J·M·C·TOYNBEE

ART IN ROMAN BRITAIN

ART IN ROMAN BRITAIN

BY J·M·C·TOYNBEE

LAURENCE PROFESSOR EMERITA OF CLASSICAL ARCHAEOLOGY
IN THE UNIVERSITY OF CAMBRIDGE

WITH 230 ILLUSTRATIONS

FROM ORIGINAL PHOTOGRAPHS

BY OTTO FEIN

PUBLISHED BY THE PHAIDON PRESS FOR

THE SOCIETY FOR THE PROMOTION OF ROMAN STUDIES

PRINTED IN GREAT BRITAIN

ILLUSTRATIONS PRINTED BY GEO. GIBBONS LTD · LEICESTER

TEXT PRINTED BY HUNT, BARNARD & CO · LTD · AYLESBURY · BUCKS

BOUND BY A · W · BAIN & CO · LTD · LONDON

FOREWORD

THE SOCIETY FOR THE PROMOTION OF ROMAN STUDIES, celebrating its Jubilee year in 1960–61, decided to mark the occasion by an Exhibition of Art in Roman Britain, and to issue as a permanent record a fully illustrated and documented catalogue of the objects exhibited. The fourfold reason for this decision was the intimate connexion of the Society and its founder-member, Professor Haverfield, with Romano-British studies, the continuing furtherance of these studies by the *Journal of Roman Studies*, the need for a well-illustrated publication of the art of Roman Britain, and the hope that an effective publication of these highly interesting works would stimulate the production of further volumes to embrace the entire field of figurative art in Roman Britain. The undertaking was further inspired by the approaching completion by Mr. R. P. Wright of the publication of *Roman Inscriptions in Britain*, a project initiated by Haverfield, and since supported by the trustees of his legacy to the University of Oxford; and also by the standing example of Espérandieu's *Recueil*, and by the series *Die römischen Bronzen aus Deutschland*, now in course of publication.

The limited resources of the Society, however, made imperative the creation of a special fund to cover the costs of the Exhibition and the preparation of material for this catalogue; and the whole task demanded a steering committee, for which the Society's Council chose the following members: Professor I. A. Richmond (Chairman), Mrs. M. J. Thornton (Secretary), Sir Douglas Veale (Treasurer), Mr. R. A. G. Carson, Mr. S. S. Frere, Miss M. V. Taylor and Professor J. M. C. Toynbee; Mr. Graham Hughes, of the Goldsmiths' Company, was later co-opted. An appeal for funds elicited a most generous response, totalling £2,900, from many Universities, Colleges, and other bodies interested in public education, particularly generous help being afforded by The Pilgrim Trust (£1,000), the Faculty Board of Classics of Cambridge University (£500) and The Worshipful Company of Goldsmiths (£300). The latter, in addition, put their rooms at the Society's disposal for the Exhibition. The Committee was also much encouraged by the splendid response, unmarred by a single refusal, from Museums, Public Authorities and private owners to their requests for the loan of objects and facilities for photography. It was now possible to secure the services of Mr. Alan Irvine for the presentation of the Exhibition, which, under the chairmanship of the President of the Society (Professor F. W. Walbank), was opened at the Goldsmiths' Hall on 26 June, 1961, by Lord Crawford, in the presence of the Lord Mayor and Lady Mayoress of London (Sir Bernard and Lady Waley-Cohen) and a representative gathering of scholars, curators and connoisseurs. The Exhibition remained on view for four weeks and was attended by some 11,000 visitors.

The assemblage of material for the Exhibition was the prerequisite of publication, and this burden fell largely upon Mrs. Thornton, whose devoted labours deserve the highest praise. The preparation of this catalogue and its text was most generously undertaken by Miss J. M. C. Toynbee, Laurence Professor of Classical Archaeology in the University of Cambridge, whose knowledge of Roman art is second to none, and who had produced the hand-list for use in the Exhibition. The illustration, involving many difficult technical problems, was achieved with the unexaggerated elegance of the born artist, by Mr. Otto Fein, photographer to the Warburg Institute. For this magnificent photography the Society was charged costs for material and travel only, while the Warburg Institute, to whose Director, Professor E. H. Gombrich, the Society is thus deeply indebted, retains the negatives and their copyright. The text and photographs were then entrusted to The Phaidon Press, whose enthusiasm and skill in production are known the world over, and with whom the Society has had the happiest co-operation.

IAN A. RICHMOND

AUTHOR'S NOTE

IN the writing of this book an attempt has been made to keep in mind the needs of two different groups of readers, both of which are served by the Roman Society's activities. The introductory essay – a general commentary on the plates – is intended mainly for the non-specialist, the text of the catalogue chiefly for the specialist. But since the non-classicist may sometimes wish to consult the catalogue for items that are of particular interest to him, Latin and Greek terms (in most cases where they first appear in the text: see also the glossary), Latin quotations, and the less straight-forward Latin inscriptions have been translated or explained throughout. The concise bibliography has been compiled solely for the non-specialist. References of a specialised nature will be found in the bibliographies and notes appended to the individual entries.

J.M.C.T.

CONTENTS

Roman site ●
Museum □
Roman site + museum ■

Bridgeness ● ● Traprain Law
Glasgow □ W. Lothian □ Edinburgh
● Lesmahagow ● Newstead
● Tweedsmuir
● High Rochester
Housesteads Chesters Capheaton ●
Bewcastle Backworth
Netherby ● Benwell ● ● South Shields
Birrens Gt. Chesters Carrawburgh Corbridge ● Newcastle-on-Tyne
Dumfries □
● Carlisle
● Murrell Hill
Old Carlisle
Kirkby Thore ●
● Piercebridge
● Catterick
● Malton ■
Aldborough ●
York ■ ● Elmswell
□ Leeds
● Ribchester
● Hull □
Horkstow ●
● Walesby
Foss Dyke ■ Lincoln
■ Chester
● East Stoke
□ Nottingham
● Felmingham Hall
● Worthing
Norwich □
● Welshpool
Leicester ■ Castor ● □ Peterborough
Hockwold-cum-Wilton ● ● Santon Downham
● Ely ● Mildenhall
Willingham Fen ● ● Icklingham
Cottenham Fen ● ● Cavenham R. Alde
Northampton □ ● Cambridge □ ● Worlington ● Whitton
Towcester ● ● Duston ● Sandy Ickleton ● □ Ipswich
Stanfordbury ● Gt. Chesterford ●
Colchester ■
Gloucester ■ Chedworth ■
Custom Scrubs ● Oxford ● ● Horspath ■ St. Albans
Woodchester ● Cirencester (Verulamium)
Cardiff □ London ■ Strood ● Reculver ●
Bath ■ □ Reading Lullingstone ■ Canterbury ■
Devizes □ ● Silchester Holborough □ Barham ●
Banwell ● Lavington Basingstoke □ Maidstone □
Low Ham ● ● Bruton ■ Winchester
Taunton □ ● Lufton Compton ● ● Bignor
Fishbourne ●
Frampton ● ● Dorchester ● Brading
Maiden Castle ■

Drawn by H. M. Stewart

INTRODUCTION

THE EXHIBITION of Art in Roman Britain held in the Goldsmiths' Hall within the confines of Roman London, from 26 June to 22 July, 1961, offered a unique experience. In it were assembled together for the first time works (140 originals, 12 replicas, and 50 photographs) drawn from almost every area of the province, carried out in most of the many varied media that the craftsmen of the Roman world employed, and reflecting practically every facet of the social structure of this country during its Roman period.[1] It was, in fact, an artistic commentary on the whole of Romano-British life and history. What was its impact on those who visited it? What message did it bring – that imposing array of sculptures, paintings, mosaics, pieces of decorated metal-work, objects of figured lead, jet, shale, glass, and terracotta? In this introduction to the photographic record and catalogue of the exhibits an attempt will be made to answer these questions.

The most arresting over-all impression conveyed by the Exhibition was that of an immensely rich intermingling in Britain of aesthetic tastes and standards, of patrons of very diverse types, and of subjects of widely differing kinds depicted in both native and imported works of art. Complexity is, of course, a characteristic of the artistic setting of many Roman provinces. But in a distant, transmarine region such as Britain complexity of this sort is more unexpected and strikes us with especial force. Peculiarly remarkable in this connection are the pieces from abroad that linked this country directly with the homelands of Graeco-Roman civilisation.

The forging of a close cultural bond between the centre and even the most marginal of provinces was, indeed, an outstanding feature of Rome's imperial policy. The military conquest and penetration of this island and the garrisoning of its frontiers were but the means to a more important end – the establishment within it of all those amenities of civilised existence to which stability and peace formed the essential background. The Romans came to Britain, not as a master-race to hold down the natives permanently as subjects and inferiors, but to live alongside of them, to turn them into partners in the Empire, into true 'Romani', who could share their laws and social customs, their administrative system, their urban organisation, their religious cults, their literature, their architecture, and their art.

As regards art, the way had been to some extent prepared before the conquest by the Romanising interests of the Belgic kings and nobles, whose domination of south-east Britain had begun round about 110–100 B.C., half a century before the raids of Julius Caesar.[2] These people continued to maintain their taste for the brilliant Celtic art, native to the country, in the late–La Tène abstract style, an art which consisted mainly of costly metal-work characterised by flowing scroll-patterns and the very formal rendering of animals and of human heads. That tradition did, in fact, hold its own to the very end of British independence and, as the Exhibition showed, was carried on, to

1. A very successful Exhibition, on a smaller scale, of Romano–British antiquities from many parts of the country was held in the summer of 1950 in the Castle Museum, Colchester, to commemorate the nineteenth centenary of the foundation of the Roman *colonia* at Camulodunum. But this was arranged on a regional basis and included many items that were not works of art; while the works of art themselves, the majority of which were decorated metal objects, comprised comparatively few stone or marble sculptures and no paintings or mosaics. The display did not claim to be representative.

2. Ed. S. S. Frere, *Problems of the Iron Age in Southern Britain*, 1958, pp. 14, 84–6.

some degree, beyond it. Yet, while still unconquered, members of the British dynasties and aristo-cracies imported from the Continent works of Roman art such as figured red-gloss pottery from central Italy and southern Gaul and figured bronze vessels and bronze figurines of gods, men, and beasts from Italy and Gaul; and from about A.D. 1 the local monarchs issued coins with designs (almost certainly the work of immigrants) that were wholly classical in style and often fully classical in content. But after A.D. 43 crafts hitherto unknown to Britain – for example, monumental carving in stone and marble, mosaic-work, and large-scale painting – made their appearance as the result of imports and of the arrival of sculptors, masons, and other artists who followed in the wake of the invading and occupying soldiery.

And the army itself played, as we shall see, an important role in the artistic education of the newly won province. Not only did the soldiers need works of art for their own ornamental, sepulchral, and votive purposes, but the colonies of veterans, of which the first was Colchester, were largely founded to be centres of civilising influence among the native population. In and around those cities, in the public buildings and open spaces and in the homes and cemeteries of the colonists, the Britons would have seen, and been impressed by, the sculptures carved locally in British media by Roman army artists, together with the marbles, the bronzes, the terracotta figurines, and the figured pots and glass-ware imported from abroad. It is likely that in the early days of Roman Britain the great majority of its works of art came from overseas. Gradually more local workshops would have been established by immigrants, some from Italy and many more from Gaul, and by the Britons whom they trained, as military requirements expanded, as more foreign traders and in-dustrialists settled in the country, and as new demands were created by native patrons, drawn from very varied strata of society. But until the end of the second century A.D. at least a steady stream of artistic objects still flowed into this island from the central areas of the Empire.

Among the products of Mediterranean workshops yielded by Roman Britain are marble sculp-tures in the round that would grace any modern gallery of high-class statuary derived from Greece or Italy. The Hadrianic bust from Lullingstone (no. 10), carved in Pentelic marble and depicting a gentle, dreamy-looking individual, seems to have belonged, together with the somewhat later piece discovered with it, to a wealthy foreigner who may have held some official post, possibly in London, during the closing decades of the second century and used this Kentish villa as a summer or vacation residence. There, at any rate, he kept two over-lifesize portraits, perhaps of his own relatives, of a quality that sets them on a par with the heads and busts, more than seventy in number, that came to light in a sumptuous Roman country house at Chiragan near Toulouse. And there, in circum-stances unknown, they were abandoned– to be found, after many years of dereliction, preserved, and accorded some form of religious cult by the new owners of the villa in the late-third and fourth centuries. The story of these two portraits, so far as the evidence enables us to read it, throws new and important light on the role that could be played by monumental foreign sculptures in the life of Roman Britain.

The larger and more varied series of imported marbles from the Walbrook Mithraeum[2a] (nos. 20, 24, 29, 32, 36–8) owed its arrival in Britain in the late-second century to foreign patrons of a different type. These were the wealthier members of the only Mithraic congregation in Londinium of whose existence we as yet know. Here again the names both of those who commissioned the out-

---

2a. Nos. 12, 20, 24, 36–8, 61, 110 in the catalogue were recovered from the Mithraeum in 1954 by Professor W. F. Grimes for the Roman and Medieval London Excavation Council.

standing pieces and of the artists who fashioned them are not recorded. But in every case the medium is Italian marble; and it is clear that the most important sculptures – the superbly modelled heads of Mithras the Bull-Slayer (no. 36), of Minerva (no. 24), and of Serapis (no. 38) and the sensitively worked colossal right hand of the bull-slaying god (no. 37 – symbolic of the central act of sacrifice whereby Mithras had 'saved' mankind) – had been carved in the workshops quite independently of the bodies, or portions of bodies, with which they were once united. Of those bodies we know nothing, since only the heads and the hand, detached from the rest, were carefully concealed in hollows below the temple floor about the middle of the fourth century, at a time when Mithraism and Christianity had come into open conflict. Assuming, as we may, that all had adorned the Mithraeum, we can win from them, from the elegant marble statuette of Mercury (no. 20) found with them, and from the fine marble River-God and marble Genius retrieved from the site (then not known to be that of a Mithraeum) in the late-nineteenth century (nos. 29 and 32), a vivid picture of the building as a 'museum' of works of art from Mediterranean sources, highly prized by the fourth-century heirs of the original collectors.

But the whole Mithraic collection included, besides these first-class marbles, carvings of other origins and orders. For one thing, it is likely that the bodies belonging to the marble heads, and the arm of the marble hand, were locally made in native media (stone or stucco). Again, the only large relief in marble from the temple, also unearthed in the late-nineteenth century, the gift to Mithras of a legionary veteran, Ulpius Silvanus, is carried out in a relatively rough provincial style (no. 69). Provincial, too, in character is the marble Bacchus group (no. 12), which seems to have been dedicated in the temple at a later stage in its history than were the other marble works and finds its closest parallels in stone reliefs from the Danubian areas. Furthermore, carvings in British stone (no. 61), the offerings of the god's poorer and less sophisticated worshippers, had found a place alongside the costly marbles. Discovered in a battered and fragmentary state, since no attempt had been made to conceal and save them, these stones are classical in content and derived from Graeco-Roman prototypes, but obviously executed by provincial craftsmen. At any rate there can be little doubt but that the group of persons by whom all these varied sculptures were set up in London were, for the most part, foreigners, oriental and continental merchants and soldiers of non-British birth. Given the exclusive and secret nature of Mithraism as a 'mystery-cult', we may believe that in this case, as in that of the sculptural outfit of all Mithraea, the pieces representing specifically Mithraic themes had been produced in workshops owned and staffed by Mithraists. Those of a 'neutral' content could have been commissioned from the ordinary studios; and some may have even been the private property of worshippers before being offered to Mithras. To sum up, quite apart from their intrinsic aesthetic and stylistic interest, the Walbrook finds are significant as implying the establishment in the heart of Roman London of a diverse, highly organised, 'international' community of patrons of the arts and for the witness that they bear to the vicissitudes of the province's religious history.

This cultivated taste for bringing into Britain works of Mediterranean origin did not confine itself to marble carvings. Italy or southern Gaul may have been the source of such bronze statuettes as the slender Venus from Verulamium (no. 28) and the stocky Cupid found at Cirencester, where it functioned as a lamp-stand (no. 13). The magnificently naturalistic bronze eagle from Silchester, once, perhaps, perched on a globe held in the hand of a statue of Jupiter or of an Emperor, could have come from Rome itself (no. 60). From the Walbrook temple site again comes a figured silver casket with scenes of hunting in relief (no. 110), probably of late-antique date and cast in an east–

Mediterranean workshop, as was also the Corbridge *lanx* (no. 108); and the finest figured vessels in the fourth-century Mildenhall (no. 106) and Traprain Law (no. 107) silver treasures were certainly of southern manufacture. Nor was this type of importation restricted to immigrants. Just before, or just after, the Roman conquest wealthy British notables were importing figured bronze jugs and casseroles from Italian factories (nos. 114-5); and thereafter, for a century at least, objects of this kind poured into civilian sites (nos. 111-2, 116-20), where we can imagine Britons, as well as army officers and other foreigners, owning them. Specimens of the decorated red-gloss table-ware produced by central-Italian potters ('Arretine', from Arezzo in Tuscany, and 'pseudo-Arretine', made by Italians in southern Gaul) also reached this country both before and just after A.D. 43 (no. 148) and a glass bowl with Nilotic ornament from Egypt of early-imperial date, found in a Roman grave near Cambridge (no. 140), represents yet another class of Mediterranean imports.

Probably the largest section of foreign patrons of the arts in Britain for whom provincial works were either locally produced or imported from northern and western continental countries were the occupying Roman armies. From the mainly military Mithraea and other temples in the frontier regions, from Caerleon, Chester, York, and the stations on Hadrian's Wall, come sculptures (nos. 33, 62, 65, 67, 70-1, 74, 80, 92, 94) by the hands of carvers who were either directly attached as draftsmen, masons, architects, etc. to the regiments or drawn from the civil settlements on the outskirts of fortresses and forts. Such pieces are, like the stone carvings from the Walbrook shrine, somewhat roughly executed in native media, but they impress us by the care with which the details of their Graeco-Roman iconography are rendered. Similar in type are the reliefs with Roman scenes associated with building inscriptions on secular military structures (no. 97). Among the earliest Roman sculptures to be worked in the province are military tombstones from the south, from Colchester and Gloucester. The relief of the centurion Facilis (no. 81) must date from the initial occupation of the site of Colchester, before the founding there, in A.D. 49-50, of Britain's first veteran colony, since the subject, whose square-built skull and flap-like projecting ears are typically Italian, is not described, in the accompanying inscription, as time-expired. The army artist who carved it in British stone must have learnt his craft in a workshop in which classical traditions were preserved and taught. For while the content of the relief is as Roman as it could be, the art-type of the figure stems from fourth-century B.C. Greek sculpture. Also fully classical is the seated Sphinx, sensitively modelled in the round, again sepulchral and from Colchester, guarding between her paws the realistic portrait of the dead, probably a legionary veteran, carved in Flavian style (no. 46). The lively renderings in relief of the trooper Rufus Sita (no. 82), dating from the early military phase of Roman Gloucester's history, and of the trooper Longinus (no. 83), erected in the early, pre-*colonia* days of Roman Colchester, have also at least one classical Greek forerunner; but they emanate from units of provincial auxiliaries and lack the elegance of the legionary stones. In these early stages of the occupation both the soldiery and members of the Roman administration would have had to rely almost entirely on military sculptors for all the votive and funerary local carvings that they needed. It was not until later that there could have been established in Britain independent civilian workshops run and manned by immigrants from Gaul or by Britons. Then, in the second and early-third centuries, the tomb-reliefs of soldiers and of their wives and children are among the most distinctive and attractive examples of northern Romano-British sculpture (nos. 88-9). All these reliefs would once have been brightly painted.

A small class of specifically military provincial works of art is composed of the items of 'sports-equipment', in particular, the bronze and iron decorated helmets, some having face-mask vizors with idealised youthful features, that were worn by the auxiliary cavalry-units of the army for tournaments and at other ceremonial displays (nos. 98–104). In view of their close analogies with continental pieces of the same type, we may guess that the examples from British sites were imported from Gaulish or Danubian factories. Other imports from continental provincial sources serving military circles were the terracotta figurines found in first-century A.D. graves at Colchester and associated with the families of early veteran colonists. They include a vivid group of men and women reclining at a banquet, while reciters entertain them as they dine (no. 143). These date from before the development of the potteries for which the district became noted from the first half of the second century onwards; but a scene such as this could well have been enacted in early Roman Colchester. Its northern find-spot, in Northumberland, in the frontier zone, suggests that the Capheaton silver treasure (no. 105) had belonged to a well-to-do army officer. Both the content and style of the decorated pieces argue that they originated, not in a Mediterranean, but in a very good provincial, probably Gaulish, workshop. Votive bronze figurines from abroad were likewise in demand, at all periods, in army *milieux*.

Another northern site has provided us with a most unexpected spectacle, that of an oriental carver who worked in Britain both for an oriental immigrant and for a foreign soldier. The evidence for this is the pair of tomb-reliefs found at the fort at South Shields, in County Durham, dating from the third century and undoubtedly produced by a sculptor from Palmyra, where a very distinctive style of funerary carving had been evolved. The architectural and other accessory details of these scenes, and the attributes of the persons who are portrayed, can all be paralleled on Palmyrene tomb-reliefs, and the style in which the stones are cut is likewise Palmyrene. Moreover, one piece (no. 87), commemorating the British wife of a Palmyrene maker of military standards (*vexillarius*) for the Tyne-Solway garrisons, bears below its Latin text another text in Palmyrene script and language. The second relief (no. 85), clearly by the same hand or from the same workshop, shows the Moorish freedman of a trooper serving in a Spanish regiment; the dead man reclines at the funerary banquet which is here presented in a specifically Palmyrene manner. The artistic implications of these stones are indeed most striking; so too is their testimony to the intermingling of races in the Roman Empire. An instance of a Celtic artist using an oriental pattern-book for depicting Syrian dress may, perhaps, be detected in the imposing statue of Juno Regina from Chesters (no. 35), since a figure from Carnuntum, in Austria, shows the same type of costume with ornamental border. Or do we, more probably, see in both of these statues the work of immigrant Syrian sculptors?

The majority of art-patrons whom we have encountered so far were either members of special foreign groups, civilian or military, or individual wealthy Britons with a taste for fine and expensive objects of Mediterranean origin. Until the early decades of the third century all such patrons were, of course, using freely as their best table-ware the decorated red-gloss and black-gloss pottery manufactured in the kilns of Gaul, the so-called 'samian', with figure-designs carried out in the mould-cast, the *appliqué*,[3] the *en barbotine*,[3] and the incised techniques (nos. 149–52). The place of this was taken at a later time by vessels from the Rhineland with relief- and painted ornament (no. 154). But during the same periods these provincial works of art also circulated widely among the broader sections of the civil population, among the natives, no less than among the immigrants, both in town and country. And it was to meet the needs of patrons drawn from the more generally re-

3. For an explanation of these terms, see p. 11.

presentative British circles that many other products of the workshops of the northern and western continental provinces entered this island. Imports of this kind included mass-produced votive terracotta figurines (nos. 144–7), examples of late glass-ware, with engraved decoration, from the Rhineland (nos. 141–2), and of late silver-ware from Gaul (no. 106); decorated relief-mounts and sculptures in the round, large and small, from the bronze-workers' studios for which Gaul was famed. Among the most classical of such provincial bronzes are a small, round cuirass-decoration (*phalera*) from Sandy, in Bedfordshire, with the mask of a Medusa in relief (no. 125); the lifesize head of Claudius, recognisable, indeed, as the Emperor, but differing in some respects from his official Roman portraits (no. 1), which probably adorned a public building in the colony of Camulodunum, before being hacked from its body, looted, and then abandoned by Boudicca's followers in A.D. 61; a once-helmeted head of Minerva, also sundered from its body, found at Bath (no. 25); and a svelt statuette of Mercury that may well have been dedicated in the rustic shrine, near which it came to light, at Gosbecks Farm, to the west of Colchester (no. 21). The statue of Claudius would have been commissioned by the colony's authorities as part of the standard equipment of a Roman town. But it also served to educate the local natives in Roman art and ways; and there is every reason to suppose that British initiative lay behind the importation of the Bath Minerva and of the Gosbecks Farm Mercury into what were basically native sanctuaries.

In the case of the frontier areas of Britain from about the second quarter of the second century onwards, it is often impossible to say of any given locally made sculpture whether the person who commissioned it was military or civilian; or whether its carver was strictly an army artist or plyed his craft as a civilian in one of the quasi-civil settlements that surrounded the military strongholds. Some northern cult-reliefs (p. 4) and religious statuary (pp. 8–9) and the tombstones of members of soldiers' families (p. 4) could, indeed, claim a place in either sphere. So can an outstanding object, the figure in the round of a reclining River-God from Chesters (no. 30), found near the commandant's house inside the fort, but displaying that splendidly decorative treatment of the patterned drapery which so often distinguishes the best native sculptures. Many of the army artists would themselves have been Celts; and all works of this kind share a common background in that they were made in Britain for British purposes by artists who were almost certainly of Celtic origin. In other words, they are Romano-British in the true and proper meaning of the term as applied to art; although a few of the most classical in style among the later pieces could still have been by the hands of legionary carvers of Mediterranean origin. Such could, in fact, have been the case with a mid-third-century female portrait, with softly contoured, youthful cheeks but worked in unprepossessing local gritstone, from York (no. 11); while the commanding head of Constantine the Great, also from York and also in a local medium (no. 6), might have been the work of a visiting court sculptor. But all sculptures worked in British stones from civil sites in the south are Romano-British in the strict sense: so also are some bronzes from both north and south that seem to bear a definitely native stamp (nos. 2–5, 8, 15–7, 22–3, 26, 43–4, 50–2, 54, 57).

There are, naturally, seldom any means of deciding with absolute precision whether a specific bronze sculpture showing strongly provincial characteristics was a Gallo-Roman import or genuinely Romano-British in that it was cast in this country for a British context by a Celtic artist. Nor can we know quite certainly whether such a work of Romano-British art came from the hand of a native Briton or from that of an immigrant Gaul. Small bronzes obviously travelled easily: so did the workers; and even some of the finer pieces, which we are inclined, on grounds of style, to regard as of continental origin, could have been cast in this island, just as there are some first-class carvings from the south in British stone that were obviously made in native *milieux* (p. 7). But among the bronzes found in Roman Britain there are some which show peculiarly striking, non-classical traits both of style and of content that most strongly suggest local workmanship.

The small head of a broad-faced girl from Compton, near Winchester (no. 8), has hair demurely waved on either side of a central parting according to the Graeco-Roman manner; but short, sharp strokes of hatching, born of the Celtic love of patterning, outline the ears and eyes, and the pupils of the eyes are made of black, glinting, natural pebbles. Native in its unorthodox proportions, in its cast of countenance, and in its emphasis upon the great, flaunting crest on the helmet is the Foss Dyke Mars from Lincolnshire (no. 16), a votive piece commissioned by two men with Celtic names, as we learn from the inscription on the base. Of the *cache* of figurines of deities from the temple site at Bruton, in Somerset, the most unusual and arresting is the Hercules, who wears his huge lion-mask breastplate-wise across his chest, while the beast's furry pelt and sturdy tail hang down behind him (no. 15). Unquestionably British both in content and in treatment is a tiny lead-filled mask, used as a steelyard-weight, that was found at Old Carlisle, in Cumberland (no. 44). Here we have the visage of a local god, somewhat Silenus-like in its flat, coarse features, but with lentoid eyes of typically Celtic form and a frame round the face of chunky hair and stiff, stubbly beard that are ordered in a non-naturalistic, symmetrical design. Among the most intimate of the figurines with subjects drawn from daily life are the hooded ploughman with his ox-team from Piercebridge, in County Durham (no. 54), and the girl from Silchester who grasps a long pipe and is watching for the signal to begin to play (no. 52). The latter's native origin is evident in her disproportionately large head and in her excessively broad and heavy shoulders and upper-arms. But in her distinctive tall headdress of spiky, upright leaves, in the thick roll in which her tunic terminates round her throat, and in the regular, unbroken, vertical folds of her skirt there are an unconventional charm and a freshness of approach which attract us far more strongly than does the unadventurous correctness of some classicised pieces.

Of the small bronze renderings of animals which were probably of local manufacture one makes a special impact in that it proclaims the survival, well on into the Roman period, of the late-La Tène art-tradition. This is an ox-head bucket-ornament from a hoard of objects recently found at Welshpool, a piece that is as splendidly and bluntly stylised as any representation of a beast could be (no. 57). The enormous, lentoid eyes, to which the crisp fringe of hair below the short, inturned horns, the small, neat ears, and the smooth, slender nozzle are mere accessories, dominate the whole and lend to the creature the mournful, abstracted air that is the special mark of the pre-Roman Celtic artist's handling of living forms, whether animal or human. The fact that a work of this kind could co-exist with the much more intimate, naturalistic, Graeco-Roman treatment of birds and quadrupeds (nos. 58–60) reveals in a special way how diverse were the tastes of British patrons. An ultra-'geometric' iron ox-head, probably a waggon-ornament, in a hoard of iron-work from Great Chesterford, in Essex (no. 56), tells the same intriguing story.

The sculptures in the round and in relief from civilian sites in southern Britain, worked in local stone and all Romano-British in the sense in which that term has been defined, display a wide variety of styles and of standards of workmanship. At the one extreme we note such plastically carved and naturalistic pieces as the best productions of the 'Corinium school' at Cirencester – the powerfully conceived Mercury (no. 19), the 'baroque' River-Deity (no. 31), and the relief of the three Mother-

Goddesses with children grouped in easy, lively attitudes (no. 72). These would seem to have been by first-rate Gaulish sculptors who had set up workshops in the largest British canton-capital. Wholly different in character is a second Mother-Goddesses relief from the same site, in which the three are seated side by side in rigidly frontal, monotonously hieratic poses (no. 73). Still more naïve are yet another votive plaque from Corinium with a triad of hooded godlets (Genii Cucullati) cut out in low relief in a single plane flush with the background (no. 76), two reliefs found at Custom Scrubs, in Gloucestershire, of Mars and a Genius respectively, both by the same hand (nos. 63, 66), and, to turn to the northern area, the almost barbaric head of a local god from Netherby, in Cumberland (no. 42a). An inscription on the Mars relief from Custom Scrubs gives the name of the Celtic dedicator, Gulioepius, and of the carver, Iuventinus, where a Roman form had been adopted. At this end of the scale comes also one of the most primitive and moving pieces in the Exhibition – a male limestone head from Gloucester (no. 7), which may well have been carved by a quite exceptional native artist in the early days of the Roman occupation. The build of the skull and the structure of the brow are three-dimensional and Graeco-Roman – the carver would have seen and studied some examples of mid-first-century A.D. Roman portrait-sculpture. But all the details are Celtic – notably the patterned hair, the stylised ears, the tapering face, the slit-like mouth, the great lentoid, projecting eyeballs, and the wrapt, aloof expression. The kinship of this face with the faces of the bronze heads of warriors on the late-La Tène bucket found at Aylesford, in Kent,[4] is, indeed, self-evident. In the same tradition is the later stone head of a northern local god found at Corbridge (no. 42).

Half-way between these two extremes stand what are probably the best-known of all Romano-British sculptures. One of them, the famous Corbridge lion (no. 47), is again a northern work and might have been made initially for a military patron from abroad. It was clearly carved in the first instance to stand on the coping of a wall or balustrade round a tomb – its role as a fountain-piece was secondary; and its content, the wide-spread Graeco-Roman funerary motif of a lion de-vouring its prey, as well as its three-dimensional, plastic modelling, proclaim its debt to a classical copy-book. But in the boldly stylised treatment of the lion's mask, mane, and bony structure and of the forms of its limp, exhausted victim we can trace the Celtic carver's hand. A no less famous sculpture, the pedimental relief from the temple of Sulis Minerva at Bath (nos. 90–1), brings us back to the southern civil area and is a piece worked specifically for a British sanctuary of 'inter-national' repute by a craftsman who could have been a Gaul. The balanced scheme of composition, a central shield upheld between two flying Victories, with a Triton filling either angle, is completely classical: so is the idea of setting on a shield a glowering, ferocious face. On the other hand, the conflation in that face of the head-wings and snakes of a classical Medusa with the beard and moustache of a male Water-Deity is wholly local and provincial, while the flat, linear, two-dimensional technique, more graphic than sculptural, stems directly from the late-La Tène tradition. Less familiar, but no less striking, in its own way, in its fusion of classical and native features, is the great figured column-capital from Corinium (no. 95). This piece, in the type of its acanthus-foliage and in the notion of introducing into it human figures, is Graeco-Roman. But the busts of the four native deities emerging from the leaves are in style, technique, and attributes eloquently Celtic. Yet another piece belonging to this intermediate class, little known, but, to the present writer's mind, the most arresting object in the Exhibition, is the head of Antenociticus, probably a north-British local god (no. 41), found in his shrine just outside the fort on Hadrian's Wall at Benwell

4. *Archaeologia*, lii, 1899, pp. 360–4, fig. 11.

(Condercum), in Northumberland. Here the contours of the face are soft and rounded. But the eyes are enlarged and bean-shaped and the lanky, winding locks of which the heavy mop of hair is formed are drawn into the splendidly ornamental pattern that only a Celtic artist could have fashioned.

The small decorated metal objects which we can describe with some assurance as truly Romano-British, made in this country by Celtic craftsmen, show almost as marked a diversity of function and content as do the sculptures in stone and bronze. Of the bronze mounts in the Exhibition the earliest is a harness-plate found in a native grave at Santon Downham, in Suffolk (or at Santon in Norfolk), and dating from about the time of the Roman conquest (no. 122). Its style is pure late-La Tène – trumpet-scrolls worked in burnished bronze against a background of red enamel. Only the 'fold-over' symmetry of the composition suggests, perhaps, Roman influence, although such symmetry is sometimes found in earlier Celtic work. Slightly later, probably produced between A.D. 60 and 70, is a bronze panel, once almost certainly applied to the wall of a casket, from Elmswell, in Yorkshire (no. 123). This bears in its main decorated zone a formal, lyre-pattern scroll-design, again of late-La Tène type, worked in *repoussé*. But a narrow cast-bronze, horizontal frieze at the top shows a running scroll, with *champlevé* red and green enamel and of mainly Graeco-Roman inspiration, which the artist has adapted from a foreign model. Another instance of this kind of borrowing on a British piece is the running floral scroll that forms the chief motif on the outer surface of a bronze casserole found in West Lothian and brilliantly adorned with polychrome *champlevé* enamelling (no. 113). How the classical human figure could sometimes fare at the hands of a local bronze-worker can be seen from yet another mount, a small plaque from Lavington, in Wiltshire (no. 124). It portrays Minerva in a pose that recalls the famous Hellenistic sculptural type of the Victory of Brescia, and the goddess's costume is traditional, consisting of a tunic and a cloak, the latter even reproducing the mannered zig-zag fold found in Greek drapery from archaic to Hellenistic times (*cf.* nos. 27, 30, 72–3). But the Medusa mask of her *aegis* is oddly sited on her flank, instead of on her breast; her raised left foot is resting on an owl, where the prototype has a helmet; and on her head, in the place of her usual helmet, she wears a bear-skin mask, while her square-shaped face, her enormous, staring eyes, and her ungainly nose and mouth all betray her native origin. This mount displays, in fact, a well-worn theme spiced with lively and unexpected variations.

Both Roman and British elements are combined again in a small series of rare native objects, that is, bronze ritual crowns and diadems worn by local priests. Two such crowns, from Cavenham, in Suffolk, had once attached to them small metal plaques, the scars of which remain and show figure-work, in the one case, classical *aediculae* or niches, each enshrining the form of a god or goddess, while the content of the decoration in the other case cannot now be deciphered (no. 127). A second *cache* of priestly headgear, from Hockwold-cum-Wilton, in Norfolk, comprises five bronze diadems and a bronze crown (no. 128). The diadems carry silver plaques with crudely drawn figure-subjects, a man with a stick and ball, perhaps a native god, and a rendering of the birds-and-chalice motif, which, debased as it is, is classical. On the crown are four bronze roundels, each adorned with an unequivocally native male mask characterised by the thick frame-work of stylised hair and beard, the lentoid eyes, the wedge-shaped nose, and the trap-like mouth that betoken the late-La Tène handling of the human head and reveal the nature of this craftsman's artistic ancestry.

Yet a further example of the British treatment of a Graeco-Roman theme is a small disc from Verulamium with a bronze back and a silver facing of *repoussé* work (no. 126). This depicts a Medusa

mask, whose classical components, the head-wings and the snake-entwined locks, breathe an un-
mistakably native air. The disc has behind it a hinged pin and it could have served either as a military
cuirass-decoration (*phalera*) or as a civilian brooch. And two bronzes that were definitely brooches
are among the most attractive and most native of all the small metal objects that were shown in the
Goldsmiths' Hall. Both of them illustrate types of brooches (*fibulae*) that were virtually unknown
outside this island and both are significant as being masterpieces of pure Celtic craftsmanship under
Roman rule. Of the fan-tailed type of *fibula* the most magnificent representative is the famous piece
from Aesica (Great Chesters), on Hadrian's Wall (no. 130). It dates from the late-first century
A.D., is made of gilt-bronze, and bears a richly 'baroque', more or less symmetrical, relief-
design of late-La Tène trumpet-scrolls. The representative of the dragonesque type of *fibula* chosen
for display comes from a Flavian context at Carlisle (no. 131). It shows how the British artist's
creative genius could transform the marine dragon of the classical, naturalistic art-tradition into
a two-dimensional, S-shaped, neatly balanced, Celtic trumpet-scroll. Here the red and the
bluish-green enamelling, contrasted with the gilt-bronze ground, enhances the pattern's joyous
buoyancy.

Of the British raw materials that supplied the native craftsmen with media for their arts, lead, jet,
shale, and clay are represented in this collection. With regard to objects fashioned in the first three of
these media, it is interesting to note how important a role was played in their designing by Graeco-
Roman copy-books (*cf.* pp. 11, 13–6), that is, by drawings and sketches on such light, portable
materials as rolls of papyrus, sheets of parchment, thin wooden boards, or even strips of cloth, which
circulated from workshop to workshop throughout the Roman world and were handed down from
generation to generation of artists of all types.[5] The child's lead sarcophagus from Holborough, in
Kent (no. 132), which was undoubtedly produced in Britain, has in relief upon its lid Bacchic figures
cast from wooden or terracotta stamps that were either imported from some Mediterranean area
or designed in this country from a foreign sketch-book. Their nearest parallels in the same medium
must be sought in Syria and Palestine. Again, the fragment of what was probably a lead baptismal
tank (no. 133) shows a Chi-Rho monogram and figure-groups that were clearly of southern origin.
The miniature jet bear from Malton, in Yorkshire, if in itself somewhat schematised (no. 135), is based
on a naturalistic rendering (*cf.* no. 139); while the closest counterparts to the two jet pendants with
portrait-groups from York (no. 138) are the painted portraits on glass medallions, and the marble
relief-busts in shells or roundels on sarcophagi, of contemporary, fourth-century date, from Italian
sites.[6] Even the much more provincial-looking jet pendant from Strood, near Rochester, in Kent (no.
137), combines a kindly, classical Medusa shown in profile with a markedly native treatment of the
hair, of the detached head-wings, and of the radiating snakes. The majority of the surviving Kimmeridge shale carvings are legs, with claw-feet and Griffin-heads, from small, three-legged tables (no.
134). These, too, show native details, but were ultimately drawn from Mediterranean models, namely
the table-legs of wood, stone, or marble shaped to form heads and legs of Griffins, panthers, or birds.[7]
Most articles of carved Romano-British furniture would have been, of course, of perishable wood.

5. No such copy-books, or vestiges of copy-books, have, to the present writer's knowledge, come to light. But their one-time existence
can be reasonably inferred from the familiar fact of the appearance and re-appearance of the same motifs and often of the same compositional schemes on works of art in many different media in widely separated areas of the Empire and sometimes throughout a period
covering several centuries.

6. M. Gough, *The Early Christians*, 1961, pls. 61–3.

7. E.g. J. Liversidge, *Furniture in Roman Britain*, 1955, figs. c, d, e, pls. 55–6, 62–3.

On the other hand, the models of the decorated pots made in British kilns came from Celtic *milieux*, in part from the central-Gaulish factories, but mainly from those of the east-Gaulish, Rhineland areas. It was the Gaulish potters who had first evolved the three main techniques for figure-ornament employed on the British pots, which, from the late-second century onwards, gradually replaced the mass-imported, mould-cast Gaulish red-gloss wares. Of these techniques the most popular throughout the province and the most characteristic of the leading industries, those in the Nene Valley ('Castor'), on the borders of Huntingdonshire and Northamptonshire, and at Colchester, was the so-called *en barbotine*. By this term is meant the trailing of a thick paste of clay, squeezed through some tube-like implement, across the outer surface of the pot, before it had received its dark colour-coating, to form relief-designs – animal-hunts (no. 155), gladiatorial combats (no. 158), circus-scenes (no. 156), or figures of deities (no. 157). A number of these subjects occur on Rhenish pots and the British potters must have originally learnt the technique from craftsmen who emigrated from the Rhineland to open kilns in Britain. But the figure-subjects on *en barbotine* beakers found on British sites are, on the whole, more ambitious and more complicated than are those on their continental counterparts. Some are unique, as, for instance, the hunting of hunch-backed Genii Cucullati on a fragment from Colchester (no. 159). And for the lithe and lively movement of their hares and hounds, the best 'Castor' hunt-cups are unrivalled by any Rhineland vessels decorated with the same theme.

A second technique, freely practised in the Rhineland but more rarely used in Britain, was that of ornamenting the pot, after it was colour-coated, with designs carried out in thick, opaque, white paint, to which a touch of brown or yellow was occasionally added here and there. Often this ornament consists of stylised floral scrolls and of jovial mottoes that are in type so close to those on pots from Rhenish sites that it is not always easy to decide whether any given piece was native or imported (no. 154). But some sherds from the Nene Valley region carry painted deities and other figures, human and animal, so much cruder in style than the figures that appear on definitely Rhenish painted pots that we can regard them as of local manufacture (no. 160).

The third, or *appliqué*, technique, whereby the body of the pot was adorned with a series of figures, each of which had been separately cast in its own mould and then luted onto the vessel's wall, was employed for decorating large, globular, locally made jars of grey or buff clay. Some of these figure-types are classical, others very definitely native, as in the case of the outlandish 'Wheel-God', Tanaris (or Tanarus), whose mould was found at Corbridge (no. 161). A jar from Colchester has smith's tools in *appliqué* (no. 162) and was probably a votive pot, offered to some British form of Vulcan. Other types of pots with applied decoration that Gaulish potters had invented and native potters copied were the face-urns, on which lumps and strips of clay were laid by hand to form lewd-looking facial features (no. 164), and the jugs with neck-masks, cast in separate moulds of which specimens have come to light in Britain (no. 163). A small British class consists of pots very roughly mould-cast in the shape of a human head, with the details added, at a later stage, by painting or incising (no. 165).

The main impression that this native pottery conveys is that of British craftsmen adapting and developing, with verve, inventiveness, and enterprise, their foreign models.

When we turn to the large-scale decoration of private houses, to the figured wall-, and, very rarely, ceiling-paintings and to figured and 'geometric' floor-mosaics, we are dealing with works of art made for rich civilian patrons, mostly Romano-Britons, who could afford the services of well-trained craftsmen from abroad; although some of the cruder figured pavements (no. 184) and paintings (no. 173) may be assumed to have come from the hands of natives using, sometimes with imperfect understanding, imported sketch-books. These domestic paintings and mosaics are not Romano-British in the strict sense. They present no specifically Celtic traits, no adaptations of Graeco-Roman themes to native taste, such as can be found in other arts; and it seems very likely that, with the exceptions just mentioned, not only their designers, but also their executants, were of Mediterranean, not of Celtic, stock. This would be particularly true of figured painting, an art which demanded more individual skill, experience, and initiative than did the craft of shaping and setting *tesserae*, but the hands of some very fine immigrant mosaicists can also be detected; and both they and the mural painters were attracted to the province by the prospects of patronage and profit that it obviously offered.

The survivors of the figured paintings from the houses of Roman Britain, both in town and country, are naturally, compared with the figured floors, few in number; and the whole idea of seriously attempting to preserve and reconstruct their fragments is a new development, dating from 1949, when spectacular discoveries in this line were made at Lullingstone. Since that year some important pieces have come to light on urban sites and been retrieved, making striking contributions to our knowledge of the art as it was practised in this country. Furthermore, as one result of these recent finds, the scanty relics of domestic paintings that earlier investigations had revealed have taken on a fresh significance.

Paintings and mosaics from Romano-British dwellings are a useful index, where they can be dated, to the pattern of the province's social and economic history. It would seem that in the late-first and second centuries members of the native gentry, encouraged and, perhaps, directed by the Roman administration, moved into the newly established towns, making their headquarters in their well-equipped and often richly decorated urban homes.[8] At this period the villas or farm-houses, that were the foci of the landed properties from which the gentry drew its wealth, while planned and constructed according to the principles of Roman building, lacked, for the most part, such civilised amenities as hypocausts, baths, wall-paintings, and mosaic pavements. It may be that there, for most of the year, bailiffs were mainly in charge, in the case of the smaller villas, at any rate, the owners perhaps making only short occasional stays, when inspecting their estates; although at Chedworth, in Gloucestershire, for instance, the presence of baths in the house in its quite extensive second-century form may indicate that its then owner was in residence for longer spells. At Verulamium and other town sites most of the mosaics and all the figured paintings, for which dating evidence exists, are of the second century; and some of them would appear, from their state of preservation, to have lasted in good shape for at least a hundred years, if not for longer. It was not until the fourth century, to judge from the finds at Verulamium, for example, that new mosaics were replacing old ones, or being laid for the first time, in pre-existing houses, and that new houses were being built and equipped with elaborate pavements, as urban life, while vigorously enduring, changed its character, by becoming more industrialized. It is, in fact, clear from these late mosaics that residential life of a quite high, but probably more restricted, order still flourished in the cities in the second half of the fourth century. In the towns, the late mosaics represented an earlier tradition carried on by the owners of the new industrial concerns. What is remarkable is the first appearance of figured pavements in the countryside in late Romano-British times; and the notable development and growth of the rural villas after A.D. 300 appear to indicate that at this period the bulk of the British landed gentry moved their domiciles from town to country. For in the fourth

8. *Cf.* Tacitus, *Agricola* 21.

century throughout the civil areas of Britain pre-existing country houses were being extensively enlarged and reconditioned, while a number of great new rural mansions were being built; and all, both old and new, were now provided with large and elaborate baths and spacious living-rooms, in which were laid the finest, most ambitious, and most complex of the polychrome figured pavements known in Roman Britain. A number of these, the fruit of modern scientific excavation, have been securely dated in the fourth century, while the close analogies in style and content between the new dated pieces and the earlier undated finds leave us with few figured pavements from the countryside that we should be tempted to regard as pre-fourth-century. Figured villa mosaics of established earlier date are extremely rare.

If this pattern of villa history has been correctly traced, it follows that nearly all mural paintings from country sites are of late, fourth-century date. Such works were represented in the Exhibition by the lifesize foot of a dancing female figure, perhaps a Nymph or Maenad, with the hem of her skirt swirling round her ankle, which was found in the villa at Ickleton, in Cambridgeshire (no. 174). It must come from a monumental figure-scene; and it gives us an inkling of the splendour of the painted rooms in some of these rural residences. The Lullingstone villa in the late-second century was exceptional in that it seems to have been the home, not of a British family, but of official persons from abroad (p. 2); and its baths in their first stage, with fish painted on the walls, and its fine group of Water-Nymphs, painted in a niche in a kind of 'basement-room', date from that time. But the Christian paintings, for which this Kentish site is chiefly famous, once adorning what is probably the earliest Christian place of worship in this country so far known, an upper room above the 'basement', were all, of course, carried out in the mid-fourth century and almost certainly by foreign painters, perhaps from Rome or Italy. The most important of them are the Chi-Rho in a wreath, symbolic of the Resurrection, and the row of six persons, one with a curtain behind him, indicating that he was already dead when the painting was done, some of the others in the early-Christian attitude of prayer with the arms extended (nos. 175–6).

To turn to town paintings, a lovely leaf-spray from London is undated (no. 168), but in view of its exquisitely naturalistic style it may well be of the second century and by a foreign artist. The second-century painted house which has recently come to light in the heart of Roman Leicester, was destroyed about A.D.200 to make room for a large public building and its frescoes are on that account in a very fragmentary state. In the Cupid (no. 173) and in what looks like a tragic mask we may, perhaps, detect a provincial hand, since the drawing is not a little crude and the colouring is stylised rather than naturalistic. But the best-preserved and most interesting of the second-century urban frescoes are recent discoveries at Verulamium; and among these a substantial section of a horizontal frieze, that ran along the top of the wall which it once adorned, has pride of place (no. 169). It shows a running floral scroll worked in brilliant greens, reds, and browns against a golden back-ground and inhabited by animals and birds, one in the centre of each spiral. This motif, a favourite one in works of art in many media throughout the Hellenistic and Roman worlds, was clearly brought to Britain from abroad and this particular example was surely by the hand of a Mediter-ranean painter. Yet it presents two peculiarities so far unknown in 'peopled' scrolls elsewhere. As regards the animals, neither the whole, nor the foreparts, but the mask only of each beast is shown; and between the spirals are large, funnel-shaped flower-buds that are never found in classical scrolls from other countries. This second feature must have circulated in the province in a copy-book, or copy-books, since it re-appears in a number of mosaic running-scroll borders, including one brought to light in Verulamium itself. Yet another strikingly Graeco-Roman composition is a portico of columns with elaborate capitals standing on a dado, both the intercolumniations and the dado being painted with imitation marbling (no. 172). More unusual still are two portions of the painted ceiling of a corridor (nos. 170–1). These show imitation coffering carried out in yellow lines against red and purple grounds, with the figure of a bird or beast in the centre of each coffer. In all these again we may assume foreign workmanship.

Of the six figured pavements that have so far been found at Verulamium, two are of the fourth, the rest of the second, century; and the four earlier pieces were represented in the Exhibition. All are very well preserved and worked in polychrome, three of them by skilful craftsmen. The subjects depicted cover a varied range – a scallop-shell in an apsidal space (no. 177), a bust of Oceanus (no. 178), a fountain with jets of water and dolphins (no. 180), and a lion devouring a stag (no. 179). This might seem to be a strange assortment of motifs for adorning domestic 'reception-rooms', until we recollect that all find a place in the repertoire of Graeco-Roman funerary art and that ordinary folk of the Hellenistic and Roman periods were much more pre-occupied with after-life ideas than are their modern counterparts (*cf.* p. 15). Another almost certainly second-century town mosaic is a large, richly coloured piece from Cirencester, once consisting of a grid of eight octagons, each of which contained a figured roundel. Of the roundels that survive, three hold busts of Seasons shown as girls with appropriate attributes (no. 181). Here we can observe the contrast between the excellent drawing of Summer and Autumn, both the work of a master, and the clumsiness of Spring, who may have been left to a British apprentice employed by a foreign firm of mosaicists established at Corinium. A marine piece from Cirencester, now lost, but recorded in a drawing (no. 182), would seem to be again of second-century date and is as good in style and execution as any pavement of the same kind from a central, Mediterranean region. On the other hand, the Cyparissus scene from Leicester (no. 183) and the Wolf and Twins from Aldborough (Isurium Brigantum), in Yorkshire (no. 184), may be assigned, on stylistic grounds, to the fourth century; and the former is probably, the latter certainly, of native workmanship.

The most popular theme represented on the late polychrome villa pavements is that of Orpheus and the Beasts. Nine certain versions of this theme are known in Britain and four more recorded pieces may have depicted it. In view of the fourth-century date of these mosaics, of the evidence that we have for Christianity in British country villas at this time (pp. 13, 15), and of the well-known appearance of Christus-Orpheus in the paintings of the Roman Catacombs, we may well believe that the Orpheus pavements of this province carried a Christian meaning. One version was, indeed, a town mosaic, a lost piece from Cirencester known from a drawing. in which it shows such close affinities with an Orpheus pavement from the villa at Barton Farm, just outside Corinium (no. 185), and with one in the villa at Woodchester (no. 186), in the same Cotswold area, that there can be little doubt but that all were the products of the same firm. That firm, we can imagine, was, like its second-century predecessor (cf. nos. 181–2), centred in the Roman city and sent its craftsmen out to work for rich country patrons. The quality of these mosaics suggests foreign workmanship, as does also that of the mosaics in the dining-room in the Chedworth villa (no. 187), where the Seasons, idyllic figure-groups, and a fine running scroll are represented, and that of the figured pavements from the Sussex villa at Bignor, where we have a hooded bust of Winter (no. 188), a Medusa mask (no. 189), the Rape of Ganymede (no. 190), and an apsidal scene with Venus and a frieze of Cupids in the guise of gladiators (no. 191). The variously coloured fish on the mosaic margin of the plunge-bath of the villa at Lufton, in Somerset (no. 194), come from a Graeco-Roman copy-book and their executant was very probably again a foreigner. At Lullingstone the Rape of Europa (no. 192), the main figures in the group of Bellerophon on Pegasus slaying the Chimaera, and the busts of the Seasons (no. 193) were clearly by a master, whereas the marine accessories (shells and dolphins) in the Bellerophon picture and the whole of the 'geometric' setting betray the hands of native pupils. Such scenes of rape (cf. no. 190) and of the overthrow of evil monsters could allude to death and to the soul's victory over it (cf. p. 15). The very varied scenes on the pavements in the Brading villa, in the Isle of Wight, reveal a similar collaboration between immigrant and local craftsmen. There the hand that worked the Orpheus group (no. 195) would appear to have been better than the hands that carried out the Astronomer (no. 196) and the enigmatic group – perhaps from 'mystery-cult' ritual – with a cock-headed personage (no. 197). The chariot-race on a pavement from the Horkstow villa, in Lincolnshire (no. 198), is a further instance of a Mediterranean subject copied from a foreign sketch-book probably by a native artist.

Two villa pavements are of special interest from the standpoint of their content. A large and elaborate piece from Frampton, in Dorset, long since inaccessible, was the work of a good foreign craftsman, to judge by the fine style and careful execution that are shown in the drawing that records it for us (no. 199). It consists of two figured square areas, linked by a 'geometric' strip and with an apse projecting from one side of one square. In the centre of the chord of this apse is prominently displayed the Chi-Rho monogram, but in curious, ostensibly pagan, company, that of Neptune, with Latin verses in his honour, of Cupid, of Bacchus, of groups of mythological persons, and of a hunting-scene. The presence of the Chi-Rho would appear to indicate that the villa owner was a Christian or had close Christian contacts. If that were so, he would have looked upon the pagan themes, as his contemporary pagan neighbours would have done, as symbols of the after-life, of death, re-birth, and paradise. At any rate, the reference to Christianity is here, as at Lullingstone, unequivocal (cf. nos. 175–6).

If the chief interest of the Frampton pavement lies in its religious implications, that of the mosaic from the cold bath (*frigidarium*) of the Low Ham villa, in Somerset (no. 200), resides in its literary connections and in the questions that it raises as to both the use of copy-books and the origin of book-illustrations under the later Empire. This pavement is divided into five scenes, each self-contained in the sense that each is in a separate framed panel, while together they present continuously the story of Dido and Aeneas as related by Virgil in *Aeneid* I and IV. We see (i) the Trojan ships arriving at the coast of Carthage and Achates bringing from the foremost ship the jewelled wreath that was Aeneas' gift to his royal hostess; (ii) a paraphrase of the last hundred lines of *Aeneid* I – Venus, accompanied by Cupid in the guise of Ascanius, kindling in the hearts of the two protagonists a mutual *vivus amor*; (iii) the hunting-episode of *Aeneid* IV; (iv) its sequel, the embrace of Dido and Aeneas in the cave; and (v), in the centre, Venus as author of the whole romance, with a pair of Cupids, one alert, running rapidly, with torch erect, representing life (Aeneas), the other standing cross-legged, with eyes closed and torch reversed, representing death (Dido). The nearest parallels to these mosaic scenes that we possess are the miniatures in the well-known illustrated codices of Virgil in the Vatican, generally held to have been respectively produced c. A.D. 400 and A.D. 500.[9] But while these miniatures are scattered through the texts of the codices, the mosaicist has arranged his pictures within the compass of a single 'page' so that we can 'read' them in sequence. The drawing

9. Codex Vaticanus Latinus 3225 (ed. 3, 1945); Codex Vaticanus Latinus 3867 'Romanus'.

of the Low Ham figure-scenes, if lively, is naïve and their executant could have been a Briton or some other, not very highly skilled, provincial, using a copy-book imported from abroad, perhaps from a workshop in Africa, where these particular Virgilian subjects would have had a topical significance. That this British pavement was laid for a patron conversant with Virgil, and that it had some connection with illustrated texts of the *Aeneid*, cannot be in doubt. The problem is, Was the copy-book from which its scenes were taken made directly from such an illustrated text?; and, Were those text-illustrations drawn *ad hoc*?; or, Did mosaicist and book-illustrator both use copy-books derived from a common source? If we adopt the last theory, we must admit the possibility that there was in Roman times a class of draftsmen professionally employed in compiling copy-books from a great variety of sources – from statuary, reliefs, mural and other paintings, mosaics, decorated metal objects, gems, etc. – and in selling them to firms plying different crafts or to individual artists (*cf.* pp. 10–1, 13–4, 16).

It may be claimed that the Exhibition of Art in Roman Britain was able to present a fully representative cross-section of the varied arts and crafts of the Roman Empire as a whole. It was, as we have seen, an art that was basically classical throughout and an art in which Graeco-Roman copy-books played a consistently important role. The use of such copy-books was, indeed, Empire-wide. Yet it is a noteworthy fact, both in Britain and elsewhere, that when we get motifs and compositions that were obviously derived from a single source, a set of pictures of the same scheme of content, for example, we practically never find figures or scenes that are in every detail precisely identical replicas of one another – apart, of course, from metal or terracotta objects that were cast from the same moulds. There are always points of difference in drawing, colour, or design. It would seem, then, that the function of copy-books was to provide the essential elements of certain stock figures or the outlines of compositions, leaving the artist to complete the details of the former, and fill in the latter, according to his own or his patron's preferences. They did not supply models for mechanical and slavish copying, but allowed considerable scope to individual taste and imagination. And in Britain, when the artists were of Celtic origin, and had a Celtic stylistic tradition behind them, the use of copy-books did not kill, or even stultify, their native genius.

For more than half a century before A.D. 43 the Belgic notables of south-east Britain had been importing from the Continent works of Roman craftsmanship – figured bronze vessels, bronze figurines, and figured red-gloss pottery (*cf.* p. 2); while of the Romanising coin-types issued by the Belgic kings the majority were fully classical in presentation, many also in their subject-matter (*cf.* p. 2).[10] The cultural conquest had, indeed, already started, to some extent, before the legions came (*cf.* p. 1). But it was with its annexation as a province of the Empire that this country felt the full impact of Graeco-Roman art in all its varied manifestations. Monumental sculptures in stone and marble began to be brought in or worked here; along with architecture, floor-mosaics and wall- and ceiling-paintings were introduced; many hitherto unknown minor forms of craft made their appearance (*cf.* p. 2). The traditions of representational, naturalistic art, as the Romans knew it, were, in fact, now firmly established in this country for the first time; and from those traditions have ultimately stemmed all the arts which have flourished in the British Isles from the seventh century until the advent of the modern abstract schools. On the other hand, the British Celts had evolved, during two-and-a-half centuries before the conquest, their own superb, non-naturalistic late-La Tène art, an art of pattern for its own sake, the influence of which maintained its hold well on into the period of Roman occupation

10. For these, see *Archaeologia*, xc, 1944, pp. 1–46, pls. 1–4; *Proceedings of the Prehistoric Society*, n.s., xxiv, 1958, pp. 43–63, pls. 1–10; R. P. Mack, *The Coinage of Ancient Britain*, 1953.

(*cf.* pp. 9–10); and Romano-British art represents the varied ways in which the Celtic artists with their own artistic heritage responded to the challenge of the classical tradition. Those artists learnt the basic principles of naturalistic art and could render men, animals, and plants as living things, not as mere designs. But in depicting human beings, in particular, they emphasised special features, the eyes, for instance, or the hair, simplified the facial forms, omitted details; and so they could infuse into their work a solemnity, serenity, and dignity (e.g. nos. 7, 42) or a gripping, fiery ferocity (e.g. nos. 42a, 91, 95) which immediately distinguish it from superficial copying of Graeco-Roman models. Even in the more sophisticated renderings by Celtic artists of purely Roman subjects, of Mercury (no. 19), for example, or of a River-Deity (nos. 30–1), there are a directness of approach and an inner dynamism which vitalise the classical themes by interpreting them in a native idiom. This enduring marriage of the principles of Celtic art with those of Graeco-Roman art was, in fact, brilliantly illustrated in the Exhibition; and it actually produced a type of stylised figure-sculpture that should make a very powerful appeal to modernistic taste. Thus art in Roman Britain in its two main aspects, the Celtic and the classical, may be reckoned as the first, decisive chapter in our national artistic history.

It is true that between the end of Chapter I, *c.* A.D. 450, and the opening of Chapter II, *c.* A.D. 600, there is a gap. During the Dark Age of the Anglo-Saxon invasions, when artists and works of art ceased to cross to these shores from the Continent of Europe, when the Roman towns decayed or were destroyed[11] and country villas disintegrated or were burnt, the painted walls would have fallen, earth would have concealed the mosaic pavements, small decorated objects would have been lost or broken, and the sculptures in the public buildings, houses, shrines, and cemeteries would, for the most part, have been overthrown and smashed or have vanished under ground. Some minor sculptures and some small works of other arts might still have been preserved and cherished by the Celtic populations that survived alongside of the invaders; and some monumental carvings, tomb-stones, for example, may still have borne their witness to what had once existed. These would have helped, to some extent, to bridge the gulf between the latest art of Roman Britain and the earliest art of Christian England. But, in the main, Graeco-Roman art, both pagan and Christian, came to Saxon England either directly, through the Augustinian mission, or indirectly, through her contacts, religious and commercial, with the western and northern Irish world; and that Irish world had itself received Graeco-Roman culture, again by way of trade and Church activities, straight from the eastern Mediterranean, North Africa, Italy, and Gaul.[12] The direct artistic legacy of the Roman province to the new English kingdoms was, so far as we can tell, very slight.

None the less, the works of art that were made in, or imported into, Britain during a period of four hundred years form an impressive portion of our heritage from the past. There are, moreover, probably many persons living in England today with an ancestry (could they trace it back so far) that links them with those Romano-Celtic peoples of whose lives the sculptures, paintings, mosaics, metal-work, glass, pottery, etc. represented in the Exhibition were in part the background. Finally, art in Roman Britain offers a visual expression, second to none in its vividness and immediacy, of one phase of that impact of classical civilisation upon the young, vigorous, local populations of the British Isles which is among the most perennially fascinating aspects of our early history.

11. *Cf. Council for British Archaeology Report No. 11*, 1961, pp. 42–3.

12. *Cf.* the transmission via fifth-century Scandinavia, and not via Roman Britain, of animal-ornament derived from Roman craftmanship to the Germanic 'Jutish Style A' of late-fifth and early-sixth-century Southern England (*Archaeologia*, xcviii, 1961, pp. 29–79).

PLATES

1. *Head of Germanicus* (?). Marble, 11½ in. high (Cat.no.1a)

2. *Head of Hadrian* (?). Bronze, 4½ in. high
(Cat.no.2)

3. *Bust of Antoninus Pius*. Bronze, 3¾ in. high
(Cat.no.3)

4. *Bust of Lucius Verus* (?). Bronze, 5¼ in. high
(Cat.no.4)

5. *Bust of Commodus* (?). Bronze, 8 in. high
(Cat.no.5)

6. *Bust of a Man*. Marble, 28 in. high (Cat.no.10)

8. *Head of a Man.* Stone, 8 in. high (Cat.no.7)

7. *Head of Claudius.* Bronze, 13 in. high (Cat.no.1)

10. *Head of a Woman. Stone*, 11 in. high (Cat. no. 11)

9. *Head of a Girl. Bronze*, 5 in. high (Cat. no. 8)

11. *Head of a Man*. Marble, 10½ in. high (Cat.no.9)

12. *Head of Constantine the Great.* Stone, 18 in. high (Cat.no.6)

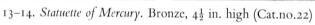

13–14. *Statuette of Mercury.* Bronze, 4½ in. high (Cat.no.22)

15. *Statuette of Mars.* Bronze, 3¼ in. high (Cat.no.17)

16–17. *Statuette of Hercules.* Bronze, 4 in. high (Cat.no.15)

18. *Statuette of Venus.* Bronze, 8 in. high (Cat.no.28)

19. *Statuette of Mars*. Bronze, 10 in. high (Cat.no.16)

20. *Head of Minerva*. Bronze, 9¾ in. high (Cat.no.25)

21–22. *Statuette of Mercury*. Bronze, 2¼ in. high (Cat.no.23)   23–24. *Statuette of Minerva*. Bronze, 3¼ in. high (Cat.no.26)

25. *Statuette of a Genius*. Marble, 20½ in. high (Cat.no.32)

26. *Statue of Minerva*. Stone, 50 in. high (Cat.no.27)

27. *Statue of Mars.* Stone, 69 in. high (Cat.no.18)

29. *Head of Mercury*. Stone, 6½ in. high (Cat.no.19)

28. *Head of Minerva*. Marble, 10 in. high (Cat.no.24)

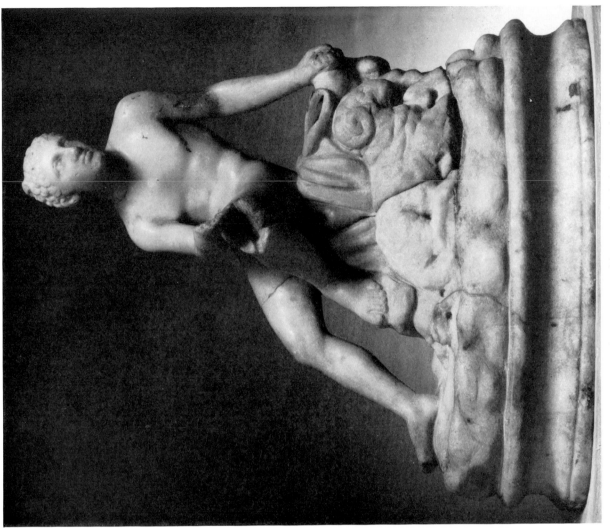

31. *Group of Mercury*. Marble, 10 in. high (Cat.no.20)

30. *Statuette of a Genius*. Stone, 13 in. high (Cat.no.33)

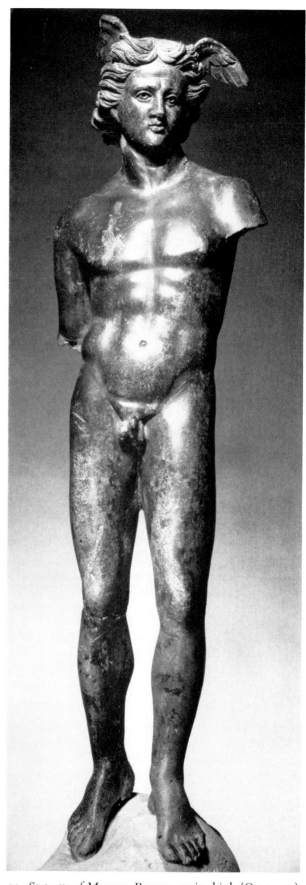

32. *Statuette of Cupid.* Bronze, 16 in. high (Cat.no.13)   33. *Statuette of Mercury.* Bronze, 21 in. high (Cat.no.21)

34. *Bacchus with a Satyr, a Maenad, Silenus, and Pan.* Marble, 13½ in. high (Cat.no.12)

35. *Head and Chest of a River-God.* Marble, 13½ in. high (Cat.no.29)

36. *Statue of a River-God.* Stone, 35½ in. long (Cat.no.30)

37. *Head of a River-God*. Stone, 12½ in. high (Cat.no.31)

38. *Head of Jupiter Dolichenus.* Bronze,
1¾ in. high (Cat.no.34)

39. *Head of Atys.* Bronze, 2½ in. high
(Cat.no.39)

40. *Colossal right Hand of Mithras holding a Knife-Hilt.* Marble, 10¼ in. long (Cat.no.37)

41. *Statue of Juno Regina.* Stone, 63 in. high (Cat.no.35)

42. *Head of Mithras.* Marble, 14½ in. high (Cat.no.36)

43. *Head of Serapis*. Marble, 12¾ in. high (Cat.no.38)

45. *Statuette of a Three-Horned Bull.*
Bronze, $3\frac{3}{4}$ in. high (Cat.no.40)

44. *Head of a Celtic God.* Stone, $7\frac{1}{4}$ in. high (Cat.no.42a)

46. *Mask of a Celtic God.* Bronze,
2 in. high (Cat.no.44)

47. *Head of a Celtic God.* Bronze, 6 in. high (Cat.no.43)

48. *Head of a Celtic Goddess* (?). Stone, $8\frac{1}{2}$ in. high (Cat.no.45)

49. *Head of a Celtic God.* Stone, 7 in. high (Cat.no.42)

50. *Figure of a Sphinx.* Stone, 33 in. high (Cat.no.46)

51. *Lion Devouring a Stag.* Stone, 34 in. high (Cat.no.47)

52. *Head of an Underworld-Goddess.* Stone, 22 in. high (Cat.no.48)

53–55. Bronze Statuettes of two Priests and a 'Flute'-Girl
(2¼ in. high, Cat.no.50; 3¼ in. high, Cat.no.51; 4¼ in. high, Cat.no.52).

56. Ivory Figurine of a Gladiator
(3⅜ in. high, Cat.no.53)

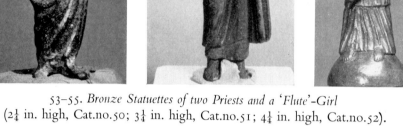

58–59. Ornaments in the Form of Stylised Ox-Heads.
Iron, 4¼ in. high (Cat.no.56); Bronze, 2¾ in. high (Cat.no.57)

57. Statuette of an Athlete. Marble,
11½ in. high (Cat.no.49)

60. Statuette of a Ploughman. Bronze,
2 in. high (Cat.no.54)

61. *Statuette of an Eagle.* Bronze, 6 in. high (Cat.no.60)

62. *Statuette of a Dog.* Bronze, 1½ in. long
(Cat.no.59)

63. *Lamp or Oil-Flask
in the Form of a Sleeping Slave.*
Bronze, 3½ in. high (Cat.no.55)

64. *Statuette of a Dog.* Bronze, 2¼ in. long
(Cat.no.58)

65. *Mars.* Stone, 18¼ in. high (Cat.no.63)

66. *Genius.* Stone, 19¾ in. high (Cat.no.66)

67. *Venus (?) and Two Water-Nymphs.* Stone, 28 in. high (Cat.no.65)

68. *Altar of Diana.* Stone, 23 in. high (Cat.no.64)

69. *Dioscurus.* Stone, 22 in. high (Cat.no.61)

70. *Three Water-Nymphs.* Stone, 20 in. high (Cat.no.68)

72. *Victory. Stone, 41 in. high (Cat.no.67)*

71. *Hercules Slaying the Hydra. Stone, 34 in. high (Cat.no.62)*

73. *Mithras the Bull-Slayer*. Marble, 17 in. high (Cat.no.69)

74. *Egg-Birth of Mithras*. Stone, 50 in. high (Cat.no.71)

75. *Altar of Mithras*. Stone, 47 in. high (Cat.no.70)

76. *Three Mothers*. Stone, 16 in. high (Cat.no.72)

77. *Dea Brigantia*. Stone, 37 in. high (Cat.no.80)

78. *Celtic God and Goddess.* Stone, 10¾ in. high (Cat.no.79)

79. *Hunter-God,* Stone, 17 in. high (Cat.no.78)

80. *Water-Goddess Coventina.* Stone, 29 in. high
(Cat.no.75)

81. *Mother-Goddess.* Stone, 38 in. high (Cat.no.74)

82. *Genii Cucullati*. Stone, 10 in. high (Cat.no.76)

83. *Genii Cucullati*. Stone, 16 in. high (Cat.no.77)

85. *Tombstone of a Woman.* Stone, 49½ in. high (Cat.no.87)

84. *Three Mothers.* Stone, 31 in. high (Cat.no.73)

87. *Tombstone of a Cavalryman.* Stone, 57 in. high (Cat. no. 82)

86. *Tombstone of a Mother and Child.* Stone, 51 in. high (Cat. no. 89)

88. *Fragment of the Tomb-Relief of a Boy-Charioteer.* Stone, 7½ in. high (Cat.no.86)

89. *Funerary Banquet.* Stone, 39 in. high (Cat.no.85)

90. *Family-Tombstone.* Stone, 58 in. high (Cat.no.88)

91. *Male Medusa Head, pediment of a Tombstone. Stone, 26 in. high* (Cat.no.84)

92. *Tombstone of a Cavalryman. Stone, 72 in. high* (Cat.no.83)

93. *Tombstone of a Centurion. Stone, 72 in. high* (Cat.no.81)

94. *Arch with Mars Thincsus*. Stone, 44 in. high (Cat.no.93)

95. *Part of a Frieze from the Temple of Jupiter Dolichenus, Corbridge*. Stone, 60 in. long (Cat.no.92)

96. *Medusa Mask on the Central Shield of the Pediment of the Temple of Sulis-Minerva, Bath.* Stone, 78 in. diameter (Cat.no.91)

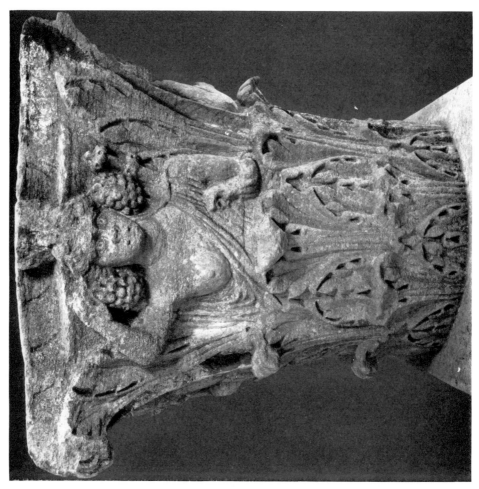

98. *Capital with Native Gods*. Stone, 41 in. high (Cat.no.95)

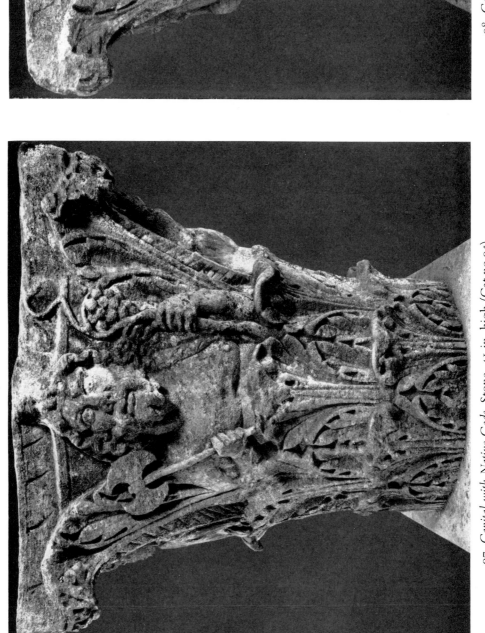

97. *Capital with Native Gods*. Stone, 41 in. high (Cat.no.95)

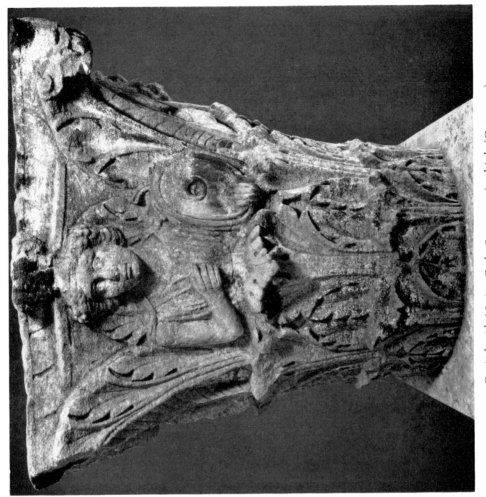

100. *Capital with Native Gods.* Stone, 41 in. high (Cat. no. 95)

99. *Capital with Native Gods.* Stone, 41 in. high (Cat. no. 95)

101. *Capital with Water-Nymphs.* Stone, 11½ in. high (Cat.no.94)

102. *Distance Slab from the Antonine Wall.* Stone, 47 in. high (Cat.no.97)

103. *Antefix*. Stone, 27 in. high (Cat.no.96)

104. *Face-Mask Helmet.* Iron, 9½ in. high (Cat.no.99)

105. *Face-Mask from Helmet.* Bronze, 8½ in. high (Cat.no 100)

106. *Helmet.* Brass, 11 in. high (Cat.no.98)

107. *Visor-Mask from Helmet.* Bronze, 8 in. high (Cat.no.103)

108. *Face-Mask Helmet*. Bronze, 11 in. high (Cat.no.101)

109. *Helmet.* Bronze, 10 in. high (Cat.no.102)

110. *Cheek-Piece from Helmet.* Bronze, 7½ in. high
(Cat.no.104)

111–112. *Casket with a Lid.* Silver, 2½ in. high (Cat.no.110)

113. *Flanged Bowl and Cover.* From the Mildenhall Treasure. Silver, 9 in. diameter (Cat.no.106)

114. *Bowl with Vine-Scroll.* From the Mildenhall Treasure. Silver, 6¾ in. diameter (Cat.no.106)

115–116. *Two Bacchic Platters.* From the Mildenhall Treasure. Silver, 7¼ in. diameter
(Cat.no.106)

117. *Oceanus Dish*. From the Mildenhall Treasure. Silver, 24 in. diameter (Cat.no.106)

118. *Scalloped Bowl*. From the Mildenhall Treasure. Silver, 16 in. diameter (Cat.no.106)

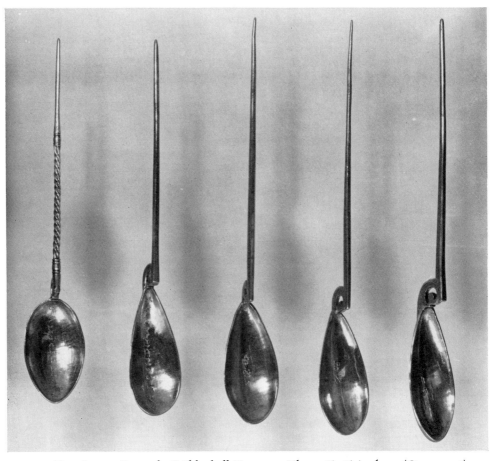

119. *Five Spoons*. From the Mildenhall Treasure. Silver, 6½–8¼ in. long (Cat.no.106)

120. *Scalloped Bowl.* From the Traprain Law Treasure. Silver, 12 in. diameter (Cat.no.107)

121. *Lanx with Apollo, Leto, Asteria-Ortygia, Athene, and Artemis.* Silver, 19 in. wide (Cat.no.108)

122. *Skillet-Handle with Diana, Mercury, and Bacchus and Ariadne*. Silver, 7¾ in. high
(Cat.no.105)

123. *Flagon with Biblical Scenes*. From the
Traprain Law Treasure. Silver, 8½ in. high
(Cat.no.107)

124. *Ladle with Handle in the Form of a Dolphin*. From the Mildenhall Treasure. Silver, 3¾ in. long (Cat.no.106)

125. *Skillet with Floral Scroll*. Enamelled Bronze, 7¾ in. long (Cat.no.113)

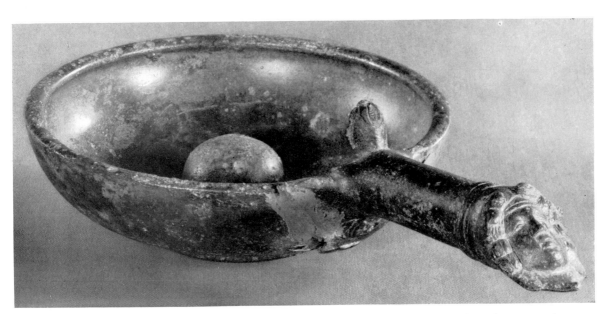

126. *Skillet with Heads of Bacchus and Two Satyrs on the Handle*. Bronze, 12 in. long (Cat.no.111)

127. *Skillet with Dog's Head on the Handle*. Bronze, 11½ in. long (Cat.no.112)

128. *Jug with Figure-Groups on the Handle.* Bronze, 10½ in. high
(Cat.no.120)

129. *Skillet with Inscribed and Decorated Handle.* Silver, 9¼ in. long (Cat.no.109)

130. *Jug with Masks and Female (?) Bust on the Handle.*
Bronze, 6½ in. high (Cat.no.114)

131. *Jug with Lion on the Handle.* Bronze, 5½ in. high
(Cat.no.115)

132. *Jug with Mask and Horse on the Handle.*
Bronze, 7½ in. high (Cat.no.116)

133. *Jug with Boy Hercules Killing Snakes on the Handle.*
Bronze, 9 in. high (Cat.no.117)

134. *Jug-Handle with Mask of Oceanus*. Bronze, 8¼ in. high (Cat.no.118)

135. *Jug-Handle with Ox-Head and Lioness and Cubs*. Bronze, 5⅞ in. high (Cat.no.119)

136. *Fragment of Dish with Fish-Symbol*. Pewter, 7 in. long (Cat.no.121a)

137–138. *Dish with Christian Symbols.* Pewter, 8½ in. diameter (Cat.no.121)

139. *Ritual Crown*. Bronze, 6½ in. high (Cat.no.128)

140. *Ritual Diadem*. Bronze, 3 in. high (Cat.no.128)

141. *Ritual Crown*. Bronze, 5¼ in. high (Cat.no.127)

142. *Mount with Scroll-Design*. Bronze, 9½ in. wide (Cat.no.123)

143. *Fragment of a Tank*. Lead, 20 in. high (Cat.no.133)

144. *Table-Leg*. Shale, 19 in. high (Cat.no.134)

145. *Lid of Sarcophagus with Bacchic Figures on the Lid*. Lead, 41¾ in. long (Cat.no.132)

147–148. *Two Phalerae with Medusa Masks*
(Bronze, 2¾ in., Cat.no.125; Silver, 2½ in., Cat.no.126)

149. *Medallion with Medusa Head*
(Jet, 1¾ in., Cat.no.137)

150–151. *Two Medallions with Family-Groups* (Jet, 2¼ in., Cat.no.138)
152. *Relief with Atys* (Jet, 2⅜ in., Cat.no.136)
153. *Buckle and Stylised Horses and Dolphins* (Bronze, 3¾ in., Cat. no. 129)

146. *Mount with Figure of Minerva.*
Bronze, 5 in. high (Cat.no.124)

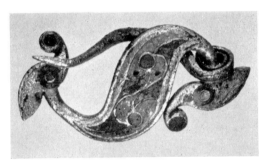

155. *Dragonesque Brooch.* Bronze, 2⅛ in. high
(Cat.no.131)

156. *Bear.* Jet, ⅞ in. long
(Cat.no.135)

154. *Fan-Tailed Brooch.* Bronze,
4¼ in. high (Cat.no.130)

157. *Harness-Mount with Scroll-Design.*
Bronze, 2¾ in. wide (Cat.no.122)

158. *Cameo with Bear devouring Goat.*
Sardonyx, 1⅞ in. wide (Cat.no.139)

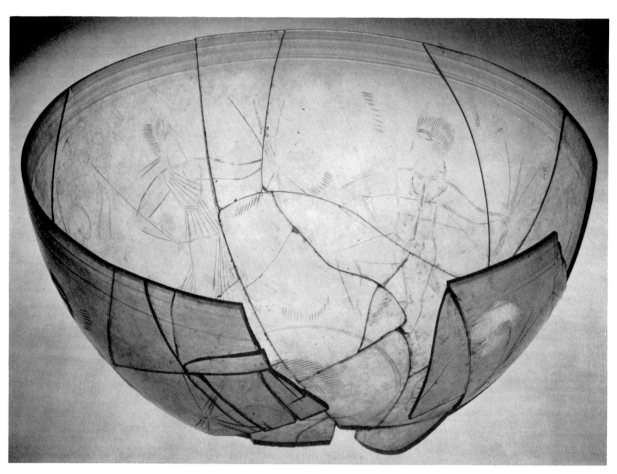

159. *Bowl with Bacchic Scene*. Glass, 7½ in. diameter (Cat.no.141)

160. *Bowl with Nilotic Motifs*. Glass, 7⅜ in. diameter (Cat.no.140)

161. *Bowl with Hunting-Scene*. Glass, 7½ in. diameter (Cat.no.142)

162. *Unguent-Pot in the Form of an Ibex*. 3 in. high (Cat.no.153)

164–165. *Mould for the Appliqué Figure of a 'Wheel-God', and Cast*. 5¾ in. high (Cat.no.161)

163. *Unguent-Pot in the Form of a Hare*. 4¼ in. high (Cat.no.153)

166–168. *Mould of a Mask for a Jug-Neck, Cast, and Exterior*. 2⅜ in. high (Cat.no.163)

169. *Sherd with Maenad and Vine*. 3⅛ in. high (Cat.no.148)

170. *Lamp with Vine-Scroll*. 4⅜ in. long (Cat.no.167)

171. *Figurine of a Genius Cucullatus* c.6 in. high originally (Cat.no.144)

172. *Figurines from a Child's Grave.* Tallest figure 6⅜ in. high (Cat.no.143)

173–175. *Figurines of Seated Mother-Goddess with Dog* (5½ in. high, Cat.no.145), *Venus and Cupid* (5⅝ in. high, Cat.no.147), and *Seated Mother-Goddess with Two Infants* (4½ in. high, Cat.no.146)

176–177. *Jar with Gladiators, Hunters, and Animal-Hunt.* 8½ in. high (Cat.no.158)

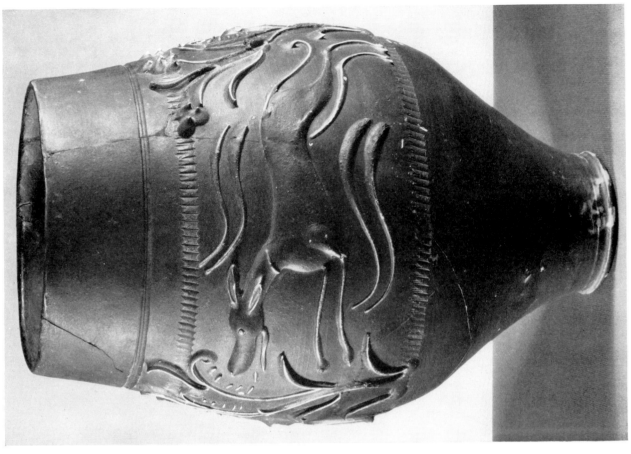

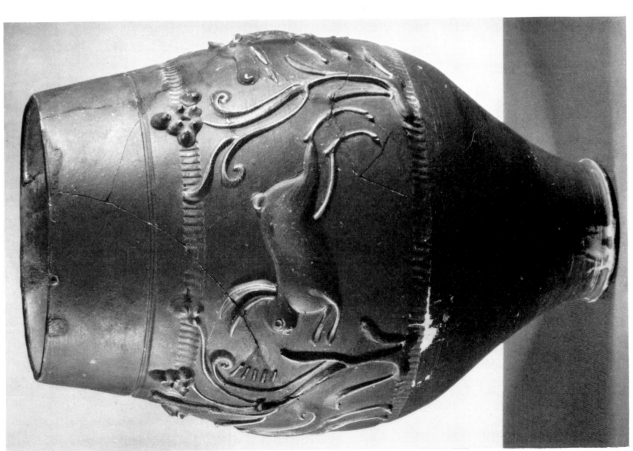

178–179. *Jar with Hare and Hounds. 9 in. high (Cat. no. 155)*

180–181. *Sherds with Pan and Medusa Masks.* 1¾ and 1⅞ in. (Cat.no.150)

182. *Pot with Vine-Leaves, Maenad Mask and Silenus Mask.* 4⅞ in. high (Cat.no.152)

183. *Sherd with Gladiator.* 3 in. high (Cat.no.149)

184. *Cake-Mould with Imperial Sacrifice.* Diameter 4¼ in. (Cat.no.166)

185. *Face-Pot.* 10⅛ in. high (Cat.no.164)

187. *Sherd with Silenus Mask.* $1\frac{3}{8}$ in. diameter (Cat.no.151)

186. *Fragment of Jar with Hunt of Hunchbacked Genii Cucullati.* 9 in. high (Cat.no.159)

188. *Fragment of Jar with Jupiter Dolichenus.* $2\frac{1}{4}$ in. high (Cat.no.160)

189. *Face-Pot.* $10\frac{1}{2}$ in. high (Cat.no.164)

190. *Jar with Mithras, Hercules, and Mercury.* 8¼ in. high
(Cat.no.157)

191. *Jar with Smith's Tools.* 8⅝ in. high
(Cat.no.162)

192. *Jar with Motto and Floral Design.* 8 in. high
(Cat.no.154)

193. *Jar with Arena- and Circus-Scenes.* 9⅞ in. high
(Cat.no.156)

194. *Head-Pot depicting a Woman.* 11⅝ in. high (Cat.no.165)

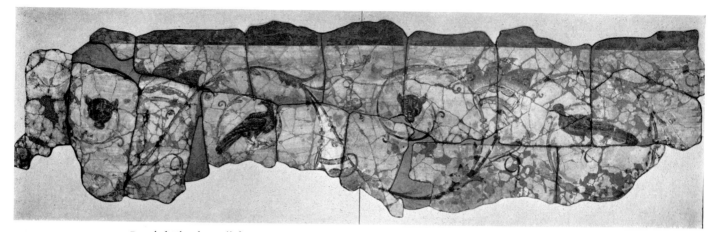

195. *Peopled Floral Scroll from a Frieze.* Fresco, 12 ft. long. From Verulamium, Herts. (Cat.no.169)

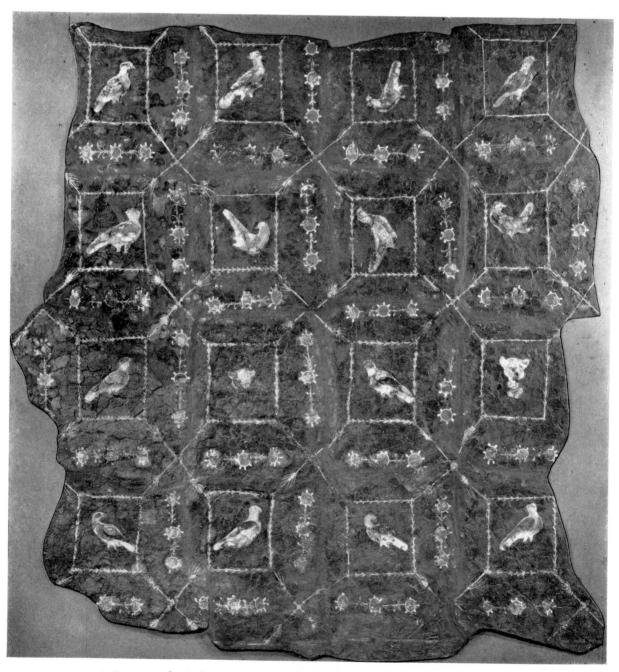

196. *Fragment of a Ceiling.* Fresco, 81 in. high. From Verulamium, Herts. (Cat.no.179)

197. Detail from plate 195

198. Detail from plate 196

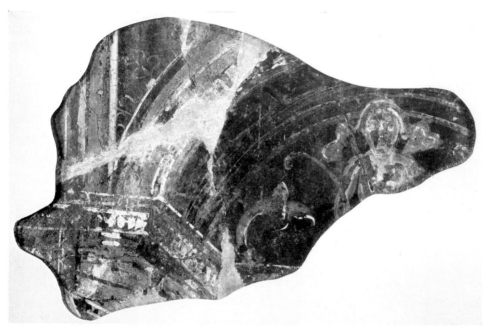

199. *Figure of a Cupid*. Fresco, 11⅝ in. high. From Leicester (Cat.no.173)

200. *Floral Spray*. Fresco, 5½ in. high.
From the Basilica, London
(Cat.no.168)

201. *Portico of Columns on Dado*. Fresco, 81½ in. high. From Verulamium, Herts. (Cat.no.172)

202. *Fragment of a Ceiling*. Fresco, 24 in. high. From Verulamium, Herts. (Cat.no.171)

203. *Female Foot*. Fresco, 9 in. high. From the Ickleton Villa, Cambs. (Cat.no.174)

204–205. *Fragments of two Christian Paintings*. Fresco, each c.32 in. high. From the Lullingstone Villa, Kent (Cat.nos.175–6)

206. *Scallop-Shell*. Mosaic Pavement, 15 ft. 9 in. wide. From Verulamium, Herts. (Cat.no.177)

207. *Oceanus*. Mosaic Pavement, 8 ft. high. From Verulamium, Herts.
(Cat.no.178)

208. *Lion devouring a Stag*. Central Panel of a Mosaic Pavement, 11 ft. 9 in. square (whole pavement).
From Verulamium, Herts. (Cat.no.179)

209. *Fountain*. Part of a Mosaic Pavement, 8 ft. wide. From Verulamium, Herts. (Cat.no.180)

210–211. *Summer and Autumn*. Parts of a Mosaic Pavement. 4 ft. 9 in. diameter each. From Cirencester
(Cat.no.181)

212. *Spring*. Part of a Mosaic Pavement. 4 ft. 9 in. diameter. From Cirencester (Cat.no.181)

213. *Marine Scene*. Drawing after a lost Mosaic Pavement from Cirencester (Cat.no.182)

214–215. *Spring and Summer*. Parts of a Mosaic Pavement, 4 ft. 10 in. long.
From the Chedworth Villa, Glos. (Cat.no.187)

216. *Winter*. Part of a Mosaic Pavement, 4 ft. 10 in. long. From the Chedworth Villa, Glos. (Cat.no.187)

217. *Floral Scroll*. Part of a Mosaic Pavement. 8 ft. 4½ in. long. From the Chedworth Villa, Glos. (Cat.no.187)

218. *Winter*. Part of a Mosaic Pavement. 2 ft. 2¼ in. wide. From the Bignor Villa, Sussex (Cat.no.188)

219. *Cyparissus and his Stag*. Mosaic Panel, 3 ft. 4 in. wide.
From Leicester (Cat.no.183)

220. *Wolf and Twins*. Mosaic Panel, 4 ft. 4½ in. wide.
From Aldborough, Yorks. (Cat.no.184)

221. *Orpheus and the Beasts.* Mosaic Pavement, 14 ft. 8 in. wide. From the Barton Farm Villa, Cirencester (Cat.no.185)

222. *Orpheus and the Beasts.* Mosaic Pavement, 49 ft. square. From the Woodchester Villa, Glos. (Cat.no.186)

223. *Medusa Mask*. Mosaic Panel, 3 ft. 2 in. diameter. From the Bignor Villa, Sussex (Cat.no.189)

224. *The Rape of Ganymede*. Part of a Mosaic Pavement, 7 ft. 2 in. diameter. From the Bignor Villa, Sussex (Cat.no.190)

225–226. *Venus and Cupids as Gladiators*. Mosaic Frieze, 14 ft. 8 in. long. From the Bignor Villa, Sussex (Cat.no.191)

227. *Chariot-Race*. Engraving after a Mosaic Panel from the Horkstow Villa, Lincs. 19 ft. 5 in. long (Cat.no.198)

228–229. *Bellerophon and the Chimaera; The Rape of Europa.* Parts of a Mosaic Pavement, 8 ft. and 7 ft. wide.
From the Lullingstone Villa, Kent (Cat.nos.192–3)

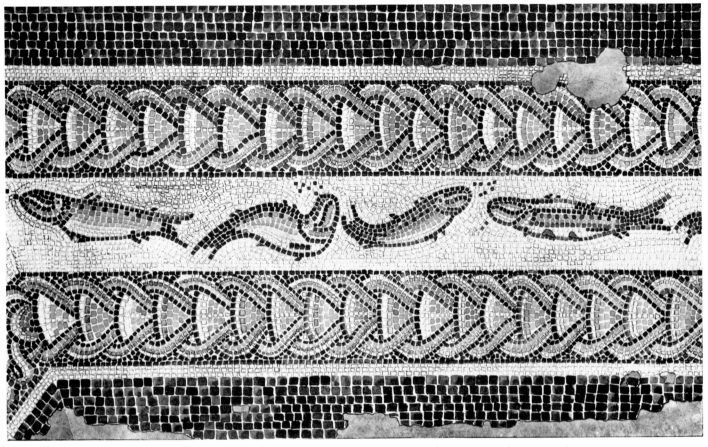

230. *Fish*. Mosaic Panel, 8 ft. long. From the Lufton Villa, Somerset (Cat.no.194)

231. *Scene with a Cock-Headed Man*. Mosaic Panel, 2 ft. 5 in. high. From the Brading Villa, Isle of Wight (Cat.no.197)

232. *Orpheus and the Beasts.* Mosaic Pavement, 8 ft. 2 in. high. From the Brading Villa, Isle of Wight
(Cat.no.195)

233. *Astronomer.* Part of a Mosaic Pavement, 3 ft. 6 in. high. From the Brading Villa, Isle of Wight
(Cat.no.196)

234. *Neptune, etc.* Engraving after a Mosaic Pavement from the Frampton Villa, Dorset (Cat.no.199)

235. *Scenes from Virgil*. Mosaic Pavement, 13 ft. square. From the Low Ham Villa, Somerset (Cat.no.200)

APPENDIX OF
COMPARATIVE MATERIAL

THE illustrations on plates 236–262 are reproduced by courtesy of the following: Dr. M. J. Vermaseren, Amsterdam (pls.236,242,245); Schweizerisches Landesmuseum, Zürich (pl.237); Römisches Museum, Augst (photo Elisabeth Schulz, pl.238); Rijksmuseum G. M. Kam, Nijmegen (pl.239); Museum of Antiquities, King's College, Newcastle (photo Otto Fein, pl.240; photo C. M. Daniels, pl.256); His Grace the Duke of Wellington (photo Otto Fein, pl.243); Musée des Antiquités Nationales, St. Germain-en-Laye (photo Hurault, pl.244); Yorkshire Museum, York (photo Otto Fein, pl.246); Württembergisches Landesmuseum, Stuttgart (pl.247); Kunsthistorisches Museum, Vienna (pl.249); Museum of Antiquities, Istanbul (pl.250); Rheinisches Landesmuseum, Bonn (pls.251,254); Straubing Museum (pls.252–253); Lt.-Col. G. W. Meates (photo Otto Fein, pl.255); Musei Vaticani (pl.257); Landesmuseum, Trier (pl.258); Biblioteca Apostolica Vaticana (pls.260–261); Roman Baths Museum, Bath (photo Otto Fein, pl.262). Pl.241 is from a photo by R. Johnson, Cambridge; pls.248,259 are from photos by J. B. Ward Perkins, Rome.

236. Marble Statue of Mercury, from Merida (*cf.*Cat.no.20)

237. Bronze Statuette of Mercury, from Thalwil (*cf.*Cat.no.21)

238. Bronze Statuette of Venus, from Augst (*cf.*Cat.no.28)

239. Bronze Head of Trajan (?), from Nijmegen (*cf.*Cat.no.1)

240. Bronze Head of Pomona(?) from Benwell (*cf.*Cat.no.21)

241. Head of the Varvakeion. Copy of Pheidias's Athene Parthenos (*cf.*Cat.no.24)

242. Stucco Head of Serapis, from the S. Prisca Mithraeum, Rome (*cf.*Cat.no.38)

243. Stone Head of Serapis, from Silchester (*cf.*Cat.no.38)

244. Head of Mercury, from Lezoux (*cf.*Cat.no.44)

245. Relief of Phanes-Aion, Modena
(*cf*.Cat.no.71)

246. Tombstone of Julia Brica, from York
(*cf*.Cat.no.88)

247. Relief of Three Water-Nymphs, from Unterheimbach
(*cf*.Cat.no.68)

248. Stone Relief of Male Sea-Medusa.
from Hatra, Mesopotamia (*cf*.Cat.no.91)

249. Gilt-Bronze Helmet from Nicopolis, Moesia (*cf*.Cat.no.98)

250. Silvered Bronze Face-Mask Visor Helmet from Vize, Thrace (*cf*.Cat.no.99)

251. Ritual Bronze Crown from Xanten (*cf*.Cat.no.127)

252–253. Mars and Victory on a Bronze Horse-Chamfron from Straubing (*cf*.Cat.no.103)

254. Engraved Glass Bowl with Hare-Hunt, Bonn (*cf*.Cat.no.142)

255. Black-Gloss Beaker from the
Lullingstone Villa, Kent (*cf*.Cat.no.154)

256. Sherd with *Appliqué* Smith-God,
from Corbridge (*cf*.Cat.no.161)

257. Central Panel of Marble Sarcophagus from the Domitilla Catacomb,
Rome (*cf*.Cat.no.176)

258. Mosaic of an Astronomer, from Trier
(*cf*.Cat.no.196)

259. Mosaic of the Three Graces, from Sabratha, Tripolitania
(*cf*.Cat.no.200)

260–261. Aeneas at Dido's Court. Miniature, c.A.D.400. Aeneas and Dido in the Cave. Miniature, c.A.D.500. (*cf*.Cat.no.200)

262. Hound Devouring a Deer, from Bath (*cf*.Cat.no.47)

CATALOGUE

CATALOGUE

SCULPTURE IN THE ROUND

Portraits of Imperial Persons

1. HEAD OF CLAUDIUS   Plate 7

From the River Alde, Rendham, Suffolk. Mid-first century A.D. Bronze (hollow-cast). Height: 13 inches. *British Museum (on loan from Mrs. D. M. E. Hollond)*

First published by Sir George Macdonald in 1926, this piece was cleaned and rephotographed in the British Museum on the occasion of the nineteenth centenary in 1950 of the foundation of the *colonia* of Camulodunum. The lower line of the neck is torn and ragged; and there can be little doubt but that this head was violently hacked from its body and carried off as loot from some important Roman centre. The find-spot suggests that Camulodunum was that centre; and since the portrait is of Julio-Claudian date, the looters are likely to have been the followers of Boudicca, who sacked the *colonia* in A.D. 61. The fact that the head is not colossal probably precludes it from having belonged to the cult-statue of a deified Emperor erected in the temple of Claudius. The statue could have stood in some other public building or in an open space in the city; and the slight backward tilt of the head may indicate that the figure was equestrian. The eyes, now hollow, would once have been completed with enamel or coloured stones or glass-paste, representing eye-balls, pupils, and irises.

The identification of the personage portrayed with Claudius has been widely accepted; and the bronze certainly re-produces some of the features familiar from well-authentic-ated coin-, cameo-, and sculptural portraits of that Emperor, namely the flat crown of the head, the thick, neat hair, and the sharply angular bridge of the nose. On the other hand, there are certain characteristics of those portraits which are missing here – the high, vertically furrowed brow, the marked distance between the nostrils and the slightly pro-truding upper lip, the folds of flesh round the mouth, the double chin, and the powerful and stocky neck; while the huge flap-like ears, so prominent on the River Alde head, are distinctive of some, but not of all, Claudius' portraits. Furthermore, portraits of Claudius normally show an even, unbroken fringe of locks across the brow, whereas here the hair forks above the forehead, much in the Augustan style. None the less, this bronze, despite these discrepancies, is more like Claudius than it is like any other Emperor or prince of the Julio-Claudian period whose features are known to us; and obviously no other claimant fits the context of its provenance so well. But if it were intended to depict Claud-ius it could hardly have come from a Roman or Italian

workshop, given its iconographical anomalies, but must be reckoned as a very good provincial product, classical in its inspiration and perhaps by a well-trained Gaulish artist who had never seen the Emperor in the flesh (life-like in appear-ance as this rendering is) and idealised his subject by showing him as leaner and more refined in features than he looked in actuality and as definitely younger than he was at the time at which the portrait would have been commissioned. The bronze busts of Augustus and Livia in the Louvre, found at Neuilly-le-Réal (Allier) and fortunately provided with incised inscriptions stating their identity, reveal the trans-formations that imperial faces could undergo at the hands of provincial portraitists.[1] That the River Alde head depicts no Emperor or prince, but some outstanding individual in the Roman province, is very improbable. But it is a possibil-ity that cannot be entirely ruled out.

Journal of Roman Studies, xvi, 1926, pp. 3–7, pls. 2–3; *Catalogue of an Exhibition of Romano-British Antiquities in the Castle Museum, Colchester, July, 1950*, p. 8, no. 2, pl. 1; *Transactions of the Essex Archaeological Society*, n.s., xxv, 1955, pp. 10–2, pl. 2.

1a.* HEAD OF GERMANICUS (?)   Plate 1

From Bosham (?), near Chichester, Sussex. Early-first century A.D. Marble. Height: 11½ inches. Tip of the nose restored. A section of the back hair has been broken off and clumsily replaced. Bust modern. *British Museum.*

At first sight it might appear unlikely that this lifesize marble head of a youngish man, worked in late-Augustan or Tiberian style, reached Bosham, near Chichester (Noviomagus Regnensium), where it is said to have been discovered, during the Roman period; and, indeed, its almost 'mint-condition' might be deemed to support the suspicion that it was a 'Grand Tour' import. If the subject is, as seems probable, a member of the ruling House, he could well be Germanicus, who died in A.D. 19; and it is not very easy to

---

1. A. de Ridder, *Les bronzes antiques du Louvre*, i, 1913, p. 11, nos. 28–9, pl. 5. Similar divergencies from Trajan's official portraits are displayed by a bronze head of provincial workmanship found in the River Waal near Nijmegen in Holland and very probably depicting Trajan. This head, which is roughly lifesize, has lank locks of hair combed forward to form a straight, horizontal line running low across the brow and deep, strongly accented creases furrowing the lower portion of the face (Rijksmuseum Kam, Nijmegen: *Bulletin van de Vereeniging tot Bevordering der Kennis van de Antieke Beschaving te 'S-Gravenhage*, xxxi, 1956, pp. 26–30, figs. 1, 3; *Fasti Archaeologici*, x, 1957, no. 3719, fig. 91; H. Hinz, *Xanten zur Römerzeit*, 1960, fig. on p. 22). Plate 239.
*No. 201 in the Exhibition Hand-list.

envisage a Roman official who arrived in Britain in, or after, 43 bringing with him a portrait of so much earlier a date, even as an heirloom. On the other hand, local tradition in the area (in which there is, incidentally, no country mansion) has it that the find-spot of the marble was Bosham not far from the place in which large Roman buildings of the late-first and early-second century have recently come to light at Fishbourne[1] about a mile to the west of Chichester. Could the head have come from an earlier building near that site, perhaps a shrine of the Imperial House[2] erected by Cogidubnus, in which a portrait of Germanicus might have been set up? This would have been in keeping with the king's honouring of the *domus divina* in the famous Chichester inscription;[3] which might itself have come originally from the Fishbourne site; and with the numismatic tribute paid by Claudius to his brother's memory.[4]

Sussex Archaeological Collections, liii, 1910, p. 272, pl. 25; *Jahrbuch des Deutschen Archäologischen Instituts: Archäologischer Anzeiger*, xxvi, 1911, cols. 305-8, fig. 12; *VCH Sussex*, iii, 1935, p. 50 and pl. opposite.

2. HEAD OF HADRIAN (?)   Plate 2

From Worlington, Cambridgeshire. Second quarter of the second century A.D. (?). Bronze (hollow-cast). Height: 4½ inches. *Museum of Archaeology and of Ethnology, Cambridge*

This head is one of a group of small male, portrait-like heads (*cf.* nos. 3–5), all with beards and plastically rendered eyes. Three come from East Anglia, one from near-by Northamptonshire, and all are from rural find-spots. In the case of two certainly, and of the other two most probably, each was attached to the top of some object, such as a ceremonial staff or sceptre. This fact of their one-time attachment would seem to preclude their being portraits of private persons; and despite their very provincial style, they are, for the most part, too conventional and classical in type to depict Celtic gods. They are more likely to show native versions of the features of a series of second-century Emperors, perhaps mounted on batons and carried either by local administrators at civil functions in the countryside or by priests or magistrates conducting some rustic form of Emperor-cult.

In small provincial works of this kind, most probably made in Britain by British or visiting Gaulish craftsmen, it would be idle to expect realistic and striking likenesses. The Worlington head, which seems to be the earliest of the group, has a broad face, a low brow, above which runs a neat row of curls, large staring eyes, a thick moustache, and a trim 'archaised' curly beard, which meets the hair in front of each ear; and it is conceivable that this could be a very poor and very local rendering of Hadrian's features. Apart from the fringe of curls above the brow and a conventional-

ised, twisted rope of hair running down behind each ear to the nape of the neck at the rear, the crown and back of the head are completely smooth and unworked. But since there is a rivet in the centre of the crown, while a round hole pierces the base of the neck behind, a helmet or some form of headdress must once have been attached to hide the bald area. Three round holes at the base of the neck in front indicate that the head was at one time fixed to the top of a staff or sceptre, perhaps of wood or iron.

In front, at the base of the neck, is an object which could be just an ornamental finish to the piece, but which might, as has, indeed, been suggested (see bibliography below), be a torc, with mouldings not unlike those on a series of torcs from the Brigantian region.[5] If this is a torc, then we must explain the bronze as being either a native deity or chieftain with unusually classical hair and beard or a Roman Emperor depicted quite abnormally with a native ornament indicating high distinction. It should be borne in mind that the three other bronzes of the group can hardly be explained as other than imperial portraits.

Proceedings of the Cambridge Antiquarian Society, xlix, 1955, p. 89, pl. 7, c.

3. BUST OF ANTONINUS PIUS   Plate 3

From Willingham Fen, Cambridgeshire. Third quarter of the second century A.D. Bronze (hollow-cast). Height: 3¾ inches. *Museum of Archaeology and of Ethnology, Cambridge*

Next in date within this group of bronzes (*cf.* no. 2), to judge by its hair- and beard-style, is the piece from Willingham Fen – a head with a long neck that terminates in the upper portion of a draped bust. Into the bust, which is partially broken in front and pierced by a round hole behind, the shaft of some baton-like object was obviously inserted. This is the most classical and naturalistic member of the group; and the narrow face, the short curly beard, and the way in which the thick hair grows low on the centre of the brow in a kind of triangle immediately suggest that the subject is Antoninus Pius. On the crown and back of the head the rendering of the locks in low relief is careful. But the crude treatment of the features, of the slanting and somewhat staring eyes in particular, betrays the hand of the provincial craftsman.

Journal of Roman Studies, xxxix, 1949, p. 19, pl. 2.

4. BUST OF LUCIUS VERUS (?)   Plate 4

From Duston, Northamptonshire. Second half of the second century A.D. Bronze (hollow-cast). Height: 5¼ inches. *Northampton Museum*

More like Marcus Aurelius' colleague, Lucius Verus, than it is like any other Emperor, and very different from no. 3 in style, is the draped bust from Duston. The actual resemblance of its features to those of Lucius is relatively slight, but the hair might be regarded as a stylised version of his familiar mop of curls; and although the piece is superior to the other

1. *Antiquaries Journal*, xlii, 1962, pp. 15-23, figs. 1-3, pls. 8-13.
2. As suggested by I. A. Richmond. For the story of the head's discovery, see K. M. MacDermott, *Bosham Church: its History and Antiquities*, 1911, p. 7.
3. *Corpus Inscriptionum Latinarum*, vii, no. 11.
4. *Catalogue of the Coins of the Roman Empire in the British Museum*, i, 1923, pp. 193-4, nos. 214-8, pl. 37, nos. 2, 9.

5. *Archaeologia Aeliana*, ser. 4, xix, 1941, pp. 23-5, pl. 2.

bronzes of the group in delicacy of workmanship, it has a decidedly more abstract, patterned, and generally Celtic character than they have. The artist was probably a Gaul, less imitative of the classical, naturalistic manner than faithful to his native art-traditions in the rendering of the human form. The face, which is very thin and narrow, is crowned by a kind of diadem of ten spiral curls above a row of seven puffed locks that grow low across the brow. The back of the head is slightly flattened, and there the hair, which ends on the nape of the neck in a thick mat, is more summarily treated than in front. The eyes are large, almond-shaped, and slightly slanting and the ears are sketchily worked. The drapery of the bust is carried out in straight, regular, unrealistic folds, in a style that is the hall-mark of some local Gaulish, and many Romano–British (in the strict sense: cf. p. 6), sculptured stones. Apart from the hair-style, which is definitely that of the second half of the second century, not of the fourth century, we might almost describe this small provincial bronze as a foretaste of the late-antique. The back of the bust is hollow and the piece must have been soldered onto the object that once carried it.

Archaeologia, xliii, 1871, p. 129, no. 50; *The Antiquary*, xxx, 1894, p. 103 with drawing; *Catalogue of an Exhibition of Romano–British Antiquities in the Castle Museum, Colchester, July, 1950*, p. 14, no. 33.

5. BUST OF COMMODUS (?)   Plate 5

From Cottenham Fen, Cambridgeshire. Last quarter of the second century A.D. Bronze (hollow-cast). Height: 8 inches. *Museum of Archaeology and of Ethnology, Cambridge*

The fourth bronze of the group, from Cottenham Fen, is, like no. 4, hollow behind and depicts either Marcus Aurelius or, more probably, his son, Commodus. Here the curly hair and beard are much more naturalistic than they are on no. 4, but the drapery, which appears to consist of tunic and mantle, displays rigid, patterned folds very similar to those that we have noted there; while in front, above the mantle, is what seems to be an *aegis*, against which a snake is writhing. An *aegis* is worn on some coin- and medallion-portraits of second-century Emperors. The eyes are, again, strikingly large, almond-shaped, and slanting. The head is topped by a species of Corinthian helmet, bowler-hat-shaped, with downturned peak and detachable bonnet, the front of which is moulded in the form of a grotesque human face. In official portraiture second-century Emperors are not helmeted; and the whole piece presents us with a curious blend of Celtic and classical Roman elements.

Proceedings of the Cambridge Antiquarian Society, xxxvii, 1937, p. 54, pl. 4, a.

6. HEAD OF CONSTANTINE THE GREAT   Plate 12

From York (Eburacum). Early-fourth century A.D. Local stone. Height: 18 inches. *Yorkshire Museum, York*

This colossal laureate head, roughly twice lifesize, was rescued by I. A. Richmond in 1944 from its limbo in the basement of the Yorkshire Philosophical Society's Museum.

Its precise find-spot is not specified, but it came to light sometime before 1823, the year in which the Museum acquired it. Despite its badly weathered state, it wears a commanding aspect and reveals the hand of a skilled and sensitive sculptor who had his workshop in York. This artist is unlikely to have been a Briton, but may well have been a highly trained Gaul, or even a man of Mediterranean origin, who came to Britain in the service of the imperial court at Eburacum. The thick fringe of straight locks above the brow, the way in which the pupils of the eyes are bored, the absence of a beard, and the broad, 'geometric' treatment of the facial features are all distinctive of the late-antique; while the refined classicism with which those features are combined points to a date not later than the early decades of the fourth century. This may, indeed, be the earliest portrait of the Emperor in the round that has come down to us, perhaps executed at the time of his elevation to the purple at York in 306 and erected in one of the public buildings of the fortress or *colonia*.

Antiquaries Journal, xxiv, 1914, pp. 1–5, pl. 1; *Royal Commission on Historical Monuments (England): York i (Roman)*, 1962, p. 112, no. 8, pl. 42.

Portraits of Private Persons

7. HEAD OF MAN   Plate 8

From Gloucester (Glevum), site of Bon Marché, Northgate Street. First century A.D. British limestone. Height: 8 inches. *Gloucester City Museum*

This male, beardless head offers a remarkable example of a genuinely Romano–British product in which the principles of three-dimensional classical carving and features that can be recognised at once as Celtic are harmoniously and most effectively combined. The general build of the skull and the structure of the brow are Graeco–Roman; and, indeed, it might be said that without the stimulus of classical portrait-sculpture the piece could never have been conceived. But the treatment of its individual forms is Celtic – the heavy locks that form an ornamental pattern above the forehead, each lock being engraved with a series of regular, grooved lines; the stylised ears; the wedge-shaped nose; the narrow, tapering face; the slit-like, lipless mouth; the enormous lentoid, projecting eyeballs; and the aloof, almost wrapt, expression. All this recalls immediately the heads of warriors on the Aylesford bucket (cf. p. 8 and note 3). Yet for all its stylisation and its air of unearthly spirituality, this is obviously a portrait of a kind, the schematised likeness of some Romano–British personage. The very markedly native treatment of the eyes and the rendering of the hair, which appears to imitate the Julio-Claudian style, place it early in the history of the province. The straight, vertical line in which the head and neck terminate behind would seem to indicate that the sculpture, which shows traces of reddish colouring, either was set against a flat background or formed part of an architectural element.

Transactions of the Bristol and Gloucester Archaeological Society, lvi, 1934, pp. 78–9, pl. 8; *Journal of Roman Studies*, xxv, p. 218, pl. 37, fig. 2; T. D. Kendrick, *Anglo-Saxon Art to A.D. 900*, 1938, pp. 4, 13, 20, pl. 4; *Antiquity*, xxxv, 1961, pl. 32.

8. HEAD OF GIRL   Plate 9

From Silkstead, Otterbourne, near Compton, Hampshire. First or early-second century A.D. Bronze (hollow-cast). Height: 5 inches. *Winchester Museum*

This bronze is clumsier in workmanship and aesthetically less impressive than no. 7, but exhibits a similar fusion of classical and Celtic traits. Roman are the three-dimensional structure of the skull, the full, plump face and small mouth, and the realistically rendered, shortish hair, which is simply waved on either side of the central parting and ripples down over the crown and back of the head as far as the junction of the neck and shoulders. Celtic are the completely unrealistic ears outlined by hatching and the large, almond-shaped eyes also outlined by hatching to indicate lashes, while the pupils consist of tiny black inset pebbles from the Reading Beds. The treatment of the eyes is reminiscent of that on the late-La Tène bronze masks from a Celtic burial at Welwyn, in Hertfordshire.[1] This portrait is difficult to date. The coiffure could be either a variant of a Julio–Claudian style or influenced by the simple, classicising hair-do affected by Sabina, Hadrian's Empress, in her later stage.

Journal of Roman Studies, xxviii, 1938, p. 196, pl. 26, fig. 1; T. S. Drew, *Compton, near Winchester*, 1934, frontispiece; *Catalogue of an Exhibition of Romano–British Antiquities in the Castle Museum, Colchester, July, 1950*, p. 17, no. 42, pl. 7.

9. HEAD OF MAN   Plate 11

From Hawkshaw, Tweedsmuir, Peebleshire. Early-second century A.D. Marble. Height: 10½ inches. *National Museum of Antiquities of Scotland, Edinburgh*

This over lifesize head was found far from the site of any Roman road or fort, in the wilds of Tweedsmuir. It represents an elderly, clean-shaven man. The nose is broken and the lower portion of the chin is lost. The face wears a severe and somewhat forbidding expression and is undoubtedly a portrait by the hand of an accomplished artist. The eyes are plain, the hair on the back of the head is sketchily worked, as though the piece were not intended to be seen from the rear, and the brow is crowned by a fringe of straight, striated, lank locks, of which the side ones curve in very slightly towards the centre. The mouth is a wide, close-set slit, with very markedly drooping corners. The style of the sculpture would seem to be Trajanic, but it is not a likeness of Trajan, whose mien is normally more open and genial and whose portraits never show the downturned mouth. Again, although Trajan's hair falls across the brow in lanky locks, they are never so rigidly regular as are the locks on the Hawkshaw head, and their tendency is to fork, not inwards towards the centre, but outwards towards the

sides.[2] Who, then, was the subject of the marble? How did it get to Peebleshire? And what class of artist carved it? The features are of Roman or Italian type and the piece must, in view of its large dimensions, depict some important personage, such as a general or provincial governor. There is no country seat near Hawkshaw whose one-time owners could have brought the sculpture back as a 'Grand Tour' souvenir; and the odds are definitely in favour of it having reached Scotland during the Roman period. The best explanation of its presence in the district is that it once formed part of a triumphal monument erected in the countryside to commemorate the Roman conquest of the Lowlands in Flavian times and their domination by Rome into the early years of Trajan's principate.[3] If such a monument existed, it is likely to have been worked in Britain in foreign marble imported for the purpose. The sculptor could have been in some way associated with the army, a man well trained in Mediterranean iconographic traditions, but possibly betraying in his treatment of the hair a Gaulish origin. For the nearest parallels to this treatment are to be found on two Gallo–Roman bronzes – the head of a youth from Bordeaux, now in the St. Germain-en-Laye Museum,[4] and the head of a Helvetian chieftain from Prilly (Vaud) in Switzerland, now in the Historical Museum in Bern.[5]

Proceedings of the Society of Antiquaries of Scotland, lxvi, 1931–2, pp. 326–9, figs. 28, 30.

10. BUST OF MAN   Plate 6

From the Lullingstone Villa, Kent. Second quarter of the second century A.D. Greek marble. Height: 2 feet, 4 inches. *British Museum (on loan from the Kent County Council)*

This bust was unearthed in 1949 in the 'basement-room' on the eastern side of the house. With it came to light another, slightly larger and slightly later, bust, the head of which had been sundered from the body and was found a few feet distant from it. Both are carved in what is probably Pentelic marble by Mediterranean sculptors and depict men of Mediterranean origin; and they would undoubtedly have been suspected of being 'Grand Tour' imports had they not appeared in an unimpeachable archaeological context. Since the bodies of the busts are hollow behind, each with its supporting vertical shaft left visible, they were clearly meant to stand against a wall or in niches or recesses; and since they are of slightly different sizes and show divergencies of technique and style, they were obviously not made as pendants. Both were evidently intended to be realistic likenesses.

Apart from the loss of the nose and a few minor abrasions, no. 10 is comparatively well preserved. The form of the bust is that characteristic of the Hadrianic and early-to-mid-

---

1. *Archaeologia*, lxiii, 1911–2, p. 21, pl. 2, figs. 3–5.

2. For the latest full-dress survey of Trajan's iconography, see W. H. Gross, *Bildnisse Traians*, 1940.

3. I. A. Richmond, *Roman Britain*, 1955, p. 148. Alternatively, the head might represent an unusual, but not unparalleled, survival of Trajanic hair-style into late-Hadrianic and early-Antonine times, and be connected with the early-Antonine re-occupation of Southern Scotland.

4. *Proceedings of the Society of Antiquaries of Scotland*, lxvi, 1931–2, p. 327, fig. 29.

5. W. Deonna, *L'art romain en Suisse*, 1942, fig. 46.

Antonine periods; and with this the absence of heavy drilling in the curly hair and short, pointed beard is in harmony. The hair is combed forward over the crown of the head in thick locks, which make a neat fringe above the brow, and a luxuriant thatch covers the nape of the neck. The pupils of the eyes are rendered by two very shallow, linked depressions. The head, slightly turned towards the spectator's left, reveals a benign, if serious and somewhat dreamy, countenance; and the sculpture as a whole exhibits the soft texture and gently modulated surfaces that we associate with Roman portraits of east-Mediterranean, rather than of Italian or western, provenance. This bust cannot be identified with any Emperor of its period. It has not the features or the hair-style either of Hadrian[1] or of Antoninus Pius.[2] Nor has it the features and deeply drilled eyes, hair, and beard of Marcus Aurelius and Lucius Verus.[3] We must describe the piece, carved not much later than c. A.D.125–135, as depicting an unknown Roman of distinction, aged about forty-five or fifty, and wearing semi-military dress – tunic and fringed cloak.

It would seem to be highly improbable that the two busts from Lullingstone were carved in Britain for Romanised natives by imported artists working in imported marble. More reasonable is the view that they represent part of the family portrait-gallery of some foreign individual in the imperial service, stationed in Britain for a longish term; and that they were brought by him into the province. Such an individual could have lived, partly at least, at Lullingstone during the period of the site's late-second-century occupation, c. 180–200, when the villa was remodelled and redecorated on luxurious lines.[4] The other bust, carved c. 155–165, or even later, possibly portrays the one-time villa owner, while this one could feature one of his relatives. Or both busts may depict the owner's relatives, the subject of neither having ever landed on these shores.

When the villa was deserted by its late-second-century owners, probably during the troubles that attended Clodius Albinus' departure from Britain for the Continent in A.D. 196, these bulky family portraits would have been abandoned to their fate, exposed in the empty and disintegrating house, for roughly eighty years,[5] to the onslaughts of the weather – hence the wear and the facial damages displayed by both busts – and to the attentions of human intruders, one of whom may have dealt the apparently deliberate blow that rent asunder the head and body of the later bust. That these two portions, found separately, do indeed belong together is beyond all doubt, since the flat lower surface of the shaft at the base of the neck precisely fits the corresponding upper surface of the shaft on the body; but the shaving down in ancient times of the shoulders of the body, for some reason at which we can only guess, makes the head when reared upon the body now appear most unpleasantly top-heavy.[6]

The earlier bust and the body of the later bust were discovered lying face-downwards on the flight of three steps that originally led down into the 'basement-room' from the north, but which were blocked up towards the end of the third century.[7] They had stood on the top and bottom step respectively and were knocked over when the ceiling of the 'basement-room' and the whole of the apartment above it collapsed in the fire that destroyed this part of the villa, probably in the early-fifth century.[8] The right-hand portion of the body of the later bust was snapped off on the edge of the lowest step, a clean, sharp break being produced. Its head had been carefully placed on a small stand, just to the east of the steps, so as to rest against the north wall of the room. There was no sign of any intention of hiding the marbles. Not only had they obviously been arranged and displayed in these positions with deliberate care, but opposite the centre of the steps three votive pots were sunk into the floor of the room, while a fourth pot was sunk opposite the head of the later bust. Of these pots, two, a third-century cooking-pot and a Rhenish motto-beaker of the mid-third century, were sunk into the original concrete floor and sealed over by its later clay floor of Constantinian date; the other two pots are of coarse fourth-century ware and both were sunk through the Constantinian clay floor. It would seem, then, that the deposition of the busts in the 'basement-room' took place contemporaneously with the re-occupation of the villa c. A.D. 280;[9] and that they continued to be cared for there well on into the fourth century.

The most plausible explanation of this strange phenomenon is that the late-third-century re-occupiers, presumably members of a new family, may, when entering into possession, have found the two busts standing or lying about in the house. To such newcomers these busts, both weathered, and one broken, as they were, would have been impressive and awe-inspiring reminders of earlier owners, portraits of persons whose *manes* were spiritual powers still to be reckoned with. What was to be done about these sculptures? The course adopted was to relegate them to honourable retirement in a species of 'mausoleum' in the 'basement-room', where the departed could be propitiated with worship and gifts. That the late-third-century occupants brought these second-century portraits to Lullingstone for the purpose of venerating them in that room is extremely unlikely. The fact that the head and body of the later bust were not juxtaposed suggests that the persons who placed them there in those positions did not know that they had belonged together. It is noteworthy that the busts and their votive pots remained in the 'basement-room', undisturbed and apparently respected, after the room above their 'mausoleum' had been converted to Christian use (nos. 175–6).

The Lullingstone portrait-busts have thus a special interest from the historical and religious standpoints. Of no less interest is their aesthetic significance as domestic ornaments. Classical marble sculptures, mythological in character, and some indeterminate fragments of marble figures, had, in-

1. E.g. M. Wegner, *Das römische Herrscherbild: Hadrian, etc.*, 1956.
2. E.g. M. Wegner, *Die Herrscherbildnisse in antoninischer Zeit*, 1939.
3. *Ibid.*
4. G. W. Meates, *Lullingstone Roman Villa*, 1955, pp. 90–102, figs. 6–7b.
5. *Ibid.*, p. xv.   6. *Ibid.*, pl. 27.

7. *Ibid*, pp. 74, 106.   8. *Ibid.*, p. 165.   9. *Ibid.*, pp. xv, 105–6.

deed, already come to light in one Romano–British villa, that at Woodchester, in Gloucestershire.[1] But as over life-size family portrait-busts of high artistic quality these pieces represent an as yet unique discovery – a modest counterpart to the impressive portrait-gallery of over seventy marble heads and busts, depicting both imperial and private persons, that was found in the great Gallo–Roman villa at Chiragan, near Toulouse.[2]

Journal of Roman Studies, xl, 1950, pp. 112–3, pls. 10, fig. 2; 12; *Archaeologia Cantiana*, lxiii, 1950, pp. 33–43, pls. 2–4; G. W. Meates, *Lullingstone Roman Villa*, 1955, pp. 70–89, pls. 17–29; ed. R. L. S. Bruce-Mitford, *Recent Archaeological Excavations in Britain*, 1956, pp. 96–100, figs. 36–7, pls. 19, b–20, b; *Catalogue of an Exhibition of Romano–British Antiquities in the Castle Museum, Colchester, July, 1950*, pl. 5.

11. HEAD OF WOMAN   Plate 10
From York (Eburacum), Fishergate. *c.* A.D. 260. Local grit-stone. Height: 11 inches. *Yorkshire Museum, York*

This lady has the coiffure of Gallienus' Empress, Salonina. The hair above the brow and on either side of the face is dressed in stiff, ridge-like waves, leaving the ears exposed, while the rest of the hair is turned up behind in a flat pad or fold, which covers the back of the head from neck to crown. The piece is competently carved, no doubt by an immigrant continental artist. The face is youthful and decidedly attractive, with large eyes, pointed chin, and faintly smiling mouth. Since the hair is very summarily rendered and the irises and pupils of the eyes are not marked in, as they normally would be at this period, we must suppose either that the portrait was never finished or, more probably, that paint, concealing the somewhat unsightly surface of the stone, once supplied the details.

The Studio, July, 1961, p. 8, fig. on right; *Royal Commission on Historical Monuments (England): York i (Roman)*, 1962, p. 131, no. 113, pl. 58.

Graeco-Roman Deities

12. GROUP OF BACCHUS, ETC.   Plate 34
From the Walbrook Mithraeum, London. *c.* A.D. 250. Italian marble. Height: $13\frac{1}{2}$ inches; width at base: $11\frac{3}{4}$ inches. *Guildhall Museum, London*

The central and by far the largest figure in this group is that of Bacchus, who stands naked towards the front, with his head turned slightly towards the spectator's right. His weight is thrown on his left leg, sending his right hip curving outwards, his left knee is slightly bent, and his left foot advanced a fraction beyond his right foot. The eyes are blank, the tip of the nose is abrased, but not broken, the thick, undrilled hair is parted in the centre and massed on

either side of the face, while a long, corkscrew curl falls forward over each shoulder onto the breast. In the hair above the brow the god wears a triangular-shaped diadem. The cheeks are full, the mouth is sensuous, the general expression of the face is mild and dreamy.

Bacchus' right arm is raised and bent across the top of his head, so that his shoulders slope down towards his left and his head is gently inclined in the same direction. With his right hand he grips the body of a large snake, the tail of which twists itself round his arm, while its neck and body are backed against a vine-branch, which follows roughly the line of his arm and then terminates in three large, flat, heavy, and summarily rendered clusters of grapes, that hang down beyond his left shoulder. The branch shoots out more or less horizontally from a gnarled tree-trunk, seen on the spectator's left: this is either the vine-stock itself or the tree on which the vine is trained. The upper portion of the tree-trunk has disappeared, carrying with it most of the figure of a Pan, who was perched upon it and of whom one shaggy leg and hoof and the lower part of the shaggy torso alone remain.

Backed against the lower section of the tree-trunk is a bald-pated Silenus, wearing a long, pointed, silky beard and seated to the front upon the back of a little ass, which stands quietly in profile towards the spectator's right, with its head turned back towards its rider. The upper half of the Silenus is naked, apart from a collar round the neck; but below he wears a garment knotted round the waist, pulled taut across the legs, and then gathered tightly round the ankles. Against his chest he clasps a large wine-cup in both hands, the fingers of which are awkwardly and stiffly drawn. His face is asymmetrical; his right eye is blank, while there is a tiny drill-hole in one corner of his left eye; the beard is un-drilled; and the drapery is flat and unplastic, with very sketchily indicated folds. The ass has no right eye, since this would have been invisible; and there is an ugly, lumpy 'bridge' attaching the creature's muzzle to its neck.

The left forearm and hand of Bacchus, and any object that he may have held in that hand, are lost. These portions of him once projected vertically forward and the left elbow rests against the chest of a young, naked Satyr, who stands on the god's left, with his legs wide apart and frontal, while his trunk is thrown back and turned three-quarters towards the spectator's left. Part of his function is to support his master, who is swaying visibly and seems to be none too steady on his legs; and the Satyr's right hand is placed against Bacchus' back, while his left arm is extended towards some vanished object (possibly once supported by his lost left hand), of which nothing now remains but a chunk of marble seen between the god's left hip and the Satyr's abdomen. Possibly the god dangled a bunch of grapes over a bowl or dish held by his henchman. The latter's head is snapped off at the neck; and so is that of his companion standing on his left, a frontal, long-robed Maenad, who holds in both hands and hugs against her breast a *cista mystica*, or sacred casket, adorned at top and bottom with slightly projecting horizontal bands and closed by a dome-shaped lid. In front of

1. S. Lyons, *An Account of the Roman Antiquities Discovered at Wood-chester in the County of Gloucester*, 1797, pls. 36–40.
2. *Mémoires présentés par divers savants à l'Académie des Inscriptions et Belles-Lettres*, ire série, xi, 1901, pp. 329–44, pls. 16–25.

her skirts a panther crouches to the right and looks up to the left in the direction of the god and Satyr. This beast lacks a right eye and nostril and teeth in the right-hand half of its maw. The Maenad's robe consists of a pouched, sleeveless tunic reaching to the feet and with folds very summarily marked. A snaky lock dangles on each shoulder; there appears to be a collar round the neck; the hands are clumsily drawn and disproportionately large; and the skirts, where the panther conceals them, are unworked.

The back of the group was not intended to be visible; for while the naked bodies of Bacchus and the Satyr are at any rate partly modelled in the rear, the three standing figures and the tree-trunk are very much flattened behind; and there, too, the hair of Bacchus, the Satyr's right hand, the tree-trunk, the vine-branch, and the Maenad's drapery are all unfinished and covered everywhere with tooling-marks. The work is, in fact, although technically statuary in the round, in all essentials a pictorial relief without a background; and it is, perhaps, an instance of religious sculpture designed for silhouetting against a glow of lamp-light (cf. nos. 70–1).

The nude forms of Bacchus and the Satyr are quite plastically and competently modelled. But Bacchus' head is somewhat over large; his torso is too broad and thick-set; and his general effect is one of top-heaviness and stumpiness. The Maenad is virtually two-dimensional; the Silenus is far too big and weighty for his little ass; and the treatment of the hands in the case of both these figures betrays the inexperienced or poorly gifted draftsman. The flesh-surfaces are smooth, but not burnished. Faint traces of red paint can be detected on the vine-branch, above the head of Bacchus, and on the back of the latter. The red stains appearing here and there are the vestiges of iron incrustation.

The group has taken punishment on no less than three occasions. First, there are a very few ancient breaks – a chip out of the Silenus' right elbow and the loss of the right hind-leg of the ass. Secondly, the pressure of earth and debris accumulating in the temple on top of the sculpture caused the tree-trunk to snap across immediately above the Silenus' head, the torso of Bacchus to split asunder just above the navel, his left arm to crack through a short distance above the elbow; and the neck of the snake, and the two right-hand grape-clusters behind it, to come detached from the rest. But apart from the very minor losses and these post-Roman-period breaks, which could easily be repaired, the group was virtually intact when unearthed. It was not until the moment of its discovery that the piece incurred its third and most disastrous series of damages. New, raw breaks betray quite modern losses, which are: the top of the tree-trunk and upper part of Pan; the right elbow and adjoining portion of the right forearm of Bacchus; Bacchus left forearm, hand, and attribute (?); the head, left hand, and attribute (?) of the Satyr; the Maenad's head; and the head of the snake. All these portions are, at present, utterly lost. The find-spot and its neighbourhood were searched for them in vain. Only the Satyr's right elbow and a small scale of marble from the back of the tree-trunk, both of which show modern breaks, were retrieved and replaced.

The base of the group carries an inscription in rough, irregular lettering, which could be, but need not be, contemporary with the sculpture. It runs HOMINIBVSBAGIS-BITAM; and there can be little doubt but that Dr. Stefan Weinstock, of Oxford, was right in pointing out that b stands for v in the second and third cases in which it occurs and that the text should read hominibus vagis vitam, 'life to wandering men'.[1] This use of b for v is normally a sign of lateness, although an unpublished graffito – a workman's scrawl – in the Severan Basilica at Lepcis Magna, in Tripolitania, carries the practice back to the first decade of the third century.[2] The meaning of this enigmatic text is discussed below (p. 130).

Scenes of Bacchic revelry, with the god half-drunk, or almost unconscious, surrounded by members of his train, and often being saved from imminent collapse by the supporting arms and shoulders of a Satyr, are a common theme of art in many media, above all in sepulchral contexts, where they serve as allegories of paradisal happiness (cf. no. 106). But the particular arrangement and combination of divine figures and accessory motifs, which the Walbrook group displays, are not widespread through the Roman world; and the closest parallels known to the present writer are two stone reliefs, each portraying the Bacchic scene within a shallow, arched niche, from Turda in Rumania[3] and Hissar in Bulgaria[4] respectively. Here again Bacchus occupies the centre of the field. But on the first relief his nakedness is modified by boots and a nebris (fawn-skin) and his weight is on his left leg. His right arm is raised above his head and entwined by an enormous snake, which he grasps with his right hand as it writhes across the top of the picture. A vine-branch and a grape-cluster can be seen beside the god's head, carved in low relief on the background; and on the spectator's left is the tree-trunk, on which is perched a bearded Pan, holding a syrinx (Pan-pipe). At the foot of the tree is a bald-pated, half-draped Silenus, this time not mounted on an ass, but walking, with the aid of a staff, towards the right. The panther crouches to the right behind the god's left foot and looks up to the left at its master. The Maenad is not present; but the faithful Satyr is at hand, striding towards the right, wearing a short cloak, holding a pedum (shepherd's curved throwing-stick) in his left hand, and supporting with his right hand the back of Bacchus, whose left arm is thrown round his shoulders. On the Bulgarian relief Pan is perched on a tree-trunk in the left-hand upper corner, but below him a Maenad beating on a tympanum (tambourine) and a Satyr playing with a panther take the place of the Silenus. On the extreme right appears the Maenad with cista mystica, while Bacchus, who rests his weight upon his right leg, raises his snake-entwined arm above his head, and wears a nebris, throws his left arm round the shoulders of the Satyr standing

1. The Times, 12 October 1954.
2. Information from Miss J. M. Reynolds, of Newnham College, Cambridge.
3. A. von Domaszewski, Die Religion des römischen Heeres, 1895, pl. 3, fig. 4, p. 54 and note 229; G. C. Tocilescu, Monumente religiose: Rumania (not dated), pp. 26–7 with fig.
4. Revue Archéologique, 1958, pp. 38–40, fig. 4.

between him and the Maenad.[1] The snake in all these scenes is likely to symbolise the blessed dead.

The Turda and Hissar stones are the work of very ordinary provincial carvers; and, according to von Domaszewski, at least nine similar reliefs found in Danubian lands were known in 1895.[2] As a work of art, the Walbrook group is, on the one hand, superior to the Turda and kindred pieces, but inferior, on the other hand, to every other monument of marble statuary that the London site has yielded; and in view of the provincial connections of its art-type and assuming that a block of Italian marble might have been imported into central Europe (cf. no. 69), a Balkan origin may with some reason be ascribed to it. Its freedom from the trammels of hieratic frontality, and the subdued movement and plasticity of its two leading figures, would seem to preclude a date much later than c. A.D. 250. Meanwhile, its flagrant errors in proportion, and the slipshod workmanship revealed by the subsidiary figures and details, would seem to lift it well out of the second century onto the threshold of the late-antique.[3] Moreover, by the middle of the third century, the late-second-century passion for heavy drilling and deep under-cutting, conspicuously absent from our marble, had already spent its force. If this dating of the group is right, it cannot have been new when it reached the Mithraeum, since it came to light above the level of the temple's latest (fourth-century) floor.

It is on the lines of the other-worldly symbolism of such Bacchic scenes that the enigmatic text on the Walbrook group– hominibus vagis vitam – is, in the present writer's view, best interpreted. The reading 'life to wandering men' un-doubtedly makes sense.[4] But when we ask what precise sense we are to give to 'life' and 'wandering men' and what the 'understood' verb is, of which vitam is the object, we are faced with a new set of problems to be solved.

At first sight, vitam would seem to be part of a well-known formula, an acclamation, in which those who use it wish 'long life' to So-and-So, some such verb as rogo (in the first or third person, singular or plural) being 'understood' as governing vitam (sometimes abbreviated to vita in inscriptions). For instance, a figured mosaic pavement in a set of public baths at Thamugadi (Timgad) in Algeria is inscribed

Filadelfis vita(m), that is, 'Long life to the Philadelphians', presumably the family, or religious guild, that earned the citizens' gratitude by paying for the building.[5] Or, again, the imperative da may be 'understood' with vitam, as in the first chapter of the Life of the Emperor Antoninus Dia-dumenus in the Augustan History – Iuppiter optime maxime, Macrino et Antonino vitam (da). In these acclamations the life wished for is length of days in this world; and if the Wal-brook inscription were to be interpreted on their analogy, it would mean that the dedicators of the group, that is, wor-shippers or initiates of Bacchus, wished 'length of days' (or 'all the best') to 'wandering men'. But who were these homines vagi? In a Bacchic context vagi would be appropriate to Bacchus and his following of divine (or quasi-divine) companions, Satyrs, Sileni, Pans, and Maenads, who journeyed through the world with him to and from India and elsewhere. Bacchus was likewise vagus when he roamed the mountains with his orgiastic train of Bacchants.[6] Vagi by itself might, then, be thought of as applied to the Bacchic thiasos (revel-rout): or to a group of Bacchic initiates. But Bacchus and his train were not homines; and the human Bacchi and Bacchae, when abandoned to their orgiastic rites, ceased, for the time being, to be homines, since they im-personated, and were assimilated to, the god's divine com-panions. Yet homines in this inscription seems to stress the humanity and mortality of those who are vagi; and it is hard to see how, in this context, mere men could be vagi in the literal sense. But if vagi were used metaphorically of homines as 'strangers and pilgrims' in this world, who seek a safe harbour and eternal life in the next world (the final goal of all the mysteries) through Bacchic initiation, and if da (addressed to Bacchus, depicted in the sculpture) be supplied to govern vitam, then the text, as erected in the Walbrook shrine, takes on a clear significance: Bacchus, himself a wanderer, is in-voked on behalf of men who are vagrants in the spiritual sense. Admittedly we cannot produce any other instance in an acclamation of vitam used of other-worldly life. Yet scenes of Bacchic jollification are, as we have seen, ubiquitous as allegories of happiness beyond the grave; and '(Bacchus, give eternal) life to wandering mortals' is an interpretation supported grammatically by the passage in the Augustan History and in content wholly in keeping with a Mithraic milieu, since Bacchus was, like Mithras, giver of life and 'saviour' from death.[7]

Journal of Roman Studies, xlv, 1955, pp. 137–8, pl. 47.

1. Cf. yet another Danubian relief, from Sistov and now in the National Museum in Sofia, which shows another variant of the same group – Bacchus clutching a snake and upheld by a Satyr, Pan, Silenus on his ass (F. Saxl, Mithras: typengeschichtliche Untersuchungen, 1931, fig. 73). See Addendum on p. 205 below.

2. von Domaszewski, loc. cit. Cf. Bulletin de la Société Archéologique Bulgare, iii, 1912–3, pp. 25–33, figs. 22–5.

3. Mistakes in proportion and shoddy craftsmanship are, of course, found in some late-second-century architectural sculptures, for instance, in those on the Marcus Column in Rome. But 'cabinet-pieces', of the category to which the Walbrook group belongs, were governed by different standards; and it is hard to believe that the defects of our marble would have been tolerated in a second-century marble-carver's studio, even in a province.

4. We can hardly accept M. J. Vermaseren's translation (Corpus Inscriptionum et Monumentorum Religionis Mithriacae, i, 1956, p. 287, no. 823) 'thou givest life to men', which assumes the existence of a verb vago or vagio, 'I give', otherwise unknown to classical Latin.

5. Bulletin Archéologique du Comité des Travaux Historiques et Scienti-fiques, 1904, p. 173, pl. 9; 1905, pp. 91–2. Cf. H. Dessau, Inscriptiones Latinae Selectae, iii, 1916, no. 8982: Pompeianis vita(m) . . . Amazoniis vita(m). The present writer owes these two references to Dr. S. Weinstock, of Oxford.

6. Catullus, lxiv, 390.

7. It is noteworthy that a marble statuette of Bacchus was found in a grave not far from the Romano-British villa in Spoonley Wood, Gloucestershire (Guide to the Antiquities of Roman Britain in the British Museum, 1922, p. 28, pl. 2; 1951, p. 55, no. 10, pl. 20; 1958, p. 55, no. 10, pl. 20).

13. STATUETTE OF CUPID   Plate 32
From Cirencester (Corinium), Gloucestershire. Second century A.D. (?). Bronze (hollow-cast). Height: 16 inches. *Ashmolean Museum, Oxford*

This is the finest and largest bronze figurine of Cupid that the province has yet produced. It probably served as a table lamp-stand. The boy's hair is dressed in an elaborate 'crest' on the crown of the head, with spiral curls falling across the brow and a series of cork-screw ringlets hanging down the neck behind. The irises of the eyes are inlaid with silver and enamel or glass-paste must once have filled the now hollow pupils. The god stands completely naked, with both heels off the ground and the right arm raised and outstretched, while the left arm, hanging by his side, is slightly flexed. The fingers of both hands are parted and in either hand he may have held the stem of a bronze scroll or branch, on which a lamp was poised. On the shoulder-blades are traces of slots (now filled in) into which the wings once fitted. Both face and body are somewhat over fleshy. But the chasing of the hair and the modelling of the trunk and limbs are excellently carried out; and this may well be the product of a Mediterranean (Italian or south-Gaulish) workshop.

Archaeologia, lxix, 1917–8, pp. 202–3, pl. 12.

14.★

15. STATUETTE OF HERCULES   Plates 16–7
From the temple site at Bruton, Somerset. Second or third century A.D. Bronze (solid-cast). Height: 4 inches. *Property of Mrs. C. M. Bennett*

This figurine, one of a *cache* of six votive bronzes (*cf.* nos. 17, 22–3, 26, 50) may well represent a native version of Hercules. The blunt facial features are framed by a 'cap' of straight hair and a thick, curly beard. The god holds a club and a wine-cup and is naked save for his lion-skin cloak. The last is very picturesquely rendered, with a huge mask covering the chest and the forepaws knotted below the chin; while the very carefully executed furry coat of the creature, its hindpaws, and long, strong tail hang down the back.

The Studio, July, 1961, p. 5, fig. on left; *Journal of Roman Studies* li, 1961, p. 187, pl. 20.

16. STATUETTE OF MARS   Plate 19
From Foss Dyke, Lincolnshire. Second or third century A.D. Bronze (hollow-cast). Height: 10 inches. *British Museum*

Mars wears a helmet with an enormous, flaunting crest upon his flowing, curly hair, but is otherwise naked. The heavy proportions of the figure, the marked twist of the torso, and the somewhat florid character of the face and crest suggest that it is of provincial, probably Gaulish, workmanship. The base bears an incised inscription to the effect that the piece was dedicated to Mars and the Emperor's divine power by the Colasuni, Bruccius and Caratius, and was made by the copper-smith (*aerarius*) Celatus.[1] The dedicators appear to

*No. 14 in the Hand-list did not figure in the Exhibition.

1. The inscription reads: *Deo Mar(ti) et nu(mini)b(us) Aug(usti) Colasuni Bruccius et Caratius de suo donarunt ad sester(tios) n(ummos)*

have Celtic names, while the craftsman's name is Roman; and the figurine may have been cast in Britain for British patrons by an immigrant artist.

Guide to the Antiquities of Roman Britain in the British Museum, 1922, p. 89, pl. 8; 1951, p. 54, no. 11, pl. 14; 1958, p. 54, no. 11, pl. 14.

17. STATUETTE OF MARS   Plate 15
From the temple site at Bruton, Somerset. Second or third century A.D. Bronze (solid-cast). Height: 3¼ inches. *Property of Mrs. C. M. Bennett*

Part of a *cache* of votive figurines (*cf.* nos. 15, 22–3, 26, 50), this Mars might be native work. The god is shown naked, apart from his helmet with its great feathered crest. The right hand held a spear, while in the left hand is what is possibly the pommel of a sword.

Journal of Roman Studies, li, 1961, p. 187, pl. 20.

18. STATUE OF MARS   Plate 27
From York (Eburacum), Micklegate Bar. Late-third or early-fourth century A.D. Local gritstone. Height: 5 feet, 9 inches. *Yorkshire Museum, York*

The figure stands on a circular pedestal which is 11 inches high. The god is beardless and wears a helmet, a tunic, a cuirass, greaves, and boots. The right forearm and hand are lost, but the latter must once have grasped a metal spear; the left hand clutches the rim of a shield; and a broad baldric, to which a short sword is attached, passes across the right shoulder. The row of curls above the brow is summarily rendered. The pupils of the eyes are marked in. The cuirass is undecorated, save for a leaf-calyx just below the navel; its base-line is edged with a single row of round, scallop-shaped lappets; and below these depends a series of tasselled leather appendages. This is, in fact, the type of simplified cuirass which late-antiquity favoured;[2] and the sculpture may well be of the late-Roman period.[3] With the figure came to light three altars, one dedicated to Mars; and, although these altars and the statue seem to represent a dump made in post-Roman times, this piece is far more likely to be a votive statue of the god than the funerary statue of a Roman soldier.[4]

Journal of Roman Studies, ii, 1912, pp. 130–1, fig. 10; G. Home, *Roman York*, 1924, pl. opp. p. 58; *Royal Commission on Historical Monuments (England)*: York i (Roman), 1962, p. 120, no. 59, pl. 46.

c(entum). Celatus aerarius fecit et aeramenti lib(ram) donavit factam★ *(denariis) III.* This would appear to mean: 'The Colasuni, Bruccius and Caratius, dedicated [this statuette] to Mars and the Emperor's divine power [*Aug* instead of *Augg* suggests a single Emperor, although *numina* instead of *numen* would normally indicate more than one person] at the cost of 100 sesterces [= 25 *denarii*, reckoning a *sestertius* as a quarter of a *denarius*] paid from their own purse. Celatus the copper-smith made the figure and gave a pound of bronze made [i.e. prepared for casting (?)] at the cost of 3 *denarii*'.
2. Cf. *Antiquaries Journal*, xxiv, 1944, p. 8.
3. For a similar dating, see *Berytus*, xiii, 1959, p. 73, no. 300.
4. As it is described on a picture-postcard sold at the Yorkshire Museum.

19. HEAD OF MERCURY   Plate 29

From Cirencester (Corinium), Gloucestershire. Second or
third century A.D. Cotswold stone (oolite). Height: 6½
inches. *Corinium Museum, Cirencester*

This head has been broken off from its body at the neck. A
petasos (round hat), carrying the stumps of head-wings,
crowns the row of curls above the brow. The forehead, the
plain eyes, the gently curving mouth, and the softly contoured cheeks are very skilfully and sensitively worked,
perhaps by an immigrant Gaulish master, who has succeeded
in combining most effectively classical naturalism with Celtic
vigour and a strong individuality of expression. The piece, a
product of the fine 'Corinium school' (*cf.* p. 7 and nos. 31
and 72), ranks as an example of Romano-British sculpture at
its best, carved, no doubt, for an important shrine in Britain's
largest canton-capital.

Unpublished.

20. GROUP OF MERCURY   Plate 31

From the Walbrook Mithraeum, London. Second quarter
of the second century A.D. Italian marble. Height: 10 inches;
length of base: 8 inches; width of base: 4⅜ inches. *Guildhall
Museum, London*

This dainty little group of Mercury, seated on a rock and
characterised by a number of his well-known attributes, was
found deliberately buried, along with nos. 37 and 38, in a
hollow, covered over and afterwards sealed by the later,
fourth-century floors of the temple, just to the west of the
entrance from the narthex. It has, as we shall see, been
severely fractured in several places. But apart from the loss
of the left knee-cap, of part of the right hand, and of the ends
of two of the toes of the right foot, all of which probably
disappeared before the marble was deliberately concealed,
the sculpture is intact, since the portions of it that had become detached from one another were found lying all
together in position and could at once be reunited.

The god is naked and lounges in an easy attitude upon the
top of a projecting lump of rock, between which and his
person he has interposed his folded cloak to serve him as a
cushion. He is hatless, but two little wings sprout directly
from his hair, which covers his head with a mass of tight,
round curls, where no traces of drilling or undercutting can
be detected. Mercury is here portrayed as very youthful,
with full lips, rounded cheeks, and a mild and somewhat
pensive expression, as he gazes dreamily towards the spectator's right with eyes of which the pupils are marked by tiny
drill-holes. Trunk and limbs are soft and slender, well knit
and well proportioned. The group was certainly meant to be
viewed all round, since the back and sides are as sensitively
and exquisitely modelled as is the front, although the sculptor
has skilfully contrived so to utilise his block that the greyer
parts of it could be restricted to the rear. All the flesh is
brightly burnished; the drapery is smooth, but not polished;
while the surfaces of rocks and other accessories have been
left slightly rough, no doubt for contrast.

Mercury's left hand rests on the end of his rugged seat and
grasps by the neck a long money-bag, presumably of leather,

which dangles downwards. In the palm of his right hand,
which is supported on his left knee, is cut a diagonal groove,
into which must have fitted the stem of a small metal *caduceus*
(serpent-staff), once held in the missing fingers and projecting
forward from the group. His right foot is set on the ground,
his left on a fold of drapery bunched upon the back of a
tortoise. Below his left knee a ram crouches towards the
right against the vertical face of the rock. These attributes
are, of course, symbolic of the god's diverse functions. The
wings and herald's staff befit him as the traveller who guides
the dead from earth to paradise; the purse denotes his patronage of commerce; the ram his gift of fertility to flocks and
herds and so to man; while the tortoise alludes to the well-
known tale of his invention of the lyre (*cf.* p. 133), which, as a
token of celestial harmony, hints at the after-life bliss of the
Mithraic *mystes* (initiate).

The piece is carved in two separate blocks of marble. From
the larger of these is cut Mercury himself, his rocky seat, his
ram, and the thin, flat, oval slab that represents the 'ground'
on which the group is supported. The smaller block has provided the sculpture with a solid base or stand, oval in shape
and consisting, below, of a large concave moulding between
two smaller convex mouldings, above, of a thin and narrow
collar of roughly modelled rocks. This collar surrounds a
shallow sunk area, designed to receive the 'ground' of the
group, which originally fitted into it with precision. The
under surface of the 'ground' and the floor of the sunk area
were both left slightly rough; and thus the two worked
blocks were neatly keyed together without any form of
fastening. Furthermore, the under surface of the base is criss-
crossed with scratches, presumably to obviate the danger of
the marble slipping off a shelf or table.

As the fractures already mentioned indicate, this Mercury
has had a chequered history. Two of these breaks took place
after the piece was buried; for it must have been the pressure
of the earth above that snapped the head clean off at the neck
and detached in a similar manner a flake of marble from the
right shoulder-blade. But the larger and more serious
fracture, which caused the figure, its seat, and its 'ground' to
split right in two, certainly occurred in Roman times and
before the marble 'went to earth', since there is evidence that
steps were taken to repair it. This break passes through the
god's right thigh and his left knee and bisects the rock, with
the ram and drapery carved upon it. It may further have resulted in the snapping of the left leg just above the ankle. In
order to remedy this damage, both sides of the main fracture,
from the 'ground' to the summit of the rock, were scratched
with diagonal keying lines, smeared with cement, and stuck
together. The breaks at the right thigh and left ankle then
closed up automatically and did not require cementing. But
since the thrust of the god's body towards the right would
have tended to pull the lower section of this fracture, where
it passed through the rocky seat, apart again, the under
surface of the 'ground' on the right side of the break and the
corresponding portion of the floor of the sunk area in the
base were clamped together by a shallow cushion of cement.
The effect of this was to raise the right-hand portion of the

group very slightly, so that it no longer dropped neatly into place on the base. Hence the joining up of the major fracture is not quite exact and some tiny fragments of marble on and near its edges have been lost. This ancient repair was, in fact, a clumsy, botched job; but the attempt to deal with the situation at the left knee may be described as desperate. Here the knee-cap has now vanished, disclosing two grooves which have been drilled right through the knee, one from the front of the leg, the other from the upper surface of the thigh, and which meet in the middle very slightly at an angle. Such grooves must have been meant for rivets, intended to hold the left leg and left thigh together, but only resulting in the knee-cap splitting off in two fragments. These fragments, and the portion of the right hand that they carried with them, were not found with the rest of the marble; and it seems almost certain that those losses were incurred before the Mercury was buried. The cementing up of the major fracture must have come unstuck while the piece was underground, for when the sculpture came to light the two edges were lying in the closest contact, but not adhering; and it is possible that the snapping of the left leg was not contemporaneous with that break, but was due to earth-pressure after the two halves of the group had ceased to be firmly held together.[1]

We can, of course, only speculate about the point in the Mercury's career at which the major fracture took place. But it seems unlikely that the marble was already injured at the time when it was bespoken for the Walbrook shrine. We can visualise the damage being done during its transit from the Continent to London and a hasty patching-up being carried out by the temple authorities or by the donor and dedicator. Alternatively, the marble may have reached the Mithraeum safely and then have fallen from its place at some point after its dedication. To this same accident, whenever and however it occurred, the loss of the two toes of the extended right foot may reasonably be attributed.

The Walbrook Mercury is a typical example of Graeco-Roman *genre* art as applied to a religious theme. Its point is not so much cult, as picturesqueness; and it stems directly from the Hellenistic tradition which prettified the gods and immersed them in the common human round, so that Mercury figures here as a dainty, graceful boy, conscious only of weariness, as he flops upon his rock, and totally forgetful of his own divinity. Compared with our marble, the famous bronze statue of the seated Hermes, found at Herculaneum, and now at Naples,[2] a Roman copy of a Greek original probably dating from the closing decades of the fourth century B.C., has dignity and poise, for all its slenderness and air of relaxation. This work has been assigned to the circle of Lysippus on the score of its affinities to the Vatican copy of that sculptor's Apoxyomenos; and it is to a later,

early-third-century, generation of Lysippus' pupils that the closest parallel to our marble is attributed. This is a bronze statuette of Hermes, seated on a rock, in the Metropolitan Museum of Art, New York,[3] which shows the same carefree turn of the head as does the Walbrook Mercury, and represents, as it does, the next stage, after that of the Naples Hermes, in the humanising and dandifying of the god.

The absence of drilling and undercutting in the hair, combined with the hard, drilled folds of the cloak, the plastic treatment of the eyes, and the burnished surfacing are all suggestive of the Hadrianic or early-Antonine period. On the other hand, it is possible that a derivative work of this type was fashioned in a conservative style at a date somewhat later in the second century. Material and craftsmanship point to Italy as the country in which the Mercury was manufactured.

Of the other instances of Mercury's appearance in Mithraic contexts the most significant is a marble statue from the Mérida (Augusta Emerita) Mithraeum, in Spain.[4] It is about five feet high and is as monumental and imposing as our piece is slight and refined. In this case the god is seated to the front, directly facing the spectator, on a rocky throne, over which he had draped his cloak. He has short, curly hair, in which no wings are visible, and he is both more mature in features and more solidly built than is the Walbrook figure. His left hand rests on the corner of the rock; his right hand, of which some of the fingers are damaged, seems to have held some object, possibly a purse; and a large portion of his left leg and the front part of his left foot are lost. His distinguishing attributes are the wings at his ankles and the tortoiseshell lyre that rests against his seat, below his left hand. This lyre is inscribed with the statue's most important and interesting element – the record of its dedication to Mithras by a *Pater* (the highest of the seven Mithraic grades of initiation) in the one-hundred-and-eightieth year of the colony of Augusta Emerita, that is in A.D. 155.[5] No evidence for the close association in the Roman mind between Mercury and Mithras could be more conclusive than this.

From Mithraea in Roman Germany and Gaul come a number of renderings of Mercury. Four stone representations were found at Stockstadt[6] and two at Dieburg;[7] while one representation comes from each of the following sites – Sarrebourg,[8] Heddernheim (Mithraeum I),[9] and Gimmeldingen.[10]

Journal of Roman Studies, xlv, 1955, pp. 137–8, pl. 46.

1. The present writer is greatly indebted to Mr. Norman Cook, Keeper of the Guildhall Museum, for help with the elucidation of these details.
2. G. M. A. Richter, *The Sculpture and Sculptors of the Greeks*, 1950, pp. 61, 294, fig. 72; M. Bieber, *The Sculpture of the Hellenistic Age*, ed. 2, 1961, pp. 41–2, figs. 106–8; *cf. ibid.*, p. 41, fig. 109 for a variation on the same scheme, a bronze statuette of Hermes in the Loeb collection.
3. Bieber, *op. cit.*, p. 42, figs. 110–1.
4. M. J. Vermaseren, *Corpus Inscriptionum et Monumentorum Religionis Mithriacae*, i, 1956, p. 274, no. 780, fig. 213. Plate 236.
5. Ann(o) col(oniae) CLXXX invicto deo Mithrae saci(um) G(aius) Accius Hedychrus Pater a(nimo) l(ibente) p(osuit).
6. Vermaseren, *op. cit.*, ii, 1960, p. 90, nos. 1176, 1178–9, figs. 312–4; pp. 95–6, no. 1210, fig. 318.
7. F. Behn, *Das Mithrasheiligtum zu Dieburg*, 1928, pp. 32–4, nos. 8–9, figs. 33–4.
8. Vermaseren, *op. cit.*, i, 1956, p. 324, no. 966 D, fig. 236. Here Mercury occurs in a group of Olympians on a Mithras Tauroctonos relief, as also on a fragmentary relief of Mithras Tauroctonos from Siscia in Pannonia (F. Cumont, *Textes et monuments figurés relatifs aux mystères de Mithra*, ii, 1896, p. 326, no. 221, fig. 193).
9. Vermaseren, *op. cit.*, ii, p. 68, no. 1089, fig. 281.
10. *Ibid.*, p. 126, no. 1317, fig. 349.

21. STATUETTE OF MERCURY   Plate 33

From near the temple site at Gosbecks Farm, to the west of Colchester (Camulodunum). Second century A.D. Bronze (hollow-cast). Height: 21 inches. *Colchester and Essex Museum, Colchester*

This is the tallest and, from the aesthetic point of view, the most impressive bronze statuette of a deity so far known in Roman Britain. The god is shown completely nude and his head-wings spring directly from his hair, which is waved in effeminate fashion on either side of a central parting.[1] Both arms are gone, but from the left shoulder, which is slightly raised, we may guess that his left hand held a *caduceus*, while in his lowered right hand he would have clutched a purse. This is no cult-image, with the eyes gazing straight at the spectator, but would seem to be an excerpt from a group, since Mercury's head is turned three-quarters towards his left and is gently inclined, as though he were addressing someone near him. That the figure was originally fixed on some steeply sloping object, as if in the act of alighting, can be seen from the angle of the feet, in the soles of which are triangular depressions for attachment. A deeply engraved, horizontal line furrows the brow and the pupils of the eyes would once have been filled with glass-paste or enamel. The general style of this graceful and skilfully modelled bronze is wholly classical, but the actual workmanship may be Gaulish. It was, at any rate, almost certainly cast abroad and represents the offering of a well-to-do worshipper of Mercury. It is worthy to be set beside the splendid, but much smaller, bronze Mercury from Thalwil, now in the Swiss National Museum at Zürich.[2]

Journal of Roman Studies, xxxviii, 1948, p. 91, pl. 14; *Transactions of the Essex Archaeological Society*, n.s., xxiv, 1951, pp. 43–6, pl. opp. p. 44; xxv, 1955, p. 12, pl. 4., fig. 1; M. R. Hull, *Roman Colchester*, 1958, p. 264, pl. 40.

22, 23. STATUETTES OF MERCURY   Plates 13–4, 21–2

From the temple site at Bruton, Somerset. Second or third century A.D. Bronze (solid-cast). Heights: 4½ and 2¼ inches. *Property of Mrs. C. M. Bennett*

These figurines from a votive *cache* (*cf.* nos. 15, 17, 26, 50) both show the same common type of Mercury. The god is standing and wears a winged *petasos*, a long, enveloping cloak with patterned folds, and winged boots. In his right hand he holds a purse, in his left a *caduceus* (which is lost in the case of no. 23). Both pieces may be native work.[3]

Journal of Roman Studies, li, 1961, p. 187, pl. 20.

1. For a similar style of coiffure, see what appears to be the bronze head of Pomona (?), wearing leaves in the hair, found at Benwell (Condercum) on Hadrian's Wall in 1927 and now in the Museum of Antiquities of the University of Durham and of the Society of Antiquaries of Newcastle upon Tyne (King's College, Newcastle upon Tyne): *Archaeologia Aeliana*, ser. 4, v, 1928, pp. 72–3, pl. 22, fig. 2. Plate 240.
2. F. Stähelin, *Die Schweiz in römischer Zeit*, 1948, fig. 112; ed. W. H. Schuchhardt, *Antike Plastik* etc., 1962, pp. 33–8, pls. 22–7. Plate 237.
3. For a more sophisticated, possibly Gaulish, version of the same type, see D. K. Hill, *Catalogue of the Classical Bronze Sculpture in the Walters Art Gallery*, 1949, p. 19, no. 32, pl. 6.

24. HEAD OF MINERVA   Plate 28

From the Walbrook Mithraeum, London. Mid-second century A.D. Italian marble. Height: 10 inches. *Guildhall Museum, London*

This piece had been deliberately buried in a hollow, covered over and afterwards sealed by the later, fourth-century, floors of the temple, just east, and slightly south, of the site of the easternmost column of the northern colonnade. It is the head of a cold, classic beauty, finely carved and attractive in respect of its majestic air of Olympian detachment and serenity. The face and neck show a brightly polished surface, somewhat marred as we now see it by the black staining, due to iron deposit, which spreads over the side of the left cheek, under the chin, and over the left ear and the portion of the head immediately behind it, while a few isolated dark streaks and patches are apparent on the right side of the chin. Under the lower edge of the polished neck there is a roughly surfaced tenon, rounded in shape, which would have been concealed in a cavity between the shoulders of the separately made body that the head once crowned. As in the case of nos. 36 and 38, each of which has a similar tenon below the neck, the head was removed from the body, probably worked in some inferior material, in order to bury it. Whether Minerva's head topped a full-length figure or a bust or a herm, we have no means of knowing, since the bodies belonging to all three heads have completely disappeared.

This head presents two obvious peculiarities. The first is the plain band of marble that passes over the brow and behind, and a little way below, each ear, and then turns at a right-angle to run across a thick, rope-like coil of hair that falls down the nape of the neck. In front this band resembles a diadem, being at its broadest in the centre, above the brow, and tapering to a relatively narrow strip for the remainder of its course. The second strange feature is the crown of the head, or rather the absence of a crown, since the skull, as viewed in profile, looks as though it had lost its top by being cleft in a slightly curved, diagonal line from the centre of the 'diadem' towards the rear. The upper surface of the cranium is very roughly tooled and completely unfinished and is pierced by two circular holes, each half an inch in diameter, set one behind the other and in depth one inch and three-quarters of an inch respectively. These holes must have been drilled to hold in place a metal headdress of some kind, concealing the whole of the top of the head, which was clearly never intended to be visible.

It is these two apparent oddities that furnish the key to the identification of the head as Minerva's. We have only to place a profile view of the Walbrook head and one of the head of the Varvakeion statuette of Pheidias' Athene Parthenos[4] side by side, to be convinced that the former's marble band represents the seating for a now vanished metal Attic helmet, of which the upturned peak was slipped over the diadem-like portion above the brow, while the raised edging of the neck-guard rested on the narrow strip that

4. A Roman-age copy in the National Museum in Athens: G. M. A. Richter, *The Sculpture and Sculptors of the Greeks*, 1950, p. 218, figs. 599–600. Plate 241.

runs behind the ears and across the back hair. The bonnet of this metal helmet was presumably held firm by two metal bars, attached to its interior, which were fixed in the two holes drilled in the upper surface of the marble. Mounted on the metal bonnet would have been a metal crest, either single or triple. The lower end of this crest probably rested, as on the Varvakeion statuette, against the coil of hair that hangs down the neck, since the back surface of this coil is flattened and unworked, whereas on the sides the individual locks are lightly indicated with the chisel. The Walbrook Minerva lacks the tresses that fall forward on either side of the breast of the Varvakeion Athene. But both versions of the goddess show the same triangle of hair coming down in front of each ear from below the peak of the helmet. There can, indeed, be no doubt whatever but that the London head presents us with a Roman version of a fifth-century B.C. Greek Athene. The helmet was probably removed and, if of bronze and not of precious metal, abandoned at the time of the concealment of the marble, on which no signs of contact with metal can now be detected.

The two triangles of hair that frame the face of the Walbrook Minerva consist of series of crisp, round curls, carved with the chisel and picked out with a number of small, circular drill-holes, of which there are more on the right side than on the left. The broken effect of the surface of the hair is also indicated by several perfectly straight, deeply incised lines cutting this way and that across the triangles. The hairs of the eyebrows are not rendered. The eyes are perfectly plain, as in all classical and Hellenistic Greek sculpture and in pre-Hadrianic large-scale sculpture of the Roman age: they lack the plastic rendering of irises and pupils that came into vogue during the second quarter of the second century A.D. and appears, from that time on, almost invariably in portraits and often, although by no means always, in the representations of deities, personifications, and the like. The clear-cut brow, long, straight nose, short upper lip, small, neat mouth, oval cheeks, and full, but not unduly fleshy, chin combine to produce an idealised and generalised, typically classical, cast of countenance. The marble's only distinctively non-fifth-century B.C. traits, apart from the brightly burnished surface, are the treatment of the hair and the very emphatic overlapping of the lower by the upper eyelid. Two horizontal creases cut across the neck, which is, perhaps, a trifle too powerful and stocky.

The Minerva is slightly asymmetrical. The line of the brows rises a little towards the spectator's right; the left eye is higher and more deeply set than the right eye; and the seating for the neck-guard descends considerably lower beneath the left ear than it does beneath the right ear. It seems that the head was meant to be turned very slightly towards the spectator's left, with the face tilted a little upwards. That, at any rate, provides the most pleasing and satisfactory viewpoint for it.

The piece is perfectly preserved, apart from the loss of a small portion of the outer margin of the upper part of the right ear and some slight chipping along the edge of the neck above the tenon.

There was probably no time during the first and second centuries of our era when there was no demand for copies and adaptations of classical Greek statuary. But Hellenising taste among the imperial Romans had its special booms, as in the Hadrianic and early-Antonine periods; and it is to the second quarter of the second century that it would be natural to assign a work so particularly classicised and idealised as the Walbrook Minerva. If we date it not later than c. 150, we should have to suppose that this marble was not roughly contemporary with the late-second-century Mithraeum,[1] but had graced some continental temple or connoisseur's collection before it was imported into Britain and dedicated in the Walbrook shrine. There is nothing inherently improbable in such a supposition. On the other hand, the philhellenic interests both of Marcus Aurelius and of Commodus ensured the survival of a fashion for classical Greek art-types throughout the second half of the second century, alongside of the new 'baroque' and pictorial developments that characterised the portraits and reliefs of mid- and late-Antonine times; and it is not impossible that our head was carved as late as c. A.D. 180-190. The peculiar treatment of the hair at the sides, with the summary straight cuts across the surface, does not suggest the meticulous technique of Hadrianic craftsmanship, while the brilliant burnishing, which the Minerva shares with the Mithras (no. 36) and with the Serapis (no. 38), is most closely paralleled in such late-second-century works as the Conservatori Commodus,[2] although it must be borne in mind that polished surfacing is also characteristic of some Hadrianic sculpture. But in view of the extremely eclectic nature of the work of Roman imperial copyists, it is best to avoid attempting to date our head too precisely between the years A.D. c. 130 and 190. That the Minerva was carved in Italy may be inferred both from its style and from its material.

While Minerva in her funerary aspect as conqueress of death is functionally akin to Mithras, the Walbrook head is undoubtedly unique as being the only large and impressive representation of the goddess that any Mithraeum in the Roman world has yet produced. Although she features in Mithraea on at least five occasions as a member of the Capitoline Triad or as part of a series of Olympians, only three times does she appear elsewhere in Mithraic contexts in her own right, as it were – in the Palazzo dei Musei di Roma Mithraeum,[3] in the Heddernheim Mithraeum,[4] and in the Gimmeldingen Mithraeum.[5]

Journal of Roman Studies, xlv, 1955, pp. 137-8, pl. 44, fig. 2.

25. HEAD OF MINERVA   Plate 20
From Bath (Aquae Sulis), Somerset. Second century A.D. Bronze (hollow-cast). Height: 9¾ inches. *Roman Baths Museum, Bath*

1. For the date of this Mithraeum, see ed. R. L. S. Bruce-Mitford, *Recent Archaeological Excavations in Britain*, 1956, p. 140.
2. For portraits of Commodus, see M. Wegner, *Die Herrscherbildnisse in antoninischer Zeit*, 1939, pls. 48-56.
3. M. J. Vermaseren, *Corpus Inscriptionum et Monumentorum Religionis Mithriacae*, i, 1956, p. 185, no. 441.
4. *Ibid.*, ii, 1960, p. 67, no. 1086, fig. 278.
5. *Pfälzische Heimatkunde*, xxii, 1926, prts. 8/9, p. 3, fig. 5.

This gilded head, roughly life-size, was found in the eighteenth century in the south-west corner of the baths. It had been violently hacked from its body in ancient times, as is betrayed by the ragged, irregular edge in which the neck terminates. The thick hair, waved on either side of a central parting, forms a kind of coronal, behind which the crown and back of the head are completely unworked and exhibit the same 'sliced off' appearance as does no. 24. Here, as there, the piece was once completed by a separately made metal helmet, but in this case by a Corinthian helmet with down-turned peak, which lacked the neck-guard fitting low and tightly across the hair on the nape of the neck, as with the Attic helmet.[1] There can, indeed, be little doubt but that this is the head of a once helmeted Minerva – of Sulis-Minerva in purely Graeco–Roman guise. A separately made *stephane* (diadem), appropriate to Juno or Venus or some local goddess associated with the sacred springs, would not have concealed the unsightly incompleteness of the skull from a spectator viewing the bronze from the side. The statue was probably cast in one of the leading and most Romanised bronze-casting centres in Gaul, a land with which Aquae Sulis is known to have been in contact.

VCH Somerset, i, 1906, p. 259, fig. 31 (the modern wax collar, with which the neck was once completed, has now been removed).

26. STATUETTE OF MINERVA   Plates 23–4

From the temple site at Bruton, Somerset. Second or third century A.D. Bronze (solid-cast). Height: 3¼ inches. *Property of Mrs. C. M. Bennett*

This figurine, another piece from a *cache* of votive bronzes (*cf.* nos. 15, 17, 22–3, 50), is classical in its type, but provincial in its style and execution. The goddess wears a long tunic with double overfold, an *aegis*, and a heavily crested Corinthian helmet. The lowered left hand once grasped the rim of her now vanished shield; and her raised right hand held her spear, not vertically, as is usual, but horizontally, in the attitude of Athene Promachos.

Journal of Roman Studies, li, 1961, p. 187, pl. 20.

27. STATUE OF MINERVA   Plate 26

From Sibson, Huntingdonshire. Late-second century A.D. Barnack rag. Height: 4 feet, 2 inches (without the missing head). *Collection of His Grace the Duke of Bedford (Woburn Abbey, Bedfordshire)*

This little-known, almost lifesize figure is the most remarkable of all the renderings of Minerva in British stone. Its find-spot lies in the centre of the extensive Romano–British potteries of the Nene Valley area, generally named after the village of Castor. In the context of this flourishing rural industry the presence of so large a statue of the patroness of craftsmen is readily explained. In her vanished right hand the

goddess held what appears to be either a sceptre with a rounded terminal or a spear reversed, with the butt-end uppermost; but of this attribute only the end and a small portion of the staff are visible against the right shoulder.[2] The left hand rests on the rim of a circular shield with a round central boss; and this shield in its turn rested on the mouth of a long-necked vase, of which only the pear-shaped body, standing on a small pedestal beside Minerva's left foot, survives. Up the body of this vessel (and once, presumably, around its neck) writhes a snake, the head and neck of which appear in low relief on the lower part of the outside of the shield. The figure wears a long tunic and a mantle, which falls in the zig-zag folds found in Greek drapery from archaic to Hellenistic times (*cf.* nos. 30, 72–3, 124) beneath the left forearm. She has no *aegis*, but a badly worn and very schematised Medusa head is carved in low relief on the breast. The snake is, of course, one of Minerva's most familiar adjuncts. The vase, a most unusual adjunct for her, might symbolise here the pottery activities of her worshippers. The back of the statue is finished and the workmanship is good throughout. The proportions are correct and the treatment of the drapery is easy and naturalistic. The hand which produced it, probably that of an immigrant provincial, had been well schooled in classical traditions. It is unlikely that this Minerva was carved before the Nene Valley industry developed in the second half of the second century.

Archaeologia, xxxii, 1847, pp. 13–5, pl. 4; *VCH Huntingdonshire*, i, 1926, pp. 226–7; A. Michaelis, *Ancient Marbles in Great Britain*, 1882, pp. 734–5, no. 111; A. H. Smith, *A Catalogue of Sculpture at Woburn Abbey*, 1900, p. 37, no 61.

28. STATUETTE OF VENUS   Plate 18

From Verulamium, Hertfordshire. Second century A.D. Bronze (solid-cast). Height: 8 inches. *Verulamium Museum, St. Albans*

Found on the floor of the cellar of a second-century house, where it had been abandoned when that cellar was filled in sometime in the fourth century, this bronze represents the most unusual and interesting type of Venus so far found in Roman Britain. The goddess is nude, save for a cloak that is knotted round her thighs and flutters out in the breeze on either side; and it is this virtual nudity that precludes the identification as Ceres that was at first suggested for the piece, since Ceres is always fully draped. Moreover, the style in which the drapery is worn can be paralleled, often very nearly and occasionally precisely, in many statues and statuettes of Venus.[3] A strand of the goddess's hair hangs

1. For similar representations of Minerva wearing a Corinthian helmet that leaves the hair visible above the brow and terminates behind at the level of the ears, see G. E. Rizzo, *Prassitele*, 1932, pp. 93–4, pls. 139–41 (bronze statue of Minerva from Arezzo, in the Museo Archeologico, Florence); M. Bieber, *The Sculpture of the Hellenistic Age*, ed. 2, 1961, p. 64, figs. 210–2 (marble statue of Minerva from the Castra Praetoria, Rome, in the Museo Capitolino Nuovo).

2. According to A. Michaelis, *Ancient Marbles in Great Britain*, 1882, pp. 734–5, no. 111, the right hand with an owl and part of the spear or sceptre was preserved separately.

3. E.g. M. Bieber, *Sculpture of the Hellenistic Age*, ed. 2, 1961, p. 144, fig. 610 (Vatican Museum); S. Reinach, *Répertoire de la statuaire*, i, 1897, p. 321, no. 1323; p. 326, nos. 1339, 1344; p. 327, nos. 1355–6; p. 334, no. 1343b; p. 337, no. 1345; ii, 1897, p. 339, nos. 1–10. For the nearest parallel in terracotta to the arrangement of the drapery on the Verulamium bronze, see F. Winter, *Die antiken Terracotten*, iii, 2, 1903, pl. 219, fig. 3. For still closer parallels in bronze, see the figurines from Augst and Trier respectively (*Ur-Schweiz*, xxv, 1961, pp. 21–30, figs. 13–6, 18). Plate 238.

forward, in the normal way, onto the shoulder on either side; whereas the attributes – the crown of fruits (if, indeed, this is not a 'bow' of hair) and the apple or pomegranate, cupped in leaves, which is clasped in the lowered left hand – are an unusual combination in representations of Venus, although they harmonise well enough with the fertility and otherworld aspects of her cult in Britain and Gaul. The mannered pose and gestures and the plastic modelling are, however, wholly Hellenistic and the technique is not distinctively provincial. The figurine could be the product of an Italian workshop, or in view of its attributes and of the fact that its nearest bronze parallels have come to light north of the Alps, of a very classicising south-Gaulish studio. The eyes show traces of silvering.

Journal of Roman Studies, l, 1960, pl. 24; *The Studio*, July, 1961, fig. on p. 3.

29. HEAD AND CHEST OF RIVER-GOD   Plate 35
From the site of the Walbrook Mithraeum, London (found in 1889). Mid-second century A.D. Italian Marble. Height: 13½ inches. *London Museum, Kensington Palace*

This marble was discovered near the middle of Walbrook at a depth of twenty to twenty-two feet below the modern surface, that is, at the same level as the 1954 finds, at a time when sewerage works were in progress in Walbrook, near Bond Court. This information was supplied soon after the discovery by James Smith, a London antique-dealer, to Mr. W. Ransom of Hitchin, who purchased the River-God from Smith along with nos. 32 and 69, which came to light with it. It was in the latter part of 1889 that were erected the office-buildings which stood above the temple site until their destruction in World War II.

The piece consists of the upper half of an elderly male figure, which, when complete, was reclining towards the spectator's left, with its head turned three-quarters towards the spectator's right (*cf.* nos. 30–1). Apart from a rather heavy abrasion on the tip of the nose, the head is intact; on the figure's right the chest is preserved as far as the waist-line; but on its left the chest is lost below a diagonal line that cuts across the body from below the left nipple to just below the navel, from which point the body terminates in a slightly convex, horizontal line running to the right flank. Below these lines nothing is left: abdomen and legs have wholly vanished. Gone, too, are the left arm and shoulder, the ends of the left-hand side locks, and the upper part of the left flank above the diagonal cut. The right arm is broken off a short way below the shoulder. Against the front side of what remains of the right upper arm is the thick, sappy stem of a bull-rush, originally held in the figure's right hand. From this stem two pointed leaves branch out to right and left and are rendered in low relief on the chest and the shoulder respectively. The section of the stem above these leaves, and most of the thick, blunt rod of flowers and fruit, are worked in the round, with the top of the rod, and the tips of the two more spiky leaves that cup it, resting against the head. From this attribute we may infer, without more ado, that the figure represents a River-God.

The god's hair flares up like a mane above the brow, twists itself into two horn-shaped curls, one above each temple, and then descends on either side of the face in long, sinuous tresses, the lower tips of which touch the shoulders. The moustache is heavy and completely conceals the upper lip; and the thickly massed locks of the beard fall like water from the cheeks and from below the full lower lip onto the left side of the chest. The effect is picturesque, despite the absence of deep undercutting and of drilling except in the side locks, where drilled grooves part the individual strands of hair. The back of the crown of the head is encircled by a fillet and there the locks, which radiate star-fish fashion from a central point, are worked in very low relief, with incised lines between them. This work, flat and unplastic as it is, is finished.

The eyes are deep-set below beetling brows and the slightly rubbed surfaces of the eyeballs show no clear traces of the rendering of pupils and irises. Between the temples, just above the nose, is a triangular-shaped depression; and a deepish longitudinal furrow runs across the centre of the forehead. The face combines benignity and strength; and the fineness of the modelling of the brow and cheeks is offset by the powerful handling of the somewhat corpulent trunk, with its full breasts and deep transverse crease in the flesh above the navel, where the left flank and left thigh formed an angle.

The surfaces are smooth, that of the flesh being smoother than those of the hair and beard, but none are brightly polished. This smoothness extends to the back and suggests that, for all the unplasticity of the treatment of the back hair, the figure could be viewed from the rear. The surviving portions of the marble, with the exception of the nose, are remarkably little damaged, with only a few slight cracks and abrasions here and there. The iron hook or rivet, which now pierces the left shoulder-blade, is modern.

The diagonal cut across the torso, already described, in the centre of which is a small hole partially filled with plaster, is completely smooth and level and almost certainly denotes a trimming down of some uneven or broken edge carried out in modern times, after the piece was unearthed – perhaps to facilitate display. It presents a sharp contrast to the rough and slightly rounded surface of the horizontal sector of the figure's present lower line, seen on the spectator's left, a sector that meets the cut at an angle and carries at the back, under the right shoulder-blade, a projecting roll of marble. It looks as if the diagonal cut had sliced away a kind of tenon, which ran in a gently curving, convex line from under the left arm-pit to the navel and which was continued by the line of the existing short horizontal sector. In other words, our marble may represent the detachable nude upper half of a reclining figure which was let into a draped lower half worked in stone or stucco (*cf.* nos. 24, 36, 38); and the projecting roll of marble at the rear, just mentioned, may be the upper transverse fold of a cloak which fitted onto the main mass of drapery below it.

We have noted the good state of preservation of the most important portion, the head and torso, of the River-God; and it seems very probable that this piece, together with nos. 32 and 69 found on the same occasion, had been, like most of the 1954 marbles, deliberately concealed beneath the temple floor. During the rough-and-ready operations of 1889 (which mercifully did not touch the 1954 discoveries), when the appearance of antiquities could hardly have been predicted, the missing arms might have been too severely damaged to be worth salvaging. The draped lower half, if of inferior material, would, like the bodies of nos. 24, 36, 38, have been abandoned in ancient times, when the marble upper part was buried.

The treatment of the surfaces, the relatively restrained use of drilling and undercutting in the hair and beard, and the absence of, or, at the most, very slight, plastic rendering of the eyes suggest that this figure was carved under Hadrian or Antoninus Pius, rather than later in the second century. It would, at any rate, seem to be earlier stylistically than nos. 36 and 38; and we must probably assume its erection in some other place before its dedication in the Walbrook temple: unless it were, as no. 24 could have been (p. 135), a conservative work of the later-second century. From the nature of its marble and from the high standard of its execution we may conclude that it was imported ready-sculptured from Italy.

In the context of the Walbrook shrine the River-God would have symbolised partly the local Thames, partly that far-distant boundary river which divides the living from the dead, and partly the great primeval stream, the cleansing and fertilising source of life, both here and hereafter. It is, at any rate, wholly in keeping with the background of a mystery-cult and with the evidence that we have from elsewhere for renderings of Water-Deities in Mithraea. Six such representations are subsidiary figures in relief. Two more renderings are closer to the Walbrook piece in that they are independent, large-scale figures in the round. These are the great stucco figure in the niche at the end of the Mithraeum underneath the Church of Santa Prisca in Rome;[1] and the marble from the temple at Mérida (Augusta Emerita), in Spain,[2] where the left thigh of the statue carries an inscription proclaiming the dedication of the piece by a Mithraist.[3]

Archaeologia, lx, 1906, pp. 45–6, pl. 8; *Journal of Roman Studies*, i, 1911, p. 163, pl. 22; ii, 1912, p. 152, pl. 9; *Royal Commission on Historical Monuments (England): London iii (Roman)*, 1928, p. 46, pl. 10; *London in Roman Times (London Museum Catalogues, No. 3)*, 1930, p. 45, pl. 15; M. J. Vermaseren, *Corpus Inscriptionum et Monumentorum Religionis Mithriacae*, i, 1956, pp. 284–5, no. 813, fig. 220.

30. STATUE OF RIVER-GOD   Plate 36
From Chesters (Cilurnum), on Hadrian's Wall, Northumberland. Second or third century A.D. British stone. Height: 1 foot, 10½ inches; length: 2 feet, 11½ inches. *Chesters Museum*

1. M. J. Vermaseren, *Corpus Inscriptionum et Monumentorum Religionis Mithriacae*, i, 1956, p. 196, no. 478, fig. 131.
2. *Ibid.*, p. 273, no. 778, fig. 212.
3. *Ibid.*, p. 274, no. 779; C(aius) Acc(ius) Hedychrus P(ater) Patrum.

This fine specimen of Romano–British carving shows a bearded figure half-draped and reclining towards the left. The right arm is the only missing portion. That the personage depicted is, not Neptune, but a River-Deity is indicated by the absence of any vestige of a trident, by the situation of Cilurnum, far inland and beside the North Tyne, and by the sculpture's find-spot in the baths of the commandant's house of the fort, which drew their water-supplies from the neighbouring river. The rough-hewn face, framed by a thick thatch of hair and by a massive, bushy beard, is turned towards the spectator, while the vigorously worked chest and abdomen show a twist towards the left and the legs are wholly in profile. The piece is especially noteworthy for the highly decorative treatment of the cloak, which sweeps in a spirally twisted roll from the left shoulder across the bottom of the abdomen, swathes the legs in a series of crinkly ridges, and falls between the legs in a boldly patterned zig-zag fold (*cf.* nos. 27, 72–3, 124). If the designer of this typically Romano-British style of drapery was a native of northern Britain, he was an uncommonly gifted artist. On the right, supporting the god's left elbow, is the large, nobly conceived mask of a Water-Deity, with parted lips and flowing hair and beard – a most unusual substitute for the overturned urn with a stream flowing from it that normally appears at this point. Is this a curious duplication of the River-Personification? Or is it Oceanus, into which the North Tyne ultimately empties itself?[4] At any rate, the type of the mask, as well as the pose and the three-dimensional modelling of the god, represent the Celtic sculptor's classical inheritance, here most brilliantly harmonised with his native feeling for ornament in its own right.

E. A. Wallis Budge, *An Account of the Roman Antiquities Preserved in the Museum at Chesters, Northumberland*, 1907, pp. 297–8, no. 3, fig. on p. 103.

31. HEAD OF RIVER-GOD   Plate 37
From Cirencester (Corinium), Gloucestershire. Second or third century A.D. Cotswold stone (oolite). Height: 12½ inches. *Corinium Museum, Cirencester*

One of the most impressive examples of the work of the fine 'Corinium school' of carvers (*cf.* p. 7 and nos. 19 and 72) is this fragment comprising the well-preserved head and upper portion of the chest of an elderly bearded personage. The twist of the head away from the chest towards the spectator's right, the thick, tousled hair, and the flowing beard combine to make it clear that we are dealing with part of the reclining figure of a River-God. The lofty brow, the slightly bulging temples, and the parted lips convey a 'baroque' effect of rude strength and latent divinity which make the technically more accomplished London marble (no. 29) look almost tame and academic by comparison. The modelling is bold and free, done by a hand that was completely master of its rough, but pliable, medium. The plastic, three-dimensional quality of the sculpture stems from a classical

4. This possibility was suggested to the present writer by Dr. Grace Simpson, Honorary Curator of the Chesters Museum.

source, but the spirit and expression reveal a Celtic carver, much more probably a Gaul than a Briton; for this head can rank beside the best stone sculptures of the Rhineland and Provence.

The Studio, July, 1961, p. 8, fig. on left.

32. STATUETTE OF GENIUS   Plate 25

From the site of the Walbrook Mithraeum, London (found in 1889). Second century A.D. Italian marble. Height: 1 foot, 8½ inches (without the missing head); width of base: 10 inches. *London Museum, Kensington Palace*

This statuette of a half-draped male personage has unfortunately parted with its head, which has snapped off at the neck – an accident that could have occurred during the building operations of 1889, when the head might easily have been completely smashed (*cf.* no. 29). The figure stands to the front, on a low rectangular and moulded base, with his weight on his right leg, which is slightly advanced beyond his left leg. Arms, torso, and feet are bare, but a thick cloak envelopes the back, hangs in heavy, vertical folds over the left arm, passes in a broad, diagonal swathe from the left wrist to just above the right thigh, and then falls again in deeply cut vertical folds to reach the ankles. This mantle must once have been drawn as a veil over the now vanished head, since it is difficult to see how it could otherwise have been held in position on the back. The two necklace-like, semi-circular objects, that wreathe the neck and dangle down, one within the other, over the chest, are not, as has been suggested,[1] parts of the drapery, but appear to represent either metal torcs or two flower-garlands very stiffly and conventionally rendered. If they are garlands, the individual blossoms may once have been filled in in paint. The navel-hole is very deeply drilled out; and below the navel, almost concealed by the transverse sweep of the cloak, are three small round drill-holes, the meaning of which is obscure.

In the left hand, of which the tips of two fingers are lost, the figure holds a *cornucopiae*. Part of its stem, just below the hand, has gone; but the bottom of it can be seen adhering to the end of a triangular-shaped 'bridge', which projects from the vertical folds of the cloak on the left side in order to support this stem. It would seem that when the statuette was found, the corner of the left shoulder together with the upper portion of the *cornucopiae* had split off from the rest, making a clean break, since this fragment has been stuck on again in modern times. The *cornucopiae* is brimming with vine-leaves, grapes, and other fruits, but the topmost tip of these contents has disappeared. The vine-leaves are picked out with small circular drill-holes. In his right hand our figure holds a *patera* (dish) over a narrow, rectangular altar, with plain mouldings at the top and bottom and flames, also picked out with drill-holes, curling up from the *focus* (fire-place). The top of the altar is connected by a marble 'bridge' with the cloak on the right side. A snake rears up from behind the altar and twines itself round the figure's right wrist; and on

1. See bibliography.

its coiled body incised lines, crossing one another at right-angles, summarily indicate the creature's wrinkled skin. To the spectator's right of the figure's left foot is the prow of a ship riding over a pile of conventionally rendered waves. The limbs and feet, and the toes in particular, are plastically worked and sensitively modelled; but the drapery folds tend to be harsh and mechanical. The statuette was obviously not meant to be viewed from behind, since its back presents a very much flattened, board-like appearance, with the folds of the cloak and the lines of the waves but faintly indicated. The surfaces of both the flesh and the drapery are smooth, but not burnished. The front shows a large number of black stains due to iron incrustation.

The Walbrook statuette belongs to a well-known series of personifications of localities (e.g. Genius Loci), classes of society (e.g. Genius Populi Romani), and abstract ideas (e.g. Bonus Eventus), by means of youthful male figures, either naked or partially draped, and distinguished by a variety of attributes and adjuncts. Of these personifications an extremely frequent, although not universal, feature is the sacrificial act implied by the *patera* grasped in the outstretched right hand. Very often, but again not always, this gesture of sacrifice is supplemented by a flaming altar onto which the contents of the *patera* are being poured; while the left hand normally holds some symbol of fertility – a *cornucopiae* or a bunch of corn-ears sometimes combined with poppies. For the Walbrook figure the name Bonus Eventus has, indeed, been suggested;[2] and Roman coin-types of the first and second centuries show a youthful male figure labelled BONVS EVENTVS or BONO EVENTVI, with a *patera* held in his extended right hand, generally over a flaming altar.[3] But there the youth is always naked and holds a bunch of corn-ears in his left hand:[4] whereas our figure is, as we have seen, characterised by the draping of the lower limbs and by the *cornucopiae*, which, together with the *patera* and flaming altar, are the hall-marks of a Genius. Genius is, in fact, a more accurate title for this statuette than Bonus Eventus, although the absence of boots, the veiling of the head (?), the torcs or garlands worn round the neck, and the ship's prow borne on waves, set it apart from the common round of local Genii. Possibly our figure wore under or over his veil the *modius* (corn-measure) not infrequently affected by these beings.[5] Such Genii were minor deities, symbolising the prosperity and fruitfulness of a place or district. In this case the locality

2. See bibliography.
3. E.g. *Catalogue of the Coins of the Roman Empire in the British Museum*, ii, 1930, pl. 46, no. 18 (Titus); iv, 1940, pl. 25, no. 14 (Antoninus Pius); pl. 32, no. 16 (Antoninus Pius).
4. *Cf.* an unpublished plaque of opaque blue glass, of unknown provenance, in the Department of Greek and Roman Antiquities in the British Museum; it bears the inscription BONO EVENTVI and shows a youth naked, but for a light cloak thrown around his shoulders, holding a *patera* in his right hand and a bunch of corn-ears and poppies in his left hand.
5. An altar from Cirencester, in the Corinium Museum, is inscribed G(enio) S(ancto) HVIVS LOC[i] and shows a Genius wearing a *modius* girt, apparently, by rays, or a mural crown, half-draped, and holding a *cornucopiae* in his left hand and a *patera* over an altar in his right hand; *Ephemeris Epigraphica*, vii, 1892, p. 280, no. 833.

intended was presumably London itself, with the ship, waves, *cornucopiae*, and torcs or garlands alluding to the wealth and activities of a busy port. But the snake suggests the living dead (*cf.* no. 12) and hints at a 'fertility' that will endure beyond the grave, in a harbour beyond the waves of ocean, for those city dwellers who have accepted Mithraic initiation.

The loss of the head makes the piece difficult to date on grounds of technique and style. The handling of the flesh and the treatment of the surfaces recall no. 29; and the Genius may belong to about the middle of the second century. It might, in that case, have been venerated elsewhere in London, or in some continental port, before it reached the Walbrook shrine. The workmanship suggests the hand of a competent, if somewhat undistinguished, Italian carver.

The evidence for Genii in other Mithraic contexts, if not abundant, is clear. Not only is a Genius Loci linked with Mithras in the inscription on an altar from Diana (Ain-Zana), in Africa Proconsularis,[1] but the Mithraeum at Dieburg in Germany has produced two provincial stone reliefs, on each of which a Genius is sculptured, half-draped, wearing boots, holding a *cornucopiae*, and sacrificing from a *patera* at an altar.[2] One of these reliefs carries an inscription recording its dedication to Mithras by three brothers.[3] Furthermore, a Genius wearing a mural crown, holding a *cornucopiae*, and sacrificing from a *patera* at an altar is depicted on one side of an altar dedicated to Mithras from Poetovio in Pannonia.[4]

Archaeologia, lx, 1906, pp. 45–6, pl. 9; *Journal of Roman Studies*, i, 1911, p. 163, pl. 23; ii, 1912, p. 152, pl. 8; *Royal Commission on Historical Monuments (England): London iii (Roman)*, 1928, p. 46, pl. 10; *London in Roman Times (London Museum Catalogues, No. 3)*, 1930, p. 45, pl. 16, a; M. J. Vermaseren, *Corpus Inscriptionum et Monumentorum Religionis Mithriacae*, i, 1956, p. 284, no. 812, fig. 219.

33. STATUETTE OF GENIUS   Plate 30
From Carlisle (Luguvalium), Cumberland. Second or third century A.D. British stone. Height: 13 inches. *Carlisle Museum, Tullie House*

The greatest possible contrast to no 32 is afforded by this crude native piece, reflecting a courageous, if somewhat ludicrous, attempt to perpetuate a Graeco-Roman art-type. There are the orthodox half-draping, the *patera* in the right hand, and the *cornucopiae* in the left hand, while, as often in the case of these Genii, a mural crown tops the thick wreath of hair. Again, in the patterned drapery, something of the special quality of British carving is retained. But the enormous head and left hand are out of all proportion to the dwarfed,

shapeless body and diminutive feet. This peculiar figure personified a century of the local garrison.[5]

F. Haverfield, *Catalogue of the Roman Inscribed and Sculptured Stones in the Carlisle Museum, Tullie House*, 1922, no. 10.

Oriental Deities

34. HEAD OF JUPITER DOLICHENUS   Plate 38
From Cirencester (Corinium), Gloucestershire. Third century A.D. Bronze (solid-cast). Height: 1¾ inches. *Corinium Museum, Cirencester*

Torn from its body, this miniature head presents an impressive countenance, framed by a bushy beard and two tiers of heavy locks and topped by the god's characteristic conical Syrian hat (*cf.* nos. 160–1). The roughness of the work and the fact that the crown of the head, if one thinks away the headdress, is far too flat and sloping, betray the hand of a provincial artist. Yet the type and inspiration are wholly classical and the bronze may well have been imported.

Unpublished.

35. STATUE OF JUNO REGINA   Plate 41
From Chesters (Cilurnum), on Hadrian's Wall, Northumberland. Early-third century A.D. British stone. Height (without the missing head): 5 feet, 3 inches. *Chesters Museum*

The slender, but commanding, figure of Jupiter Dolichenus' consort, whose head and arms are most unfortunately lost, is lightly poised, facing the spectator, upon the back of a powerfully built animal, turned towards the left, the head and legs of which are gone. The creature has been called a bull, an identification rejected, in view of its lack of dewlaps and genitals, by I. A. Richmond, who sees in it a heifer – an attractive idea, which explains the absence of sex indications, since the udders would not be developed.[6] The goddess wears a necklace and a long-sleeved tunic, piped round the neck and caught in round the waist by a girdle with heart-shaped metal terminals. The skirt of the tunic, blown by the wind back and towards the right and crinkled at the lower edge, reaches to the feet, its severe, but very decorative, vertical folds being off-set by the horizontal dipping creases in the sleeves, across the legs, and on the broad scarf-like garment drawn tightly over the abdomen and thighs and fastened at the figure's back. Especially effective are the borders, woven with a running wave-design, on the 'scarf' – a feature derived, it would appear, from oriental costume, and the way in which the outlines of the legs and knees are revealed through the gauzy tunic. The Juno is, indeed, a magnificent example of the exploitation of drapery to gratify a love of sheer designing, combined with a masterly grasp of the stance and three-dimensional structure of the human form according to classical principles. Is this the

1. *Corpus Inscriptionum Latinarum*, viii, no. 4578; M. J. Vermaseren, *Corpus Inscriptionum et Monumentorum Religionis Mithriacae*, i, 1956, p. 94, no. 140.
2. F. Behn, *Das Mithrasheiligtum zu Dieburg*, 1928, pp. 31–2, nos. 6 ,7. figs. 31–2; Vermaseren, *op. cit.*, ii, 1960, pp, 107–8, nos. 1253, 1255, figs. 328, 330.
3. *Ibid.* p. 108, no. 1256: d(eo) i(nvicto) M(ithrae) Priscinius Sedulius Primulus fratris [*sic*] v(otum) s(olverunt) l(aeti) l(ibentes) m(erito).
4. *Ibid.*, p. 196, nos. 1591–2, fig. 407.

5. Of the partly obliterated inscription on the base only *Geni[o] c[enturiae] Bassii Cresce[ntis] don[o do]navit* can be read.
6. On a relief in Rome Juno Regina is mounted on a sturdy doe (see p. 164, note 7).

work of a Celtic carver using an eastern copy-book, or, perhaps more probably, of an immigrant Syrian sculptor (*cf.* p. 5 and nos. 85 and 87)?[1]

E. A. Wallis Budge, *An Account of the Roman Antiquities Preserved in the Museum at Chesters, Northumberland*, 1907, p. 300, no. 14, fig. on p. 95: I. A. Richmond, 'A Statue of Juno Regina' (*Fritz Saxl Memorial Essays*, 1957, pp. 47–52, pl. 3), where it is suggested that the statue is a portrait of the Syrian Empress, Julia Mamaea, mother of Alexander Severus, in the guise of Juno Regina.

36. HEAD OF MITHRAS   Plate 42
From the Walbrook Mithraeum, London. Italian marble. Late-second century A.D. Height: 14½ inches. *Guildhall Museum, London*

The head and neck of Mithras, found sundered and separately, but lying close together and fitting one another perfectly when reunited, had been deliberately buried in a hollow, covered over and afterwards sealed by the later, fourth-century, floors of the temple, just east, and slightly north, of the site of the easternmost column of the northern colonnade. The god is portrayed as a handsome, beardless youth, with long, curly hair and characteristic Phrygian cap. The twist of the neck shows that his body, now vanished, veered three-quarters towards the spectator's right, while his head was turned back over his right shoulder more than three-quarters towards the spectator's left. When the head was found, most of the face and large portions of the hair were disfigured by dark smears of iron incrustation and staining. These have been cleaned off through the skill of Dr. H. J. Plenderleith in the British Museum Research Laboratory, leaving a light-yellow colouring and a slightly roughened surface. But originally the flesh parts were smooth and highly polished, as can be seen on part of the right cheek, near the ear, and over the whole of the neck, which comes down to a point in the centre. The clean break between the head and the neck cuts across just below the chin and it severed from the hair on the head the ends of the side and back locks, where they touch the shoulders. The two parts are now joined together by a dowel inserted into opposing holes drilled in the fractured surfaces. The carbon residue found in the iron incrustation suggests that the marble may have been exposed to altar-fires.[2]

Below the lower edge of the polished neck the piece terminates, as in the case of nos. 24 and 38, in a roughly surfaced tenon for letting the head into a cavity between the shoulders of a separately made body of inferior material – coarser marble, stone, or even stucco. A marble head resting on a stucco body would undoubtedly need some extra support to bear its weight; and in the base of Mithras' tenon there is a hole, about an inch square, into which a vertical metal bar may have been inserted. Assuming that the head is that of Mithras Tauroctonos ('Bull-slayer') (p. 142), such a bar could have passed invisibly through the bodies of the god and bull to the floor on which the group rested; and were this group, apart from its surviving head, of stucco the complete disappearance of the rest would be very readily explained.[3] At any rate we have no knowledge of the details, material, and provenance of the remainder of the monument of which the Walbrook head was apparently the most distinguished feature. It might have been worked abroad by the sculptor who carved the head, or by a member of the same workshop, and imported along with it into the province. If, on the other hand, we suppose that it was fashioned in this island, we must envisage the activity in Britain of a craftsman sufficiently skilled to produce both a body and other accessory figures (*cf.* no. 69) that provided a worthy and suitably proportioned setting for the head.

The Walbrook head of Mithras was clearly not intended to be viewed from the rear. Not only was it always relatively flat and unworked behind, but the back of the cap has been shaved down still further, leaving a heavily tooled surface, from which the hair on the nape of the neck and behind the right ear projects somewhat. This criss-cross tooling does not extend to the top of the peak of the cap in front; and it looks as if the head had been reconditioned to fit a group placed a short distance in front of a background that curved up slightly over it from below. Furthermore, the face of the god was meant to be seen neither full-, nor even three-quarter-, face, but almost in profile towards the spectator's left. For not only is this the view obtained when the tooled portion of the head is placed flush with some vertical surface, but the line of the brows slopes slightly up, and that of the nostrils slightly down, towards the spectator's right, producing a distinctly asymmetrical effect when the face is regarded directly from the front, while as seen from the side the perspective is perfectly correct and must have resulted from deliberate calculation. Again, the two creases that cut horizontally across the neck emphasise the sharp turn of the head, in that they are aligned, not with the chin, but with the central hollow that separates the ends of the collar-bone. The horizontal line which furrows the right temple, starting above the right pupil and ending just to the left of the nose, but not extending across the left temple, may reveal a small error, or change of idea, on the part of the artist.

No attempt was made to indicate the hairs of the eyebrows. The irises of the eyes are not incised and were probably put in with paint. The pupils are each represented by a deeply drilled-out, somewhat elongated hollow, with a small indentation in the centre of its upper side, so that the effect is

1. Precisely the same wave-design occurs on the borders of the cloak of a female statue, wearing Syrian dress, from Carnuntum, which has also been identified as a portrait of Julia Mamaea (E. Swoboda, *Carnuntum*, 1953, pl. 14, fig. 2; H. Gollob, *Götter in Carnuntum*, 1957, fig. v). Was this piece likewise perhaps by a Syrian artist working in Pannonia?
2. H. J. Plenderleith, *The Conservation of Antiquities and Works of Art: Treatment, Repair, and Restoration*, 1956, pp. 312–3, pl. 52.
3. It is, however, possible that the hole was merely for a dowel needed to steady the head, in view of its fairly sharp turn backwards, upon a stone or marble body. On the other hand, there is evidence that the cult-statue of Zeus, carved in the second half of the second century A.D. for the restored temple of Zeus at Cyrene, had head and other flesh-parts of white marble, drapery, hair, and accessories of stucco (*Papers of the British School at Rome*, xxvi, 1958, pp. 54–5).

roughly crescent-shaped. Glass-paste or enamel may once have filled these hollows, although no vestige of any filling substance now remains. Between the centre of the nose and that of the upper lip a deep, circular depression has been drilled. The inside of the mouth has also been deeply drilled out, with the suggestion of an upper row of teeth just visible between the slightly parted lips. The lower lip and projecting tip of the chin are separated by a deeply carved 're-entrant'.

The hair is treated in an impressionistic manner, with deep circular holes and deep running grooves, all drill-made, flecking the rough surface and parting lock from lock. This now results in a lace-like look, with black and white vividly juxtaposed and setting off most effectively the burnished polish of the flesh. That the contrast was originally accented by colouring the hair is very probable; but no traces of paint can now be detected. The surface of the cap is rough and un-polished and was almost certainly once painted, although here again no vestige of colouring survives. The soft mater-ial, whether wool or leather, in which this headdress is conceived to have been fashioned, is suggested by two shallow diagonal grooves, denoting folds or creases, on the left side of the peak and by two lower down on the left side of the bonnet.

Taken as a whole, the Mithras head can claim first place among all the Walbrook marbles as a work of art. It com-bines a fine mastery of the technique of marble-carving with the power to express an intense life and activity, of both flesh and spirit, which arrests the spectator's gaze and stirs him emotionally. In the wide-open, far-seeing eyes with their large, dark pupils, in the slightly dilated nostrils, and in the parted lips we can sense strength tempered with serenity and tenderness, and a deeply felt excitement and ecstasy linked with contemplation and repose. It is the face of one who is enacting, with quiet triumph and even with buoyancy, the role for which a higher power has cast him.

The backward turn of the head and the slightly upward glance of the eyes, recalling the type of the inspired Alex-ander, leave little room for doubt but that this is the head of Mithras from a variant of the famous scene that portrays him as Tauroctonos. In that scene is depicted the great elemental and symbolic act of sacrifice whereby the god brought life out of death, good out of evil, light out of darkness for man-kind. These opposing forces are normally represented by the flanking figures of Mithras' two attendants, Cautes with torch erect and Cautopates with torch reversed (cf. no. 69). Mithras performed the deed at the bidding of the Sun, who sent a raven as his envoy. He is shown holding the mouth of the bull with his left hand and with his right hand plunging his knife into its right shoulder. He averts his gaze from the sight of his victim's anguish because he takes no delight in slaughter for its own sake, but his face, if sometimes sad and 'pathetic', seldom, if ever, expresses horror and revulsion; he is generally, as here, the strong, yet pitiful, the inspired and transfigured sacrificant, who fully comprehends the holy purpose that underlies this bloodshed.

The focal point of almost every Mithraeum was the cult-image of Mithras Tauroctonos erected in sculpture, or occasionally painted, at the termination of the nave, whether straight or apsidal; it occupied a place of honour comparable to that accorded to the Crucifix above the main altar of a Christian church; and it is almost certain that the group which our marble crowned was the cult-image of the Wal-brook temple and stood on the platform in the apse at its western end. A group proportioned to the head would have filled that space exactly. What accessories it shared with no. 69 we do not know.[1]

The general style of the Mithras head and, in particular, the manner and technique in which the hair is worked, point to a date for it between about A.D. 180 and 200. Both its crafts-manship and its material strongly suggest that it was carved in an Italian studio.

Journal of Roman Studies, xlv, 1955, pp. 137–8, pl. 44, fig. 1; ed. R. L. S. Bruce-Mitford, *Recent Archaeological Excavations in Britain*, 1956, pp. 139–42, pl. 28.

37. COLOSSAL RIGHT HAND OF MITHRAS HOLDING KNIFE-HILT   Plate 40

From the Walbrook Mithraeum, London. Second century A.D. Italian marble. Length: 10¼ inches; height, with knife-hilt held vertically: 6 inches; width, across back of hand: 5¼ inches; length of iron shank: 4½ inches. *Guildhall Museum, London.*

This huge right hand was found, deliberately buried, along with nos. 20 and 38. It is just over twice lifesize, and the thumb and fingers are clenched to grasp a cylindrical knife-hilt, also of marble. The hilt has a round pommel, slightly projecting beyond the contours of the shaft, and decorated on the top with a deeply incised circle. In the centre of the end of the shaft is drilled a circular hole, one-and-three-quarters inches deep, into which a metal blade, presumably of bronze, must have been inserted. Much of the surface of the hand is polished, with a few tooling-marks visible on the back of the hand itself and on the backs of the fingers. But the shaft of the hilt, the palm of the hand, and the under side of the wrist are tooled all over; and on the hand and wrist the purpose of it seems to be to reproduce the myriad tiny creases which appear in Nature. Deeply drilled-out grooves separate the fingers, which, with the thumb, are most sensitively modelled, the utmost care having been expended on the finger-nails and transverse creases at the joints. The large crease that runs between the palm and wrist is also beautifully rendered. The hand presents, in fact, a quite ex-ceptionally fine combination of delicacy and strength.

It is clear that the hand was not an isolated hand, nor yet one that had been accidentally snapped off from a marble statue. There was never any break at the wrist, but the piece ends in a shallow tenon which starts a short way below the line of the wrist on the thumb side and tapers away to merge with the edge of the wrist on the side of the little finger. Into the base of this tenon a very rough, irregular iron shank has been lapped in with lead, a large drip of which has spilt itself

1. For the most recent discussion of the origin of the Tauroctonos group, see E. Will, *Le relief cultuel greco-romain*, 1955, pp. 169–85.

slightly over the edge of the wrist, where the tenon merges with it. Here, then, we have a detachable marble hand, to which at least an arm once belonged. For the ugly iron shank must have been embedded in an arm of another material, whether of coarser marble, stone, or stucco; and embedded in a draped arm, since the end of a sleeve must have fitted over and concealed the roughly surfaced tenon. The hand holds the knife with its blade pointing downwards and exactly reproduces the attitude of Mithras' right hand as he stabs, or is about to stab, his victim in the endlessly re-peated bull-slaying scene.[1] This, combined with the fact that the arm wore a long sleeve, leaves no room for doubt but that this colossal hand is that of Mithras Tauroctonos. But if it is easy to identify the owner of the hand and arm, the problem of the monument of which they formed part, and of their place and purpose in Mithraic worship in Roman London, is extremely difficult to solve. Were the hand all that has survived to us of a complete bull-slaying group, in the round or in very high relief, that group could never have been dedicated in the Walbrook shrine. It would have been far too large to stand on the platform in the apse; nor could it have stood in the nave, where it would have seriously interfered with the movements of the congrega-tion and where it would have needed a solid emplacement, of which no trace was found, to support it, given the boggy and unstable nature of the ground in this area. Again, it is impossible to hold that a rendering of this sacred and secret theme was erected in the street, outside the temple's narthex. Such a mammoth group, if it did exist, must have been set up at the end of another and much larger Mithraeum in Londinium; we should have to imagine the hand being brought from that 'cathedral' for burial at Walbrook; and we must suppose that the precious marble left hand and head from that group still lie concealed somewhere in or near the Roman city. On the analogy of Rome, Ostia, and other cities of the Empire, it is highly probable that a big port like London had more than one Mithraeum. Yet Lon-don was, perhaps, hardly rich and populous enough to pro-duce a Mithraic shrine of the quite abnormally large dimens-ions (even by Italian standards) required to accommodate a group proportioned to this mighty hand.

Fewer difficulties are raised by the view that the hand was never linked to an entire group, but formed, together with its vanished arm, a symbolic object, in which the immediate agent of the holy act of sacrifice was isolated from its context and erected, as a token of the whole scene, for veneration in the Walbrook temple. We have no idea how, and in what place, within the shrine such a symbol might have functioned; and instances of other dedications of this nature are, to the present writer's knowledge, wholly lacking. The absence of parallels is, indeed, the chief weakness of this interpreta-tion.[2] But we can at least set it out as a possible hypothesis

and hope that corroborating evidence may one day come to light.

Journal of Roman Studies, xlv, 1955, pp. 137–8, pl. 45, fig. 2.

38. HEAD OF SERAPIS   Plate 43

From the Walbrook Mithraeum, London. Late-second century A.D. Italian marble. Height: 12¾ inches, without *modius*; 17 inches, with *modius*. *Guildhall Museum, London*

The first thing that impresses the beholder of this piece, found purposefully buried in the same *cache* as nos. 20 and 37, is the extremely brilliant polish of its flesh-surfaces. The effect is, in fact, more striking than in the case of no. 24, since here the resplendent burnishing is offset by the broken, dark-on-light masses of cascading hair and foaming beard. Once more the neck terminates in a roughly surfaced tenon for insertion between the shoulders of a full-length body, bust, or herm.

The Serapis was, like no. 36, not intended to be viewed from the rear, at least in the last stages of its history in ancient times. The back of the head was always relatively flat and it was originally covered, from the crown to the upper edge of the tenon, by a kind of waterfall of sinuous, rippling locks, summarily carved in low relief. But the centre of this area has been reworked by the removal of a thin layer of marble, an operation that has left a bare patch, from which all traces of these locks have vanished. The reason for this mauling we do not, of course, know; but we may surmise that it was done with a view to squeezing the head more easily into a niche, or against some other form of back-ground, when it was dedicated in the Walbrook temple.

The crown of the head was flattened from the first so that it might give a steady foothold for the *modius* (corn-measure), a symbol of fertility, by which Serapis, as the Graeco-Egyptian god of fertility and after-life, is always distinguished. This cylindrical object carries at the top and bottom a plain, rounded, and projecting moulding. The drum between these two mouldings splays out slightly towards the top and it is adorned with three conventional, but not precisely identical, olive-trees, with leaves and berries sprouting from a central trunk – a further allusion to the fruitfulness that the god was expected to bestow both on

---

1. In the representations of Mithras' birth from a rock or from an egg (no. 71) the blade of his knife points upwards.
2. The closest sculptural parallel to the Walbrook hand, although it is completely lacking, so it seems, in Mithraic associations, is provided by a colossal marble bust now standing in the circular ambulatory

that surrounds the ground floor of the Mausoleum of Hadrian (Castel Sant' Angelo: no. 130) in Rome. Most of the face and the shoulders of the bust are modern restorations. But the style of the curly hair suggests that we have here the sorry relics of a portrait of Antinous – a subject that suits the site well enough. Upon the crown of the head rests an enormous hand, measuring at its greatest extent about 1 foot, 4 inches. The thumb and fingers grip firmly what appears to be the hilt of a sword or dagger, the blade of which must be thought of as buried in the left side of the head. The hand is carved in a separate block of marble from the head, but fits the latter's curve perfectly and it seems to have been finished off at the wrist as a self-contained hand, revealing no trace of an arm to which it had once been attached. The hand is set more at an angle to the wrist than is the case with the Walbrook hand, but otherwise its attitude is much the same as that of the latter. Does it symbolise the hand of death striking down Antinous? (The present writer's attention was called to this bust by Mr. Ralph Merrifield of the Guildhall Museum.)

dead and living. These trees are worked in very low and delicate relief and are paralleled on many other renderings of Serapis. The summit of the *modius* is pierced at its centre by a small, round hole, one inch deep, which is likely to have held a metal bunch of corn-ears, to complete this picture of material and other-worldly bounty.

The locks of hair that hang upon the brow, and those that descend in thick, vertical masses on either side to frame the face and hide the ears, are all deeply undercut and heavily drilled, with long, running grooves distinguishing the lateral tresses, some of which, on the right side, are connected by small, transverse 'bridges' of marble left between the grooves and for some reason not removed. The overall effect is one of painstaking virtuosity. Apart from the little 'bridges', every detail has a finished look; and we note that exact repetitions of the locks have been studiously avoided. It is clear that the brow was once overshadowed by four dangling forelocks; but of the two central ones, which must have been completely undercut, so as to hang quite clear of the surface of the forehead, only the stumps remain, while the two unbroken forelocks to right and left respectively merge slightly with the side locks. There is the same heavy drilling in moustache and beard. Below the centre of the chin the beard is dressed in large corkscrew ringlets, the lower parts of which are modelled in the round, with flanking tiers of spiral curls arranged in patterns that vary somewhat as between the two sides. It may be claimed that in the treatment of its hair, moustache, and beard the Walbrook Serapis represents a triumph of pictorial and colouristic sculpture.

There is no indication of the hairs of the eyebrows beneath the sensitively rendered temples. The pupils of the eyes are represented by small round depressions, the irises by lightly incised circles. These devices produce an air of vivid alertness; and indeed the whole face, if lacking the force and inspiration of no. 36, is instinct with life. We can almost sense the breath issuing from between the rows of teeth, the upper one of which the parted lips clearly reveal. The mutilation of the two central forelocks is the only substantial damage that the marble has sustained. The bright-brown stains on the beard and on the hair above the brow, and the darker-brown stain on the edge of the right side of the neck, are vestiges of iron incrustation.

The Walbrook head is a version of a well-known type of Serapis, of which two of the most familiar examples are a colossal marble bust in the Sala Rotonda of the Vatican[1] and a dark-greenish-grey basalt head in the Villa Albani collection in Rome.[2] The hall-mark of the type is the fringe of normally four or five vertical forelocks which dangle over the brow in straight, stiff lines, 'like icicles', to quote H. P. L'Orange's apt comparison,[3] and are sharply demarcated from the main coiffure, but which in the case before us seem to have worn a somewhat less hieratic, clear-cut, and rigid

aspect than that which is often seen elsewhere. It has been suggested that these overhanging locks were intended to denote the darkness of the underworld in which Serapis reigned.[4] But whatever their meaning may have been, they clearly distinguish the heads that bear them from those of another main series, in which the hair, instead of falling forward over the brow, either rises up from it, leaving it free and uncovered, and then streams down on either side in waving masses, or is waved laterally on either side of a central parting, or is massed thickly above the brow, of which the main area still remains empty. If we compare the technique and style of the marble heads that exemplify the two main types, we can have little doubt but that those without the dangling forelocks are earlier than those which show them. The British Museum possesses a good example of the type without the forelocks, a Roman work executed in a manner that dates it not later than the time of Antoninus Pius, but which could be several generations earlier.[5] This type may, for convenience, be labelled 'Hellenistic',[6] as opposed to the forelocks type, of which no known sculptural example would appear, from stylistic and technical criteria, to antedate the last quarter of the second century A.D. and which might, for that reason, be termed 'Roman-age' or 'Roman'.[7] Which type of hair-style reflects that of the cult-image of the god which an early-Hellenistic sculptor, Bryaxis the Younger, is alleged to have created for the Serapeum at Alexandria,[8] we cannot tell. But the forelocks type has been commonly assigned to him.[9]

When the 'Roman' Serapis type with the forelocks, which our Walbrook head exemplifies, whether going back to Bryaxis (?) or not, became the fashionable and standard one we do not know precisely. The earliest *certain* appearance of the forelocks known to the present writer is on a frontal bust of Serapis on an Alexandrian coin of Marcus Aurelius.[10] But general considerations would suggest that the sudden popularity of the forelocks type in late-second-century A.D. Roman sculpture had some connection with the history of the cult-image of the Serapeum of Alexandria, the mother temple of the religion. Recent (1943–5) discoveries at Alexandria have, indeed, revealed the remains of a large Roman Serapeum replacing the original and smaller

1. G. Lippold, *Die Skulpturen des vaticanischen Museum*, iii, 1, 1936, pp. 135–7, no. 594, pl. 36; M. Bieber, *The Sculpture of the Hellenistic Age*, ed. 2, 1961, pp. 83–4, fig. 296.
2. Bieber, *op. cit.*, fig. 297.
3. *Apotheosis in Ancient Portraiture*, 1947, p. 79.

4. G. Lafaye, *Histoire du culte des divinités d'Alexandrie*, 1884, p. 250.
5. A. H. Smith, *Catalogue of Sculptures in the British Museum*, iii, 1904, p. 5, no. 1527; M. Collignon, *Histoire de la sculpture grecque*, ii, 1897, p. 309, fig. 158; G. Dickens, *Hellenistic Sculpture*, 1920, fig. 12.
6. For a valuable assemblage of examples of this type by L. Castiglione, see *Bulletin du Musée National Hongrois des Beaux-Arts*, xii, 1958, pp. 17–39.
7. The head from Oxyrhynchus, in Egypt, with heavily drilled hair and beard, plain eyes, and traces of three irregular locks on the brow, never had a *modius* and could represent Zeus-Hades, although it has been published as a Serapis of Hadrianic date (*Jahrbuch des Deutschen Archäologischen Instituts*, lxxv, 1960, pp. 88–99, fig. 1).
8. J. Overbeck, *Die antiken Schriftquellen zur Geschichte der bildenden Kunst bei den Griechen*, 1868, pp. 253–4, no. 1325, quoting Clement of Alexandria.
9. E.g. Bieber, *op. cit.*, pp. 83–4; L'Orange, *op. cit.*, pp. 79, 83 (fig. 57).
10. R. S. Poole, *Catalogue of Coins of Alexandria in the British Museum*, 1892, p. 157, no. 1298, pl. 13. The present writer owes this reference to Mr. R. V. Nicholls of the Fitzwilliam Museum, Cambridge.

Ptolemaic building.[1] A. Rowe and A. J. B. Wace suggest that the Hellenistic temple was destroyed during the Jewish insurrection under Trajan and that the grandiose new shrine was the work of Hadrian.[2] But we have no record of any such early-second-century destruction. On the other hand we have got a record of the burning of the Alexandrian Serapeum under Commodus in A.D. 183;[3] and Commodus, whose devotion to the gods of Egypt was notorious,[4] is a likely Emperor to have sponsored the replacement of the burnt shrine on new and more ambitious lines.[5] It is, as we have seen, in the age of Commodus that the earliest 'Roman' heads of Serapis fit both in style and in technique; and it is at least a reasonable hypothesis that, of the two existing types, that with the forelocks was chosen for a new cult-image made under Commodus for a new Alexandrian Serapeum. The type was certainly well established in Alexandria by A.D. 199–201, when Septimius Severus, during his famous tour of Egypt, became an enthusiastic devotee of Serapis and adopted for himself the forelocks hair-style of his patron deity.[6] The existence of these two distinct types of Serapis hair-style is anyhow a puzzle. For Bryaxis' (?) image was a single, new creation and obviously cannot have shown both types. One or other must have been invented at a different date by someone else. As in the case of nos. 20, 24, 29, 32, 36–7, both material and workmanship indicate that Italy was the source from which the Serapis was brought to Walbrook.

Of the representations of Serapis known to have been dedicated in other Mithraea, the most impressive in some ways is the marble head from the temple at Mérida (Augusta Emerita), in Spain.[7] Its identification as Serapis is rendered certain by the flat cut across the summit of the crown which can only be explained as the seating for a *modius*. The hair flares up above the centre of the bow and then ripples down to frame the face. Here we have, in fact, a version of the 'Hellenistic' Serapis, without dangling forelocks; while the sparing use of drilling and of undercutting points to a date in the early-Antonine period. Two sculptured representations, one possibly, one certainly, of Serapis, have come to light more recently in the Mithraeum beneath the Church of Santa Prisca in Rome. One is a marble statuette, apparently topped by a *modius*, but abnormal as regards its drapery and gesture.[8]

The other, which in style is related very closely to the Walbrook marble, is a fine stucco head, which has a *modius* with olive-sprays and dangling forelocks and seems to have been fixed on or near the upper margin of a stucco relief of Mithras Tauroctonos, which occupied the end-wall of the temple.[9] This was also the position held by a bust of Serapis on a large gypsum relief of the bull-slaying scene which filled the end wall of the Mithraeum at Dura-Europos on the Euphrates.[10]

These four monuments from Spain, Rome, and Syria amply suffice to prove that there is nothing abnormal in the discovery of the Serapis head in a Mithraic context at Walbrook.[11]

Journal of Roman Studies, xlv, 1955, pp. 137–8, pl. 45, fig. 1.

39. HEAD OF ATYS   Plate 39

From Mildenhall, Suffolk. Second or third century A.D. Bronze (hollow-cast). Height: 2½ inches. *Ashmolean Museum, Oxford*

The jagged line of the neck indicates that the head has been hacked from, or broken off, a statuette. The stylised wreath of curls crowned by a Phrygian cap, the pointed face, the abnormally large eyes inlaid with blue enamel, and the crescent-shaped mouth, drooping markedly at the corners, proclaim its non-Mediterranean, probably north-Gaulish origin. The head is unlikely to be that of Mithras, since a small bronze figure in the round of that deity would be very unusual.

Proceedings of the Society of Antiquaries of London, xiv, 1892, p. 155.

Celtic Deities

40. STATUETTE OF THREE-HORNED BULL   Plate 45

From the fourth-century temple at Maiden Castle, near Dorchester (Durnovaria), Dorset. Fourth century A.D. (?) Bronze (solid-cast). Height: 3¾ inches. *Dorset County Museum, Dorchester*

This unusual votive bronze was discovered in the small Roman temple erected in the late-fourth century within the defences of the Early-Iron-Age hill-fort of Maiden Castle, some two miles from the Roman town of Durnovaria. It depicts a quartet of curious Celtic divinities. A powerfully

1. A. Rowe, *Discovery of the Famous Temple and Enclosure of Serapis at Alexandria* (Supplement aux Annales du Service des Antiquités de l'Egypte, No. 2), 1946.

2. *Ibid.*, pp. 60–4.

3. Eusebius Hieronymus, *Chronici Canones*, ed. J. K. Fotheringham, 1923, p. 290, CCXL Olymp. II: 'templum Sarapidis Alexandriae incensum'.

4. J. Beaujeu, *La religion romaine à l'apogée de l'empire*, i, 1955, pp. 377–81, pp. 386–8.

5. The coins ranging from Trajan to Geta, which were found in cavities at the four corners of the rock-cut cistern adjacent to the new Serapeum, do not necessarily suggest, as Beaujeu (*op. cit.*, p. 232) believes them to do, that the temple itself was the work of Caracalla; they only prove that the cistern was sunk in his period.

6. L'Orange, *op. cit.*, pp. 73–86.

7. M. J. Vermaseren, *Corpus Inscriptionum et Monumentorum Religionis Mithriacae*, i, 1956, p. 274, no. 783, fig. 215.

8. *Antiquity and Survival*, i, 1955, p. 33, pl. 12.

9. *Ibid.*, p. 14, pl. 4; Vermaseren, *op. cit.*, i, 1956, p. 196, no. 479, fig. 133. Plate 242.

10. Ed. M. C. Rostovtzeff, F. E. Brown, and C. B. Welles, *The Excavations at Dura-Europos: Preliminary Report of the Seventh and Eighth Seasons of Work, 1933–4 and 1934–5*, 1939, pls. 29. fig. 2; 30; Vermaseren, *op. cit.*, i, 1956, pp. 63–5, no. 40, fig. 15. *Cf.* also the marble Mithras Tauroctonos relief at Bologna (*ibid.*, pp. 252–3, no. 693, fig. 195).

11. A fine, if somewhat battered, oolite head of Serapis, 12½ inches high, with four dangling forelocks and a flattening on the crown of the head to receive a now vanished *modius*, was discovered in a garden in the modern village of Silchester (G. C. Boon, *Roman Silchester*, 1957, pp. 125–6, pl. 13). The sculpture, presumably the work of a good continental carver using a British medium, obviously came from Calleva Atrebatum; but whether from a Serapeum or from a Mithraeum or from the temple of some other deity, we cannot tell. Plate 243.

built and vigorously modelled three-horned bull, probably Tarvos Trigaranus,[1] stands towards the spectator's left. Above the centre of the creature's back rises the half-figure of a heavily draped, bare-headed goddess, while upon its tail, which is arched over its back, perches a plump, human-headed bird. Just behind the bull's horns is the bust, now headless, of a fourth personage, too fragmentary for its character to be determined. The workmanship is singularly good – three-dimensional and naturalistic – for so late a date.[2]

R. E. M. Wheeler, *Maiden Castle, Dorset*, 1943, pp. 75–6, pl. 31, b.

41. HEAD OF ANTENOCITICUS   Frontispiece
From Benwell (Condercum), on Hadrian's Wall, Northumberland. Second or third century A.D. British stone. Height: 12 inches. *Museum of Antiquities of the University of Durham and of the Society of Antiquaries of Newcastle upon Tyne (King's College, Newcastle upon Tyne)*

The head has been broken off a statue at the neck, round which is the groove for a bronze torc (?). It was found in the small apsidal temple known from inscriptions to be that of Antenociticus and it undoubtedly depicts that god. It is a fully three-dimensional piece, with a strongly constructed skull and well-rounded, if simplified, facial planes. In its build and in its faintly smiling mouth it is, indeed, not un-reminiscent of a work of archaic Greek sculpture. None the less, its Celtic origin is manifest, not only in the torc (?) and the great diamond-shaped eyes, with heavy lids and drilled pupils, but above all in the massive mop of wig-like hair that covers the crown and brow. Here the Celtic taste for patterning expresses itself magnificently in the regular, vertical locks, thrown into bright high-light by the deep, black grooves between them, which hang down symmetrically on either side of the central feature: this is a rigid, pendant-shaped tress, widening in the middle and tapering at either end and flanked by two long, sinuous, horn-like tresses that writhe diagonally and again symmetrically to right and left across the falling hair. This is a most exciting work – an art that contrives to be civilised without forfeiting the power and appeal of its native genius.

R. G. Collingwood, *Roman Inscriptions and Sculptures belonging to the Society of Antiquaries of Newcastle upon Tyne*, 1926, no. 302; *Proceedings of the Society of Antiquaries of Newcastle upon Tyne*, n.s. iii, 1927–8, pp. 124–6; T. D. Kendrick, *Anglo-Saxon Art to A.D. 900*, 1938, pp. 20–1, pl. 9, fig. 1; *Gods and Men: an Exhibition of Sculpture from Collections at Newcastle and Durham*, 1957, no. 13 with fig.; *Archaeologia Aeliana*, ser. 4, xxxix, 1961, pp. 80–1, fig. 6.

1. Pauly-Wissowa, *Real-Encyclopädie*, iv, a, cols. 2453–7. Cf. the three-horned bronze bull found at Leicester in 1936 (Leicester Museum: K. M. Kenyon, *Excavations at the Jewry Wall Site, Leicester*, 1948, p. 272, fig. 96) and that from the Roman site at Waddon Hill, Dorset (Bridport Museum: *Proceedings of the Dorset Natural History and Archaeological Society*, lxxxii, 1960, pp. 104–8, no. 68, fig. 9).
2. It is, of course, not impossible that the bronze was cast much earlier than the time of its dedication in the Maiden Castle temple.

42. HEAD OF CELTIC GOD   Plate 49
From Corbridge (Corstopitum), Northumberland. Third century A.D. (?). British stone. Height: 7 inches. *Corbridge Museum*

This head is three-dimensional in build, but wholly native in the treatment of its hair and facial features. The hair and beard are, in fact, virtually nothing but slightly raised planes, the latter sheathing the delicately pointed chin, with an element resembling a very stylised, three-pronged leaf-calyx. Two furrows spring from the root of the nose and fork away from one another diagonally across the temples. The enormous eyeballs are projecting and lentoid; the nose is wedge-shaped; the moustache droops, as do also the corners of the small, tightly closed mouth. The face is triangular; the expression is serene, if sombre, and recollected; and from the front the general appearance is almost Chinese in character. In the centre of the flattened crown of the head is a circular depression, designed to hold offerings. The personage portrayed is undoubtedly a local god – Maponus, in the view of I. A. Richmond.

T. D. Kendrick, *Anglo-Saxon Art to A.D. 900*, 1938, p. 21, pl. 9, fig. 2; Ed. D. B. Harden, *Dark Age Britain*, 1956, p. 11, pl. 3, fig. a.

42a.* HEAD OF CELTIC GOD   Plate 44
From Netherby (Castra Exploratorum), Cumberland. Second or third century A.D. British stone. Height: 7¼ inches. *Carlisle Museum, Tullie House*

This is an almost barbaric piece of awe-inspiring aspect. The brows are scowling and behind each ear is a curling ram's horn – a link with the classical type of Jupiter Ammon. The deep-set eyes are gouged-out hollows; the nose is a broad wedge; the mouth is a rectangular slot. The front and sides of the face are set uncompromisingly at right-angles to one another. The carver has, in fact, not modelled, but roughly hacked, a block of stone into the semblance of a human head.

T. D. Kendrick, *Anglo-Saxon Art to A.D. 900*, 1938, p. 21, pl. 9, fig. 4; *Archaeologia Aeliana*, ser. 4, xxxix, 1961, pp. 72–3, pl. 16, fig. 1.

43. HEAD OF CELTIC GOD   Plate 47
From Felmingham Hall, Norfolk. Second or third century A.D. Bronze (hollow-cast). Height: 6 inches. *British Museum*

This portrait of a Celtic god is classical in modelling. But its provincial, perhaps Gaulish, origin is evidenced by its highly patterned wreath of knob-like curls, stylised moustache and beard, parted lips, and generally tense expression, which would have been enhanced by the glass-paste or enamel filling of the now hollow eyes. The crown of the head has become detached.

Guide to the Antiquities of Roman Britain in the British Museum, 1951, p. 60, (c), no. 2 (ii). pl. 24; 1958, p. 60, (c), no. 2 (ii), pl. 24.

*Not in the Exhibition Hand-list.

44. MASK OF CELTIC GOD   Plate 46
From Old Carlisle (Olenacum), Cumberland. Second or third century A.D. Lead-filled bronze. Height: 2 inches. *Carlisle Museum, Tullie House*

One of the smallest, but most remarkable, of representations in the round of a Celtic god that has so far come to light in Britain is this bronze mask, filled with lead and, as the ring which tops it indicates, once serving as a steelyard-weight. The wide, flat face, snub nose, and small, coarse, thick-lipped mouth remind us of a classical Silenus. But the very elongated, lentoid eyes and the technique in which the thick hair, drooping moustache, and short, square-cut beard are carried out are essentially Celtic. The hair rises in chunky masses above the brow and envelopes the cheeks with a stubbly fringe that fans out on either side as it meets the beard, which is divided into three equal, rectangular segments. The individual locks of hair, moustache, and beard are indicated by deeply engraved lines that are ordered in simple, but highly decorative, symmetrical patterns. The treatment is symbolic and impressionistic, rather than naturalistic, yet the contrast in texture between the smooth, soft flesh-surfaces and the stout frame of stiff, wiry hair that hems them in is most effectively suggested.

Manchester Guardian, 30 April, 1956, where the bronze is aptly compared with the head of the Lezoux Mercury (O. Brogan, *Roman Gaul*, 1953, pp. 187–8, fig. 46, a; Plate 244); *Journal of Roman Studies*, xlvii, 1957, p. 203, pl. 15, fig. 2.

45. HEAD OF CELTIC GODDESS (?)   Plate 48
Probably from Birrens (Blatobulgium), Dumfriesshire. Second or third century A.D. (?). British stone. Height: 8½ inches. *Dumfries Burgh Museum*

This striking and enigmatic head, acquired by the Dumfries Burgh Museum in 1951, had been preserved for over a century at Burnfoot House, Birrens, Annandale, together with two Roman altars discovered in the *vicus* (civil settlement) outside the Roman fort of Blatobulgium; and although there is no proof of it, the likelihood is that the head is of the same provenance. It is, indeed, most probable that it is Roman, since no medieval work resembling it is known in this district of southern Scotland.

The head has been snapped at chin-level from a bust or statue. The eyes are large, wide-open, and completely framed by double lines representing the upper and the lower lids. The eyeballs are flattened – a detail for which the present writer knows no Roman parallel; and no attempt has been made to indicate the hair of the eyebrows. The upper lip is long and slightly protruding, the mouth rather tight-set and drooping, the chin full and heavy. The expression is serious, serene, absorbed, and dignified. It is an arresting face which stamps itself upon the memory.

The most unusual feature of the head is its hair or head-dress, the general effect of which is that of a 'Dutch bonnet' with projecting 'wings' that cover the ears. No known helmet, or civilian male headgear, or any male coiffure of any kind, Roman or medieval, answers to this description.

If, then, the head is unlikely to be that of a youthful god or hero or warrior, it must be the head of a woman.

It seems most probable that we are dealing here with a species of close-fitting cap or net enveloping the hair, which is bunched up over the ears. The nearest parallels to it come from the Rhine and Danube areas. In the Rheinisches Landesmuseum, Trier, is a brightly painted stone female head, a fragment from one of the Neumagen grave-reliefs, where the hair is completely hidden by a kind of 'bathing-cap';[1] a remarkable, ornamental, and no less enveloping hair-net is worn by the small bronze head of a woman in the Rheinisches Landesmuseum, Bonn;[2] and something of a parallel to the turban-like appearance of the upper part of the Dumfries headdress is afforded by the 'norische Haube' worn by two women on a second-century grave-relief from the Neumarkt, Tauchental.[3]

Supposing, for the sake of argument, that the Birrens *vicus* is the provenance of the Dumfries head, it is more likely to be that of a local goddess worshipped by the garrison than the portrait of a woman from a sepulchral monument. Its sculptor was undoubtedly provincial and was probably attached to the Roman forces, either directly as an army artist or indirectly as a native craftsman working for the soldiery.

Transactions of the Dumfriesshire and Galloway Natural History and Antiquarian Society, ser. 3, xxix, 1950–1, pp. 139–40; *Journal of Roman Studies*, xlii, 1952, pp. 63–5, fig. 3, pl. 9, figs. 3–4.

Funerary Figures

46. FIGURE OF SPHINX   Plate 50
From Colchester (Camulodunum), Essex. Late-first century A.D. British stone. Height: 2 feet, 9 inches (including base). *Colchester and Essex Museum, Colchester*

Found on the site of the Roman cemetery to the south-west of the *colonia*, this seated Sphinx is pre-eminent among the funerary sculptures in the round from Roman Britain as regards both its state of preservation and the skill and vigour of its carving. The creature's head, shoulders, chest with two full breasts, and her arms to well below the elbows, are human; but two clawed forepaws take the place of hands, and from below the chest the Sphinx is wholly cat, with powerful back, flanks, haunches, tail, and hindpaws, and two rows of swelling feline paps upon her belly. From her shoulders spring two great wings that are folded upon the back. Between her forepaws is the head of an elderly, clean-shaven man, with sketchily rendered hair, furrowed brow, plain eyes, and fleshy cheeks. The face wears the appearance of a realistic portrait, no doubt of the deceased person whose memorial this was; and the type is that of the Flavian or early-Trajanic period. The human hands, protruding on either side from beneath the creature, and the bones piled beside them, are likewise those of the departed owner of the

1. W. von Massow, *Die Grabdenkmäler von Neumagen*, 1932, p. 177, no. 193, pl. 66, no. 193a.
2. *Bonner Jahrbücher*, cl, 1950, pp. 87–90, pls. 2–3.
3. *Jahreshefte des österreichischen Archäologischen Institutes in Wien*, xxxviii, 1950, pp. 181–2, fig. 61.

tomb. Yet this is not the man-eating monster of the Theban legend, but the peaceful symbol of death's riddle and the guardian of the grave. There are no traces of agony or struggle in the man's expression, which is that of one serenely sleeping in the care of his protectress. We can picture the group as reared upon a lofty pedestal above the burial-place. The Colchester Sphinx must have been the work of a very good continental sculptor, possibly of Italian origin and perhaps attached to the occupying Roman army, who was carrying out commissions locally, in a British medium, for the ex-legionary veteran community settled in the *colonia*. It is among the best surviving Roman sculptures that were executed in the western and northern provinces.[1]

Journal of Roman Studies, ii, 1912, pp. 148–9, fig. 16; M. R. Hull, *Roman Colchester*, 1958, pl. 38, b.

47. LION DEVOURING STAG   Plate 51
From Corbridge (Corstopitum), Northumberland. Second or third century, A.D. British stone. Height: 2 feet, 10 inches; width: 3 feet. *Corbridge Museum*

It is virtually certain that this famous group was in origin a tomb-monument, later adapted, so it seems, as a fountain-ornament, since it came to light in the cistern of a house at Corstopitum on the sloping ground towards the Tyne and had been reconditioned so as to accommodate a lead water-pipe. The lion is, indeed, closely comparable in theme to a funerary group re-used in one of the bastions on the city-wall of Londinium,[2] although here its hindlegs are planted firmly on the rump, while its front claws crush the horn and rend the brow and eye, of the victim, which appears to be a stag. The hole cut through the stone at the back of the lion's mouth, and the groove contrived in the neck of the stag, are clearly secondary features; and the section of curved coping, on which the group is sculptured, could, in the first instance, have topped the balustrade or wall surrounding an architecturally elaborate tomb or mausoleum outside Corstopitum, before being brought into the Roman station.[3] The rugged vitality and stylistic unconventionality of this truly Romano–British work have often been remarked upon. The man-like face, the lashing of the tail round one hindleg, and the shape of the paws are all unrealistic. But the modelling has a solid, three-dimensional quality; and the telling contrast between the limp, helpless, flattened stag, with closed eyes and slack, lolling tongue, and the rude, vibrant strength of its vanquisher betokens the hand of a naturally gifted, if in-

experienced, sculptor. For the dating of the cistern, in which the group was found, there would seem to be little evidence. And if this sculpture was not originally a feature of the fountain, but had been pillaged for that purpose from a tomb (perhaps ruined in a raid from beyond the Wall), we must allow for a certain time-lag between its carving and its conversion into a domestic decoration.[4]

This group with its dramatic coupling of death and life finds its best British parallel in a native rendering of the same type of theme, but this time in relief, which was found near Bath. It is a fragment only, probably from an architectural frieze, representing the slaughter of a deer by a hound. The heads of both beasts survive: the deer's droops in agony, while the hound turns to snap at it with greedy, ruthless jaws. The stylisation of the carving serves but to enhance the tragedy.[5]

Archaeologia Aeliana, ser. 3, iv, 1908, pp. 234–40, pl. 2; *Journal of Roman Studies*, ii, 1912, pp. 148–9, pl. 5, fig. 2; F. Haverfield, *The Romanisation of Roman Britain*, ed. 4, 1923, pp. 53–4, fig. 23.

48. HEAD OF UNDERWORLD-GODDESS   Plate 52
From Towcester (Lactodorum), Northamptonshire. Second or third century A.D. British stone. Height: 22 in. *British Museum*

This neckless head, the chin of which rests directly on a low base, has been described as an 'antefix'. But a piece of such dimensions is much more likely to have been a funerary monument; and indeed Espérandieu's *corpus* of Gallo-Roman sculptures contains a number of large stone and marble heads resting directly on bases and attributed to sepulchral contexts.[6] Most of these are fully Graeco–Roman in style; and the Towcester head stems from classical tradition in the modelling of its face. But the doleful expression conveyed by the staring, deeply drilled eyes, the puckered brow, and the drooping mouth, together with the rendering of the hair and side locks, give the work a fierce, quasi-barbaric quality.[7] A native Underword-Goddess may well be the subject of the head, since the coiffure looks

1. For two Sphinxes in the round, each holding a human head between her forepaws, similar to, but less accomplished than, the Colchester Sphinx and found at Alba Julia, in Dacia, see S. Ferri, *Arte romana sul Danubio*, 1933, p. 283, fig. 368.
2. Guildhall Museum: *Royal Commission on Historical Monuments (England): London iii (Roman)*, 1928, pp. 102–3, fig. 26, pl. 11.
3. A funerary lion in the Grosvenor Museum, Chester, standing over its prey, which was found among sepulchral remains near the Roman road in the southern suburb of Chester, rests on just such a coping-stone and must have come from the surround of a burial-place (R. P. Wright and I. A. Richmond, *Catalogue of the Roman Inscribed and Sculptured Stones in the Grosvenor Museum, Chester*, 1955, p. 55, no. 168, pl. 40).

4. The probability that the Corbridge lion was erected initially on an extra-mural tomb site has been confirmed by the recent excavation of a building right outside the station, to the west of the Cor Burn (*Journal of Roman Studies*, l, 1960, p. 215; *Archaelogia Aeliana*, ser. 4, xxxix, 1961, pp. 37–61, pls. 10–2). There two fragmentary sculptured lions came to light, one seen crouching on the back of another animal, the head of which it pins down with its forepaws. It had been suggested that this building was a temple (*Archaeologia Aeliana*, ser. 4, xxxvi, 1958, p. 234). But its identification as a mausoleum is now accepted.
5. Roman Baths Museum, Bath: height 16 inches; width: 26½ inches: T. D. Kendrick, *Anglo-Saxon Art to A.D. 900*, 1938, p. 28, pl. 14, fig. 2. The piece came to light near the line of the Foss Way, about half a mile from the centre of the Roman town, and could have adorned an extra-mural temple or a tomb. Plate 262.
6. E. Espérandieu, *Recueil général des bas-reliefs, etc., de la Gaule romaine*, xii, 1947, pl. 17, no. 7888, 1–2; i, 1907, pp. 276–7, nos. 396–8.
7. For other Gaulish heads of similar type to the Towcester head, see *Gallia*, v, 1947, pp. 427–33, figs. 3–5; *ibid.* vi, 1948 (1949), pp. 186–7. Cf. *Bonner Jahrbücher* clxi, 1961, pp. 141–54, where it is suggested that the Towcester head and the Gaulish heads of this type all represent an *interpretatio Celtica* of the classical theatre mask. But the Towcester head lacks the open mouth and wig-like hair, one or both of which features are normally present in theatre masks proper.

feminine and the head is surrounded by a jewelled circlet.[1]

T. D. Kendrick, *Anglo-Saxon Art to A.D. 900*, 1938, p. 19, pl. 7, fig. 1; *Transactions of the Essex Archaeological Society*, n.s., xxv, 1955, pl. 7, fig. 1; *Guide to the Antiquities of Roman Britain in the British Museum*, 1951, p. 54, no. 1, fig. on p. 55; 1958, p. 54, no. 1, fig. on p. 55; H. Schoppa, *Die Kunst der Römerzeit in Gallien, Germanien und Britannien*, 1957, p. 57, pl. 95.

Genre Figures

49. STATUETTE OF ATHLETE   Plate 57
From York (Eburacum). Mid-second century A.D. Marble. Height: 11½ inches. *Yorkshire Museum, York*

This statuette, found in the Roman baths of York, may be characterised as a piece of reasonably good, if second-rate, imported sculpture. The right arm, from well above the elbow, and both legs, from above the knees, are missing. The hair is combed forward neatly over the brow and encircled by a laurel-wreath. The tough-featured man is naked, apart from a short cloak wound tightly round his left forearm; and the palm of the disproportionately large left hand, hanging beside him, is backed against some indeterminate object. The *puntelli* projecting from the right thigh, and the angle of what remains of the right upperarm, indicate that the right arm also depended by the athlete's side. The original setting of the piece was, we may presume, the *palaestra* of the baths, where it would have served, appropriately enough, a purely decorative purpose, if it did not also commemorate some specific local athlete. Style and technique are the only evidence for date.

G. Home, *Roman York*, 1924, pl. opp. p. 146; Royal Commission on Historical Monuments (England): York i (Roman), 1962, p. 120, no. 60, pl. 49.

50. STATUETTE OF PRIEST   Plate 53
From the temple site at Bruton, Somerset. Second or third century A.D. Bronze (solid-cast). Height: 2¼ inches. *Property of J. Jones, Esq.*

One *genre* figure accompanies the deities in this *cache* of bronzes (*cf.* nos. 15, 17, 22–3, 26). It presents a veiled priest, with lank locks of hair combed down across the brow. In his left hand he holds a scroll, in his right, a *patera*. The type is wholly Roman, but the rough and summary workmanship suggests a native craftsman.

Journal of Roman Studies, li, 1961, p. 187, pl. 20.

51. STATUETTE OF PRIEST   Plate 54
From Barham, Kent. Second or third century A.D. Bronze (solid-cast). Height: 3¼ inches. *Royal Museum, Canterbury*

This figurine of a veiled priest, or praying man, is, like no.

1. *Cf.* (i) the fragmentary over lifesize, neckless female head, resting directly on a square base, that was found on the site of the Roman cemetery to the south-west of the *colonia* of Camulodunum (Colchester and Essex Museum, Colchester: *Transactions of the Essex Archaeological Society*, n.s., xxv, 1955, pp. 13–5, pl. 5, fig. 2); (ii) the large broad-faced bearded male head, resting on a square base, found in or near Bath and perhaps depicting an Underworld-God (Roman Baths Museum, Bath; unpublished).

50, fully classical in type, but again of crude, probably local, execution. The left arm is raised in supplication: the right hand, extended to the front, is empty.

Unpublished.

52. STATUETTE OF 'FLUTE'-GIRL   Plate 55
From Silchester (Calleva Atrebatum), Hampshire. Second or third century A.D. Bronze (solid-cast). Height: 4¼ inches. *Collection of His Grace the Duke of Wellington (on loan to the Reading Museum)*

The so-called 'flute'-girl is conspicuous for its notable blend of classical and Celtic elements. The girl, who is poised upon a flat-bottomed, dome-shaped, hollow-cast stand, holds diagonally in both hands across her person a single pipe (described inaccurately as a flute) with projecting stops and is watching keenly for the signal to begin to play. Her head is crowned by a tall *stephane* (headdress) decorated with a series of spiky, upright leaves; and she wears a long, sleeveless tunic which descends to her feet, forms a roll round her neck, and has an overfold falling to the level of her knees. This drapery is reminiscent of a Greek *peplos*; but its stylised, vertical folds, flowing down the body at front, back, and sides in regular, unbroken lines, are essentially Romano-British. Indeed, the native craftsman is betrayed by the disproportionately large head and by the excessively broad and heavy shoulders and upperarms. But the little figure has, despite these blunders, a definite charm of its own, born of its author's fresh and direct approach to a classical subject. The headdress, the roll of drapery round the throat, and the homely, but lively, facial features were not derived from any Graeco-Roman copy-book.

G. C. Boon, *Roman Silchester*, 1957, p. 126, pl. 16; *The Studio*, July, 1961, p. 8, fig. on right.

53. FIGURINE OF GLADIATOR   Plate 56
From South Shields (Arbeia), County Durham. Second or third century A.D. Ivory. Height: 3⅜ inches. *Museum of Antiquities of the University of Durham and of the Society of Antiquaries of Newcastle upon Tyne (King's College, Newcastle upon Tyne)*

The figurine surmounts the handle of a clasp-knife and portrays a gladiator of a somewhat unusual type. The subject stands on the defensive, with his left leg, sheathed in a heavy guard, advanced; and from neck to knees his body is protected by a large cylindrical shield, with incised lattice ornament on its exterior, which he holds up in front of him. He wears a short, belted tunic and a guard on his right arm, but is unhelmeted. The hair is dressed in crisp, regular curls and the pupils of the eyes are marked. The piece is good provincial work, probably imported.

Archaeologia Aeliana, ser. 2, x, 1884, p. 267 with drawing; *The Studio*, July, 1961, fig. on p. 4.

54. STATUETTE OF PLOUGHMAN   Plate 60
From Piercebridge (Magis), County Durham. Second or third century A.D. Bronze (solid-cast). Height: 2 in. *British Museum*

This diminutive group shows a peasant wearing a hood (*cucullus*) and ploughing with a pair of oxen. It is an unpretentious, homely scene from provincial country life, worked with taste and sincerity, perhaps in Gaul, if not actually in Britain.

Guide to the Antiquities of Roman Britain in the British Museum, 1951, p. 54, no. 13, pl. 16; 1958, p. 54, no. 13, pl. 16; *Collection Latomus*, xxviii, 1957, pp. 456–7, pl. 62, fig. 3.

55. LAMP OR OIL-FLASK IN FORM OF SLEEPING SLAVE
Plate 63

From Aldborough (Isurium Brigantum), Yorkshire. Second century A.D. Bronze (hollow-cast). Height: $3\frac{1}{2}$ inches. *British Museum*

Of the Hellenistic and Roman taste for the rendering in art of quite young children a pleasing instance from Roman Britain is afforded by this figurine. The infant squats on the ground with a box or casket wedged between his bare feet. He is wrapped in a voluminous cloak which leaves the right arm free and from which the left hand emerges to support his weary head. The carefully drawn individual locks of hair, the childish features, the chubby right leg and feet, and the suggestion of the outline of the left leg concealed by the folds of the cloak reveal the sensitive hand of a gifted continental artist. The piece is very likely to have been imported. The figure's hollowness, the rings for suspension attached to its shoulders, and the truncated crown of its head indicate that it would have functioned as a lamp or as an oil-flask.

Guide to the Antiquities of Roman Britain in the British Museum, 1951, p. 54, no. 14, pl. 18; 1958, p. 54, no. 14, pl. 18.

56. ORNAMENT IN FORM OF STYLISED OX-HEAD
Plate 58

From Great Chesterford, Essex. No criteria for dating. Iron (solid-cast). Height: $4\frac{1}{4}$ inches. *Museum of Archaeology and of Ethnology, Cambridge*

This ultra-stylised version of an ox-head, perhaps once mounted on a cart, was found in a rubbish-pit in association with Roman material. It is an outstanding instance of the survival into the Roman period of native traditions of craftsmanship.

Unpublished.

57. ORNAMENT IN FORM OF STYLISED OX-HEAD
Plate 59

From Welshpool, Montgomeryshire. No criteria for dating. Bronze (solid-cast). Height: $2\frac{3}{4}$ inches. *National Museum of Wales, Cardiff (on loan from the Welshpool Borough Council)*

Carrying the same significance as no. 56, and aesthetically much more striking, is this bucket-ornament from the Welshpool hoard of Roman objects (*cf.* nos. 111 and 117). Completely Celtic is the treatment of the creature's huge lentoid eyes and of its stylised nozzle, 'fringe', knobbed horns, and ears. Other Roman-period ox-heads used as bucket-ornaments, mostly in the same late-La Tène style, have come to light at York (G. Home, *Roman York*, 1924, pl. opp. p. 130) Lydney in Gloucestershire (R. E. M. and T. V. Wheeler, *Report on the Excavation of the Prehistoric, Roman, and Post-Roman Site in Lydney Park, Gloucestershire*, 1932, pp. 75–6, fig. 11, no. 12), Manchester (ed. W. F. Grimes, *Aspects of Archaeology in Britain and Beyond*, 1951, p. 194, fig.

50, a), Gloucester (*ibid.*, p. 194, fig. 50, b), Kenchester, in Herefordshire (*ibid.*, p. 195, fig. 51), Thealby, in Lincolnshire (*ibid.*, pl. 7, fig. 5), Twyford, in Leicestershire (*ibid.*, pp. 198–9, pl. 9, figs. 3–5), Mountsorrel, in Leicestershire (*ibid.*, pls. 8, b; 9 figs. 1–2) Burrow, in Westmorland (*ibid.*, p. 196, fig. 52: for the find-spot, see *Antiquaries Journal*, xxxiv, 1954, p. 225), Ribchester, in Lancashire (?) (*ibid.*, pp. 225–8, pl. 24), Leicester (Museum no. 3354.1887; unpublished), and the Dinorben hill-fort, in Denbighshire (*Bulletin of the Board of Celtic Studies of the University of Wales*, xvii, 1958, pp. 306–7, pl. 8, a-b).

Antiquity, xxxiv, 1960, pl. 143, pl. 15; *Antiquaries Journal*, xli, 1961, pp. 25–6, pl. 10.

58. STATUETTE OF DOG
Plate 64

From Kirkby Thore (Bravoniacum), Westmorland. Second century A.D. Bronze (solid-cast). Length: $2\frac{1}{4}$ inches. *Carlisle Museum, Tullie House*

This smooth-coated, long-nosed hound is a little masterpiece of second-century naturalistic art. The raised head, the extended forepaw, and the 'expression' of the wiry tail suggest the presence of the dog's master. It is good provincial work, probably imported.

Unpublished.

59. STATUETTE OF DOG
Plate 62

From Carrawburgh (Brocolitia), on Hadrian's Wall, Northumberland. Second century A.D. Bronze (solid-cast). Length: $1\frac{1}{2}$ inches. *Chesters Museum*

No less naturalistic than no. 58 is this 'Aberdeen terrier', with shaggy coat, curly tail, and concentrated gaze. It had been thrown as a votive offering into Coventina's well (*cf.* no. 75). Again it is provincial, and perhaps imported, work.

E. A. Wallis Budge, *An Account of the Roman Antiquities Preserved in the Museum at Chesters, Northumberland*, 1907, p. 394, no. 103, fig. on p. 165.

60. STATUETTE OF EAGLE
Plate 61

From Silchester (Calleva Atrebatum), Hampshire. Second century A.D. Bronze (hollow-cast). Height: 6 inches. *Collection of His Grace the Duke of Wellington*

By far the most superbly naturalistic rendering of any bird or beast as yet yielded by Roman Britain is this famous eagle, cast by the *cire perdue* process and with legs separately made and fixed in place. The bird is poised for flight, with lifted head, and although the wings are missing, we can be sure, from the careful finish of the feathers beneath where they were, that they were raised and spread. It is also obvious, from the clumsy botching of the back, that in antiquity the original pair of wings had been replaced by another, secondary pair. The curve of the under sides of the feet suggest that the claws once clasped the surface of a globe; and indeed the most likely theory of the eagle's purpose is that it was the attribute held on a globe on the hand of a bronze statue – of Jupiter or of an Emperor.

G. C. Boon, *Roman Silchester*, 1957, pp. 99–100, pl. 15; *Catalogue of an Exhibition of Romano-British Antiquities in the Castle Museum, Colchester, July, 1950*, p. 16, no. 39, pl. 8.

SCULPTURE IN RELIEF

Graeco-Roman Deities

61. DIOSCURUS   Plate 69

From the Walbrook Mithraeum, London. Second or third century A.D. British oolite. Height: 1 foot, 10 inches; greatest remaining width: 14 inches. *Guildhall Museum, London*

This relief was discovered by the east bank of the Walbrook stream, some sixty feet south of the temple and nineteen feet below the modern street-level. There can be little doubt but that it came from the Mithraeum. It is a fragment, showing one of the Dioscuri with his horse (*cf.* nos. 92 and 104). They stand on a heavy ledge projecting from the flat background. The extreme left-hand edge of the slab is intact, from the base to a point roughly level with the Dioscurus' raised right hand. But above, the relief has been smashed and a rugged, jagged line runs diagonally from where the original left-hand edge ends to the crown of the god's head; and on the right the background is broken away round his head and left shoulder, while of the figure itself the extended left arm and hand, the top-surface of the left thigh, the whole of the left leg from the knee downwards, and the right leg from the middle of the shin downwards are lost. Of the horse, which stands towards the spectator's right, all that is left is its rump, tail, right hindleg, and a small bit of its left hindleg visible behind its master's spear. Part of the crupper is seen passing round the base of the tail. The piece is an object-lesson in the fate that overtook such of the Walbrook Mithraeum sculptures as were not deliberately concealed.

The Dioscurus stands fully facing the spectator, in front of his horse's belly, with his weight thrown mainly on his right leg. He is naked, save for a cloak, which is fastened on his right shoulder, passes across the left side of the chest, envelops the left shoulder and upperarm, and hangs like a curtain behind the back. He wears the characteristic *pilleus* (pointed cap), from under which appear the thick curls of his hair, framing the face and falling onto the shoulders. The face is round, full, and heavy; the neck and right arm are clumsily drawn and somewhat thick-set in proportion to the torso. In his right hand, which has been snapped off at the wrist, the Dioscurus grasped the shaft of his spear, the head of which is gone: the shaft is not undercut, but is joined to the background by a thin wall of stone. With his extended left hand (the left arm is bent sharply at the elbow) he must have held the bridle of his horse. The hindquarters of the animal, and, in particular, its long, sweeping tail, which almost reaches to the ground, are vigorously modelled; but the right hindleg terminates in a feature that looks more like an elephant's foot than a horse's, since, in contrast to the profile leg, the hoof is turned fully to the front.

It is almost certain that we have here one member of a pair of confronted Dioscuri; and the nearest parallel to this piece, as regards art-type, material, and context, is a relief at Vienne, found on the site of the Mithraeum to the south-east of the Halle Neuve and certainly Mithraic in its content.[1] The Gaulish sculpture is also of stone and fragmentary. It survives in two portions, of which the major one comprises the left-hand side and centre of the composition, while the other consists of a small adjoining piece from the bottom of the right-hand side of the design. In the centre, facing to the front, stands the Mithraic Aion, naked, with lion's head, four wings, claw-like feet, and a snake twined about him from feet to chin, while he clutches a key in one hand and a hook-like object in the other. To the left of Aion is a flaming altar; and on a high pedestal behind the altar there stands, in front of his horse, which faces to the right, one of the Dioscuri, wearing a Phrygian cap. With his left hand this Dioscurus holds his horse's bridle and in his raised right hand he must have clutched a spear, probably of metal, since there appear to be no signs of a stone spear broken away. On the smaller, right-hand fragment are both feet of the other Dioscurus and two of the hooves of his horse.

Whether the Walbrook Dioscurus' companion confronted him directly, or from the opposite side of a central figure, we cannot, obviously, tell.

The rather lumpish and stumpy proportions of the Dioscurus and his uncompromising frontality perhaps suggest a third-, rather than a late-second-, century date for the Walbrook fragment, which came to light unstratified. The use of British stone and the relative coarseness of the workmanship indicate that the relief was carved in Britain by a native, or north-west continental, craftsman.

Journal of Roman Studies, xlviii, 1958, p. 144, pl. 21, fig. 2.

62. HERCULES SLAYING HYDRA   Plate 71

From Corbridge (Corstopitum), on Hadrian's Wall, Northumberland. Second or third century A.D. British stone. Height: 2 feet, 10 inches; width, at bottom: 2 feet, 3 inches. *Corbridge Museum*

Hercules stands to the front, curly-haired, bearded, powerfully built, and muscular, with his left leg planted on the body of the Lernean Hydra, of which nothing now is left (the relief being broken away on the right side) but a couple of coils that are wound round his left upperarm; and in his right hand he brandishes a mighty club with which to smash the monster. On the left, in the background and hence on a much smaller scale, is the figure of Hercules' patroness, Minerva, wearing a crested helmet and a short-skirted tunic, resting her left hand on her shield, and pointing with her right-hand index-finger at her *protégé*, as though to direct

1. Vienne Museum: M. J. Vermaseren, *Corpus Inscriptionum et Monumentorum Religionis Mithriacae*, i, 1956, pp. 310-1, no. 902, fig. 230; F. Cumont, *Textes et monuments figurés relatifs aux mystères de Mithra*, ii, 1896, pp. 399-400, no. 277, fig. 320.

his blow. Classical in content, the relief is wholly local in its execution. Possibly the fragment was not strictly votive in character, but architectural, representing a portion of a frieze which originally contained other Labours.

Archaeologia Aeliana, ser. 4, xxi, 1943, pp. 171–2, pl. 10A, fig. 2.

63. MARS   Plate 65

From Custom Scrubs, near Bisley, Gloucestershire. Second or third century A.D. Local stone. Height: 18¼ inches; width: 13 inches. *Gloucester City Museum*

As depicted on a series of altars and votive plaques found in Gloucestershire, in wholly rural or suburban areas, Mars was revered in his capacity of god of agriculture, conquering sterility in crops and vanquisher of death and sickness in the case of man. Very native in its character is this plaque, which takes the form of a curved niche with flanking pilasters, topped by a steeply sloping gable and containing the frontal figure of the god. Here the style and treatment are quite distinctive, with a flat and two-dimensional over-all effect and sharply grooved lines, rigidly patterned, indicating the folds of cloak and tunic. Mars also wears boots and a triple-crested helmet that fits closely, hood-wise, round the face and terminates in a scalloped edging at the base of the neck (it recalls, in fact, the cap and bells of a jester). Eyes and mouth are mere slits, the nose is wedge-shaped. Mars is armed with a spear, an oval shield, and a sword depending from a broad belt, below which the abdomen is sheathed in a smooth-surfaced, semi-circular, apron-like feature, suggesting the lower segment of a cuirass divorced from its upper portion. Beside the left-hand pilaster of the niche is a narrow, elongated altar or pedestal surmounted by a double *cornucopiae*, emblem of fertility, very rare in the company of Mars, but betokening his agrarian functions. The piece intrigues us by its very naïvety; and by its inscription, cut in rough letters on the inner side of the slope of the gable – *deo Rom[u]lo Gulioepius donavit Iuventinus fecit* – and containing an interesting equation of Mars and Romulus (always rendered in the guise of Mars in Roman art) and the record of its dedication by a native Briton with a strange Celtic name and its execution by a native carver with a Roman name. We shall meet Iuventinus' unmistakable style again on no. 66.

Transactions of the Bristol and Gloucestershire Archaeological Society, xxix, 1906, p. 173, pl. opp. p. 176; xlv, 1923, p. 88.

64. ALTAR OF DIANA   Plate 68

From London. Second century A.D. British stone. Height: 23 inches; width: 12½ inches. *Goldsmiths' Hall, London*

Diana stands to the front, a slim, girlish figure in a cloak, a short, belted tunic, and boots, holding her bow in her left hand and with her right pulling an arrow from the quiver that is slung behind her. A hound is seated, snout in air, on the spectator's left, beside its mistress. This is the work of a good provincial carver.

Royal Commission on Historical Monuments (England): London iii (Roman), 1928, pp. 43, 120, pl. 12.

65. VENUS (?) AND TWO WATER-NYMPHS   Plate 67

From High Rochester (Bremenium), Northumberland. Second or third century A.D. British stone. Height: 2 feet 4 inches; width: 3 feet, 7 inches. *Museum of Antiquities of the University of Durham and of the Society of Antiquaries of Newcastle upon Tyne (King's College, Newcastle upon Tyne)*

Here we have a clear example of a native carver doing his best to reproduce a scene from a Graeco-Roman copy-book.[1] The relief shows three women at their ablutions, the figures being varied in both poses and activities. The central figure faces the spectator, but kneels towards the left, as she binds up, Venus-like, with both hands her long, sinuous tresses, while from an overturned urn behind her right leg a copious stream of water flows. Her companion on the right is frontal and holds a jar and a long tress of hair: the left-hand figure, also turned towards the front, screens her person with an odd, horizontal feature that could be meant to be a fringed towel. The action of the central figure, and the fact that she is on a larger scale than her companions, suggest that the group may depict Venus assisted at her bath by attendant Water-Nymphs. Alternatively, all three figures could be Water-Nymphs.

J. Collingwood Bruce, *Lapidarium Septentrionale*, 1875, p. 305. no. 584 with fig.

66. GENIUS   Plate 66

From Custom Scrubs, near Bisley, Gloucestershire. Second or third century A.D. Local stone. Height: 19¾ inches; width: 14¾ inches. *Gloucester City Museum*

This relief is clearly by the Iuventinus who carved no. 63. It has the same steeply sloping gable at the top and the same side pilasters; and the style of the carving of the frontal Genius is identical with that of the Mars. The figure wears a tunic reaching to the knees, a cloak, and, unlike most Genii, a close-fitting hood. He grasps a double *cornucopiae* in his left hand and holds in his right hand a *patera* above a narrow, elongated altar.

Transactions of the Bristol and Gloucestershire Archaeological Society, xxix, 1906, p. 173, pl. opp. p. 177; xlv, 1923, p. 87.

67. VICTORY   Plate 72

From Housesteads (Vercovicium), on Hadrian's Wall, Northumberland. Second or third century A.D. British stone. Height: 3 feet, 5 inches; Width, 1 foot, 10 inches. *Chesters Museum*

Victory stands facing the spectator within a niche. Her hair covers her ears after the manner of Julia Domna's coiffure; she wears a fine, sleeveless, clinging tunic with an overfold and a girdle below the breasts; and she holds in her left hand a palm-branch. The right arm and hand, which would have held a wreath, and the legs from below the knees are lost. The execution is provincial, but the style and type are wholly classical.

1. Cf., for instance, a mosaic from Timgad: L. Leschi, *Algérie antique*, 1952, p. 118.

E. A. Wallis Budge, *An Account of the Roman Antiquities Preserved in the Museum at Chesters, Northumberland*, 1907, p. 327, no. 129, fig. on p. 183.

68. THREE WATER-NYMPHS   Plate 70
From Carrawburgh (Brocolitia), on Hadrian's Wall, Northumberland. Second or third century A.D. British stone. Height: 1 foot, 8 inches; width: 3 feet. *Chesters Museum*

This triptych, found in Coventina's well, is composed of three rounded, equal-sized, columned niches. Beneath each arch reclines a Water-Nymph, classical in derivation, but very native in style and execution. Each figure is half-draped in a cloak with close-set, crinkly folds; and each holds in her lowered hand an urn from which a stream of water gushes forth and in her upraised hand a squat-shaped jar or beaker.[1]

E. A. Wallis Budge, *An Account of the Roman Antiquities Preserved in the Museum at Chesters, Northumberland*, 1907, pp. 310–11, no. 63, fig. on p. 151.

Oriental Deities

69. MITHRAS THE BULL-SLAYER   Plate 73
From the site of the Walbrook Mithraeum, London (found in 1889). Late-second or third century A.D. Probably Italian marble. Height: 17 inches; width: 20 inches. *London Museum, Kensington Palace*

Found at the same date and in the same circumstances as nos. 29 and 32, this slab shows as its main and central feature a slightly concave roundel, within which is carved in high relief the famous bull-slaying scene, the significance of which has been discussed in connection with no. 36. On the border of the roundel the twelve signs of the zodiac are worked in low relief between two mouldings.

In the roundel Mithras wears his usual costume – a Phrygian cap, a short, long-sleeved tunic, a cloak, and trousers. He turns his head three-quarters towards the spectator's left as he grasps the bull's nostrils with his left hand and plunges his knife into its shoulder with his right hand. He kneels with his left knee on the creature's back, while his right leg is thrust straight down beside its rump, his right foot resting on the inner moulding of the zodiac frame. The god's cloak flies out behind him, but a portion of it has been broken off. This, and the loss of part of the bull's tail, are the only substantial damages that the relief has suffered. A lump of marble below the cloak may be the relic of a corn-ear sprouting from the victim's tail, symbol of life-bringing death. On the left Cautes stands to the front with legs crossed, wearing a Phrygian cap, a sleeved tunic, a cloak, and trousers and holding a torch erect – symbol of life, light, and day. On the right of Mithras and the bull Cautopates also stands to the front with legs crossed, wearing the same costume as Cautes, but

holding a torch reversed – symbol of death, darkness, and night, not as unmitigated evils, but as the necessary preludes to immortality. A snake, of which the head and tail alone remain, and a dog rear up against the bull's flank to drink the blood that gushes from the wound. These represent the life, both natural and other-worldly, generated and nourished by the act of sacrifice. Meanwhile a scorpion, token of the powers of evil, vainly attacks the victim's genitals.

Outside the frame of the roundel, in the upper left-hand corner, is Sol driving his team of horses up the sky towards the right. In the corresponding corner on the right is Luna, also facing to the right, who sends her pair of bulls plunging headlong downwards. In the lower corners are the frontal busts of two Wind-Gods, each with wings in his flying locks. The Wind on the left is old, fierce, and bearded, with bared teeth and staring eyes: he may be Boreas. His companion on the right is young and smiling, full-cheeked and beardless: he may be Zephyrus. These four figures together with the zodiac signs, betoken Nature's co-operation with the exploit of Mithras.

Into such empty spaces as are left on the slab between the sculptured elements an inscription has been squeezed in four separate parts. On the left, below Sol, we read *Ulpius Silvanus*; on the right, below Luna, *emeritus leg(ionis) II Aug(ustae) votum solvit*; to the right of Boreas (?), *factus*; and to the left of Zephyrus (?), *Arausione*. This is best interpreted as 'Ulpius Silvanus, veteran of the Second Augustan Legion, paid his vow: he was initiated at Orange'. The reading *factus emeritus*, 'discharged', is as insipid in the present context as *factus* in the sense of 'made a Mithraist' is pointed.

This scheme of composition, with the main scene enclosed within a circular border, is relatively rare. The bull-slaying episode appears in a laurel-wreathed medallion (the laurel presumably alluding to the god's victory) on reliefs from Heddernheim[2] and Friedberg[3], in Germany, from Sarmizigetusa[4] and Turda[5], in Dacia, from Kumanovo, in Serbia,[6] from Küstendil, in Bulgaria,[7] and in a corn-wreathed medallion from Siscia, in Pannonia;[8] it is found in a circular frame

---

1. For a somewhat similar relief of three Water-Nymphs, but without the arcading and more classical in style, from Unterheimbach, in Germany, and now in the Württembergisches Landesmuseum, Stuttgart, see *Germania Romana*, ed. 2, iv, 1928, pl. 23, fig. 5. Plate 247.

2. E. Espérandieu, *Recueil général des bas-reliefs, etc. de la Germanie romaine*, 1931, p. 107, no. 159 with fig.; F. Cumont, *Textes et monuments figurés relatifs aux mystères de Mithra*, ii, 1896, p. 379, no. 263, fig. 293; M. J. Vermaseren, *Corpus Inscriptionum et Monumentorum Religionis Mithriacae*, ii, 1960, pp. 77–9, no. 1128, fig. 294.
3. Espérandieu, *op. cit.*, p. 59, no. 88 with fig.; Cumont, *op. cit.*, pp. 356–7, no. 248c, fig. 232; Vermaseren, *op. cit.*, ii, 1960, p. 58, no. 1054.
4. Cumont, *op. cit.*, p. 293, no. 165, fig. 148. Two fragments of a relief from the same site show the bull-slaying scene framed by a wreath and, outside that, by a circular frieze containing episodes from Mithras' life (*ibid.*, p. 301, no. 176, fig. 158; Vermaseren, *op. cit.*, ii, 1960, pp. 302–3, nos. 2042, 2044, fig. 538). *Cf.* the circular marble plate from Sarkeszi, in Pannonia (*ibid.*, pp. 242–3, no. 1815, fig. 469).
5. *Ibid.*, p. 275, no. 1926, fig. 503.
6. *Revue Archéologique*, 1933, pp. 185–90, no. 5, figs. 5–7; Vermaseren, *op. cit.*, ii, 1960, pp. 339–40, no. 2202, fig. 608.
7. *Germania*, xix, 1935, pp. 25–6, no. 3, pl. 2, fig. 2; Vermaseren, *op. cit.*, ii, 1960, p. 349, no. 2241, fig. 618.
8. Cumont, *op. cit.*, ii, 1896, p. 326, no. 221, fig. 193 (*cf.* also a fragment of unknown provenance in the National Museum in Budapest (*ibid.*, p. 323, no. 215, fig. 189)); Vermaseren, *op. cit.*, ii, 1960, pp. 173–4, no. 1475, fig. 377.

decorated with a bust of Helios, two snakes flanking a vase, and a variety of animals on a relief from Salona, in Dalmatia.[1] But the present writer knows of only two examples, possibly one from Stockstadt, in Germany[2] and certainly one from Siscia,[3] in which, as on the Walbrook slab, Mithras the Bull-Slayer is framed within a zodiac circle. The zodiac itself, besides symbolising the planets' co-operation with the god, denotes apotheosis, the sky where Mithras dwells and where his worshippers will find eternal life.

Style and technique, the clumsy drawing of some of the elements in the relief, proclaim the Walbrook slab to be provincial work. Since the medium is said to be Italian marble, it seems most likely that an unworked piece was imported into Britain and was carved in this country either by a Briton or by a Gaul or perhaps, in view of its compositional associations, by a Danubian, who was plying his trade as sculptor in the British province.

Archaeologia, lx, 1906, pp. 46–8, pl. 10; *Journal of Roman Studies*, i, 1911, p. 163, pl. 24, fig. 1; ii, 1912, pp. 142–4, fig. 14; *Royal Commission on Historical Monuments (England): London iii (Roman)*, 1928, pp. 43, 170, pl. 10; *London in Roman Times (London Museum Catalogues, No. 3)*, 1930, pp. 45–6. pl. 17, a; M. J. Vermaseren, *Corpus Inscriptionum et Monumentorum Religionis Mithraicae*, i, 1956, pp. 283–4, nos. 810–1, fig. 218.

70. ALTAR OF MITHRAS   Plate 75
From Carrawburgh (Brocolitia), on Hadrian's Wall, Northumberland. Third century A.D. British stone. Height: 3 feet, 11 inches; width: 18 inches. *Museum of Antiquities of the University of Durham and of the Society of Antiquaries of Newcastle upon Tyne (King's College, Newcastle upon Tyne)*

This altar was found in the Mithraeum of the *vicus* outside the fort and is of local workmanship. It carries on its main face the frontal bust of Mithras, wearing a halo of rays, which are perforated so that light from a lamp or lamps, placed on a shelf behind, within the depth of the altar, might shine through them (*cf.* nos. 12 and 71). The god holds the whip of Sol; and his cloak, which falls in stiffly patterned folds, bears traces of red paint. The inscription reads: *deo invicto Mitrae M(arcus) Simplicius Simplex pr(a)ef(ectus) v(otum) s(olvit) l(ibens) m(erito)*.

I. A. Richmond and J. P. Gillam, *The Temple of Mithras at Carrawburgh*, 1951, pp. 36–8, 49–51, pl. 12, b; C. Daniels, *Mithras and his Temples on the Wall*, 1962, pp. 18–9, fig. 17.

71. EGG-BIRTH OF MITHRAS   Plate 74
From Housesteads (Vercovicium), on Hadrian's Wall, Northumberland. Second or third century A.D. British stone. Height: 4 feet, 2 inches; width: 2 feet, 6½ inches. *Museum of*

Antiquities of the University of Durham and of the Society of Antiquaries of Newcastle upon Tyne (King's College, Newcastle upon Tyne)

Found in the Mithraeum of the *vicus* of the fort, this scene of Mithras' birth from an egg (instead of from a rock, as normally) is unique in the Roman world.[4] Above an empty panel, designed for an inscription that was either never cut or carried out in paint, is an oval frame on which the signs of the zodiac are carved in low relief. Within the frame are the top and bottom halves of an egg-shell, which have split apart to hatch the infant god, whose head and body, from the waist-line upwards, are shown in bold modelling between them. His laterally extended arms are gone[5], but the hands can be seen against the zodiac frame, one gripping a knife, the other a torch. The nose, chin, and mouth are damaged. The sculpture is indeed a relief: but the background on either side of the figure of the god has been cut away, no doubt for the purpose of silhouetting the divine form against a glow of lamp-light behind it (*cf.* nos. 12 and 70).

R. G. Collingwood, *Roman Inscriptions and Sculptures belonging to the Society of Antiquaries of Newcastle upon Tyne*, 1926, no. 277; M. J. Vermaseren, *Corpus Inscriptionum et Monumentorum Religionis Mithriacae*, i, 1956, pp. 298–9, no. 860, fig. 226; C. Daniels, *Mithras and his Temples on the Wall*, 1962, pp. 16–7, fig. 15; *Archaeologia Aeliana*, ser. 4, XL, 1962, pp. 108–13, 277–80, pl. 27.

Celtic Deities

72. THREE MOTHERS   Plate 76
From Cirencester (Corinium), Gloucestershire. Second or third century A.D. Cotswold stone (oolite). Height: 1 foot, 4 inches; width: 2 feet, 8 inches. *Corinium Museum, Cirencester*

This piece, although made locally in a British medium and by a provincial artist, stands quite apart from all the renderings of the triad of Mother-Goddesses in this country, in its style, in its composition, and in its wholly classical spirit. The three are seated in a semi-circle on a bench in easy, carefree attitudes, each with her boy beside her. The central figure is not strictly flush with the background and the lateral figures are turned three-quarters towards the right and left respectively. They recall, in fact, a group of human mothers chatting together on a bench in a park or garden while their children play. The upper part of the head in each case has gone and in one case the features of the remnant of the face are worn away. But these losses do not lessen our appreciation of the plastic, three-dimensional, naturalistic quality of the carving. Each goddess wears a cloak, which falls between her legs in a Greek zig-zag fold (*cf.* nos. 27, 30, 73, 124), and a long tunic. The right-hand Mother's arm is laid affectionately round the shoulders of her child, who rests his left

---

1. *Berytus*, xi, 1954, pl. 5, fig. 2; Vermaseren, *op. cit.*, ii, 1960, pp. 256–7, no. 1861, fig. 477.
2. Espérandieu, *op. cit.*, p. 183, no. 283 with fig.; Vermaseren, *op. cit.*, ii, 1960, p. 87, no. 1161, fig. 306.
3. Cumont, *op. cit.*, ii, 1896, p. 325, no. 220, fig. 192; Vermaseren, *op. cit.*, ii, 1960, pp. 172–3, no. 1472, fig. 375. A relief from Kadin-Most in Moesia displays the bull-slaying scene within a narrow, plain, circular border (*Berytus*, xi, 1954, pl. 5, fig. 1).

4. For a relief at Modena depicting the egg-birth of the snake-entwined Orphic-Mithraic god Phanes-Aion, within a zodiac frame, but not with a cut-out background, see M. J. Vermaseren, *Corpus Inscriptionum et Monumentorum Religionis Mithriacae*, i, 1956, pp. 253–4, no. 695, fig. 197. Plate 245.
5. The arms shown on Plate 74 are restorations.

hand upon her lap, while leaning with his right elbow against the central Mother. That Mother nurses on her lap (the laps of the other two are empty) a long-eared little 'Dachshund'[1] and grips the wrist of her son, who is straining away from her towards the left-hand Mother, eager to share the meal of the latter's own infant, whom she is suckling. There is a spontaneity and playfulness about the scene which suggests that the carver may have taken Nature for his model, rather than copy-book. It is true that, as has been pointed out,[2] a distinct resemblance exists between the composition of the group of the left-hand Mother and that of the Terra Mater or Italia group on the Ara Pacis Augustae in Rome.[3] But it would seem to be a somewhat remote possibility that the Romano–British sculptor had the Roman monument in mind or was working with a sketch of that particular relief before him. He would anyhow have had to combine that group with the other two groups, the Roman prototypes of which, if they existed, are unknown to us. Why should this not be the bold, original, and unified design, fully worthy of the fine 'Corinium school' (cf. p. 7 and nos. 19 and 31), of a local artist?

Journal of Roman Studies, ii, 1912, pp. 140–2, fig. 13; *Archaeologia*, lxix, 1917–8, pp. 183–4, fig. 10 on p. 183.

73. THREE MOTHERS Plate 84

From Cirencester (Corinium), Gloucestershire. Second or third century A.D. Cotswold stone (oolite). Height: 2 feet, 7 inches; width: 2 feet, 1 inch. *Corinium Museum, Cirencester*

Another relief of the Three Mothers from Corinium, a competent piece of work, but less attractive than no 72, and of a much more common type, shows the members of the triad seated stiffly side by side in unrelenting, hieratic frontality.[4] Each has a tunic that seems to reach no lower than the knees and a cloak that hangs between the legs in the Greek zig-zag fold (cf. nos. 27, 30, 72, 124). But here that fold is also worked into the shape of a water-beast, of which the head, narrow body, and spreading fish-tail are clearly discernible:[5] this recalls the Syrian Fertility- and Mother-Goddess, Atargatis Derkéto, whose symbol is a fish (cf. no. 91). The caps and the hair-styles of the three figures vary, as do also the ways in which they wear their cloaks and the attributes on their laps. Two hold each a tray of fruits; the third holds a tray of oblong cakes or loaves. This rigidly frontal seated type of triad appears on a number of other Romano–British votive slabs – on a small relief from Cirencester,[6]

on a piece from London,[7] on one from Lincoln,[8] and on one from Ancaster, in Lincolnshire.[9] Two similar reliefs of the trio come from Carlisle.[10]

Archaeologia, lxix, 1917–8, pp. 181, 183, fig. 8; *Journal of Roman Studies*, ii, 1912, pp. 139–40, fig. 12; *The Studio*, July, 1961, fig. on p. 2.

74. MOTHER-GODDESS Plate 81

From Bewcastle (Banna), Cumberland. Late-second or third century A.D. British stone. Height: 3 feet, 2 inches; width; 2 feet, 4 inches. *Carlisle Museum, Tullie House*

This relief bears the most attractive surviving Romano–British rendering of a seated Mother worked in Celtic style. It shows the goddess enthroned on a backed chair with curved arms and elaborately turned legs. The relief is broken on the left side, so that we cannot be absolutely certain that she is not the sole remaining member of a trio, although the chair-leg on the left, indicating that she had a separate seat, suggests that she was portrayed alone. The hair hangs, wig-like, over the ears, as in the case of Julia Domna's portraits. The features of the face are unfortunately worn away. The relief is very low and flat and the charm of the piece lies in the heavy drapery, the delightfully patterned folds of which seem to be drawn, rather than carved, by deeply incised, grooved lines. The goddess wears a mantle fastened across her breast and a trailing tunic with an overfold and long, full, hanging sleeves, from which emerge her slender hands, delicately fingering the fruits that are piled on her lap. It is a quite outstanding example of the most distinctive Romano-British sculptural style, in which the Celtic feeling for the decorative value of pure lines, both straight and curving, has found its fullest outlet.

F. Haverfield, *Catalogue of the Roman Inscribed and Sculptured Stones in the Carlisle Museum, Tullie House*, 1922, no. 132, pl. opp. p. 43; J. Liversidge, *Furniture in Roman Britain*, 1955, fig. 24 (wrongly ascribed to Netherby).

75. WATER-GODDESS COVENTINA Plate 80

From Carrawburgh (Brocolitia), on Hadrian's Wall, Northumberland. Second or third century A.D. British stone. Height: 2 feet, 5 inches; width: 1 foot, 4 inches. *Chesters Museum*

This gabled relief, found in Coventina's sacred well, shows the naïve form of the local Water-Goddess in the guise of a Graeco–Roman Water-Nymph, reclining, half-draped, on a

1. Cf. the stone statuette at Cologne of a seated Mother-Goddess nursing a lap-dog (H. Schoppa, *Römische Götterdenkmäler in Köln*, 1959, pl. 78 (lower left-hand fig.). Cf, also no. 145. The dog befits a Mother-Goddess in her capacity as deity of healing and of after-life.
2. *Archaeologia*, lxix, 1917–8, p. 184.
3. *Ibid.*, p. 184, fig. 11; E. Strong, *La scultura romana*, 1923, pl. 6.
4. Cf. the very similar Three Mothers relief at Cologne (H. Schoppa, *Römische Götterdenk mäler in Köln*, 1959, pl. 70 (upper fig.).
5. This detail was pointed out to the present writer by Miss M. V. Taylor.
6. Corinium Museum, Cirencester: *Archaeologia*, lxix, 1917–8, pp. 182–3, fig. 9.

7. Guildhall Museum, London: *Royal Commission on Historical Monuments (England): London*, iii (Roman), 1928, pp. 45, 141, pl. 6 (lower fig.).
8. British Museum: *Guide to the Antiquities of Roman Britain in the British Museum*, 1922, p. 28, pl. 2 (lower fig.); 1951, p. 54, (b), no. 3, pl. 19; 1958, p. 54, no. 3, pl. 19.
9. Grantham Museum: *Archaeological Journal*, ciii, 1947, pp.19–20, pl. 4, a.
10. Carlisle Museum, Tullie House: F. Haverfield, *Catalogue of the Roman Inscribed and Sculptured Stones in the Carlisle Museum, Tullie House*, 1922, nos. 108–9. Cf. also the relief from Housesteads: *Archaeologia Aeliana*, ser. 4, xxxix, 1961, pp. 296–7, pl. 25, fig. 1.

water-lily leaf in a recessed panel. She holds a water-plant as sceptre and rests her other elbow on an overturned urn, from which water is flowing. The inscription below the picture reads: *deae Covventinae T(itus) D(omitius) Cosconianus pr(aefectus) coh(ortis) I Bat(avorum) l(ibens) m(erito)*.

E. A. Wallis Budge, *An Account of the Roman Antiquities Preserved in the Museum at Chesters, Northumberland*, 1907, pp. 317–8, no. 90, fig. on p. 147.

76. GENII CUCULLATI   Plate 82

From Cirencester (Corinium), Gloucestershire. Second or third century A.D. Cotswold stone (oolite). Height: 10 inches; width: 12 inches. *Corinium Museum, Cirencester*

Of these hooded godlets of healing, fertility, and after-life (*cf.* nos. 77, 144, 159) Roman Britain has produced so far thirteen renderings in relief, three from the region of Hadrian's Wall, eight from Gloucestershire, one from Wiltshire, and one from London. The Genii Cucullati are in all cases erect figures; and on eight of these monuments, including this one, they feature as a triad, a specifically British aspect, so it seems, of their cult. Here they appear in very low relief in a shallow panel slightly recessed in the face of the votive plaque, which has a straight base and a rounded top. The surface of the stone is badly weathered; and all the details of the faces, dress, and attribute are gone. But it is clear that these Genii, instead of standing to the front, as they usually do, are walking, or rather trotting, to the right. Each hood rises to a point above the back of the head and each cloak reaches to the wearer's knees. A round object, faintly indicated on the surface of the central figure's cloak, near the hem, suggests a *patera*, grasped in his hand which emerges at this point from his garment. Even when freshly carved the relief can never have been more than two-dimensional, the figures being plastered flat, and in 'geometric' shape, against their background. This is local work of the simplest and most un-classical variety, and work produced for specifically British consumption. For while the northern carvings from the military zone of Hadrian's Wall might have been set up by foreign worshippers, the Gloucestershire series must represent a purely native, and largely rural, cult of the Genii Cucullati.

Collection Latomus, xxviii, 1957, pp. 461–2, no. 5, pl. 64, fig. 1.

77. GENII CUCULLATI   Plate 83

From Housesteads (Vercovicium), on Hadrian's Wall, Northumberland. Third century A.D. British stone. Height: 1 foot, 4 inches; width: 1 foot, 7 inches. *Housesteads Museum*

This piece was discovered in a small domestic shrine in the *vicus* of the fort. Behind it was a small coin-hoard consisting of five *denarii* ranging from A.D. 220 to 229. These, if they do not date the sculpture precisely, at least suggest the period in which the cult of these deities was active on this spot. Here the Genii are depicted as a triad of hooded figures standing to the front upon a ledge and set against a flat back-

ground. The carving is coarse, but competent, the work of a man who had some feeling for plasticity and volume. The heights of the three are identical, as are also the dresses – thick, enveloping cloaks forming one piece with the hoods. In each case the cloak conceals the arms and hands and reaches almost to the ankles, the feet being shod, so it seems, in soft leather shoes. Each cloak is tightly fastened down the front, but no fasteners appear; and to right and left of the central join folds in the material are somewhat summarily indicated. The face of the central Genius is square and unequivocally masculine. The faces of the lateral figures are more oval in shape and more effeminate in mien. But we need not, on that account, think of them as female. Quite a number of male hooded Genii from continental sites are youthful, not to say boyish, in countenance (*cf.* nos. 76, 144, 159).

Journal of Roman Studies, xxiv, 1934, p. 198, pl. 7, fig. 1; *Archaeologia Aeliana*, ser. 4, xi, 1934, pp. 190–1, pl. 27, fig. 2; *ibid.*, xii, 1935, p. 187, no. 1; *Collection Latomus*, xxviii, 1957, p. 460, no. 3, pl. 63, fig. 2.

78. HUNTER-GOD   Plate 79

From Chedworth Villa, Gloucestershire. Second or third century A.D. Cotswold stone (oolite). Height: 1 foot, 5 inches; width at bottom: 1 foot, 4½ inches. *Chedworth Villa Museum*

The frontal figure in the niche of this gabled slab more probably represents a British Hunter-God than the classical Silvanus. The features of the face are unfortunately smashed away, but the dress, attributes and adjuncts are clear. The figure wears a cloak, a short, girded tunic, and boots; in his right hand he holds a hare by the hindlegs above the head of a hound, which is seated beside him on the ground; while on the right, emerging from behind his legs, is seen the forepart of an antlered stag. The carving is rough and almost certainly by a native artist.

Unpublished.

79. CELTIC GOD AND GODDESS   Plate 78

From East Stoke (Ad Pontem), Nottinghamshire. Second or third century A.D. British stone. Height: 10¾ inches; width: 7¼ inches. *Nottingham University Museum*

This relief, in which a male and a female deity are shown side by side, is bisected by a vertical ridge into two narrow niches, each topped by a gable and occupied by a rigidly frontal figure. On the left is an unprepossessing, broad-faced, bushy-haired goddess, naked to the waist, but wearing a heavy torc round her neck and a flounced skirt reaching to her shoes. She holds a bowl or basket of fruits in front of her with both hands. On the right is an elderly, but apparently beardless, god, curly-haired, clad in a short, girt tunic and in boots, and grasping in his left hand a long-handled hammer. There is no inscription; but the pair distinctly recalls the renderings in the north-western continental provinces of a male and a female deity standing side by side and bearing the names of Sucellus and Nantosvelta, as, for instance, on a well-carved altar from Sarrebourg. There, indeed, the goddess's attributes, a sceptre topped by a little shrine and a *patera* held above a *candelabrum*, are not the same as on the British piece. The Sarrebourg god, too, is different in being bearded, but he has the same costume and holds a hammer.[1] It is, then, possible, but by no means certain, that the deities from East Stoke are Sucellus and Nantosvelta.

Unpublished.

80. DEA BRIGANTIA   Plate 77

From Birrens (Blatobulgium), Dumfriesshire. Early-third century A.D. British stone. Height: 3 feet, 1 inch; width: 1 foot, 6 inches. *National Museum of Antiquities of Scotland, Edinburgh*

From epigraphic evidence it would seem that Amandus, the dedicator of this relief, could not have reached Birrens before *c* A.D. 210, which is thus the *terminus post quem* for the carving of the piece. The figure of the goddess, who stands to the front in a gabled niche, is extremely syncretistic, the work of a carver who (or whose patron) was well acquainted with the cults most favoured in the Empire, in military and court circles, during the early years of the third century. Brigantia wears a cloak and a long tunic, with Minerva's *aegis* on her breast, and a conical helmet surmounted by a crest and encircled by the towered crown of a City-Tyche, presumably of the chief Brigantian Roman city, York. She holds Minerva's shield and spear, while from her shoulders spring the wings of Victory.[2] On her right hand is a globe, proudly proclaiming the world-wide rule of the Brigantian region! And by her side is the aniconic stone of Juno Caelistis or Regina, consort of Jupiter Dolichenus (*cf.* nos. 34–5) and in Syria and Africa a tutelary goddess.[3] Brigantia's attributes and adjuncts thus illustrate the connections of the reigning, or recently reigning, Emperor Septimius Severus and of the Empress Julia Domna. The wings of Victory and the globe could also allude to Septimius' military exploits and his imperial rule; and Minerva was one of Julia's special protectresses. At any rate, we have in this relief a signal example of a purely local, native goddess decked in oriental and Roman trappings and rendered in the plastic, three-dimensional manner that befits her classical associations. The inscription reads: *Brigantiae s(acrum) Amandus arcitectus* [sic] *ex imperio imp(eratum?)*.

Archaeological Journal, xcviii, 1941, pp. 36–61, pl. 1.

1. Metz Museum: E. Espérandieu, *Recueil général des bas-reliefs, etc. de la Gaule romaine*, vi, 1915, no. 4566 with fig.; *Germania Romana*, ed. 2, iv, 1928, pl. 26, fig. 2; A. Grenier, *Les Gaulois*, ed. 2, 1945, pl. 13 (left). The inscription reads: *deo Sucello Nantosvelt(a)e Bellausus Mass(a)e filius v(otum) s(olvit) l(ibens) m(erito)*.
2. *Cf.* H. Dessau, *Inscriptiones Latinae Selectae*, ii, 1902, nos. 4719–20: *dea victrix Brigantia*.
3. *Cf.* the altar from Corbridge, in the Corbridge Museum, dedicated to Caelestis Brigantia in association with Jupiter Dolichenus and Salus (*Archaeologia Aeliana*, ser. 3, vii, 1911, pl. 2; ser. 4, xxi, 1943, pl. 10 H).

Tombstones

81. CENTURION   Plate 93

From Colchester (Camulodunum), Essex. A.D. 43–9. British stone. Height: 6 feet; width: 2 feet, 4 inches. *Colchester and Essex Museum, Colchester*

Not least among the interesting aspects of this monument is the fact that it is possibly the earliest surviving Roman sculpture to be carved in Britain. It came to light in the cemetery area to the south-west of the *colonia* and it represents M. Favonius Facilis of the Twentieth Legion. Since the deceased is not described in the inscription as a veteran, his tombstone must date from the time of a military occupation of the site before the founding of the colony in A.D. 49–50.[4] The slab contains a deep, curved niche with a rounded top and stylised floral ornament cut in low relief on the flanking pilasters and on the spandrels. In the niche, worked in high relief, stands Facilis, facing to the front, the work, we may be certain, of a first-rate legionary sculptor of Mediterranean origin and trained in the classical tradition. The stone was thrown to the ground in the disaster of A.D. 61, as yet unweathered and without sustaining appreciable damage.

The stance of Facilis, with the weight resting on the right leg, and the arrangement of the *sagum* (cloak) bunched on the left shoulder and draped across the left arm, might almost be a conscious imitation of some Praxitelean model. Combined with this is the centurion's most un-Hellenic, essentially Roman or Italian cast of countenance – the most portrait-like of any face on a funerary relief from Roman Britain, with its square-shaped skull, broad cheeks, slightly frowning brows, large projecting ears, and hair combed neatly forward over the forehead. Facilis wears, besides his cloak, a tunic, a metal cuirass with two rows of leather flaps at the base of it, and a broad, richly decorated, *cingulum militiae* (metal belt), with the strap from which his dagger hangs attached to it. His left hand rests on the pommel of his sword, which is slung on a broader *balteus* (strap) across the right shoulder; and in his right hand he holds his badge of office, his *vitis* (vine-staff). Greaves and short boots complete his outfit. A few traces of plaster adhering to the surface of the stone may represent the remains of paint; and it seems not unlikely that most, if not all the carved sepulchral stones of Britain and of the kindred continental provinces were originally brightly coloured.

The inscription reads: *M(arcus) Favon(ius) M(arci) f(ilius) Pol(lia) (tribu) Facilis* ⊐ [= *centurio*] *Leg(ionis) XX Verecundius et Novicius lib(erti) posuerunt h(ic) s(itus) e(st)*.

Journal of Roman Studies, ii, 1912, pp. 124–5, fig. 7; *Archaeological Journal*, lxxxii, 1925, pl. 3; M. R. Hull, *Roman Colchester*, 1958, pl. 1, a.

82. CAVALRYMAN   Plate 87

From Gloucester (Glevum). First century A.D. Cotswold

4. *Cf. Archaeological Journal*, cxv, 1958 (1960), p. 61.

stone (oolite). Height: 4 feet, 9 inches; width: 2 feet, 7½ inches. *Gloucester City Museum*

Commemorating a provincial auxiliary trooper and probably worked by a provincial army artist, this piece is less classical in style and execution than is no. 81. For the motif – a cavalryman in combat[1] with a prostrate foe beneath the horse's hooves – no Roman or Italian and very few Hellenistic grave-relief prototypes are known. The only fully comparable earlier instance of this composition on a tombstone – one that is often quoted as the model for the Roman carvings of this class – is the famous Hellenic *stele* of Dexileos, who, so the inscription tells us, fell in the battle of Corinth in 394 B.C.[2] But it would seem to be extremely improbable that that sculpture was consciously imitated by the Roman craftsmen; and the provincial rider-type is best regarded as an independent creation dictated by army needs and possibly influenced by the figures of mounted and charging huntsmen on Roman and Italian tomb-monuments[3] or by mounted and charging warriors in large-scale early-imperial battle-scenes.[4]

The Gloucester piece, bearing the name of Rufus Sita, a Thracian cavalryman, is, like no 81, early, dating from the initial, military phase of Glevum's history. The sculpture is contained in a rectangular panel, slightly gabled at the top, and it shows the normal version of the scene with the horse riding over, and the rider in the act of spearing, the vanquished enemy, who lies on his back (here the carver has omitted to give him feet) with his long hair flopping backwards from his brow and his sword still brandished in his hand. The attitudes of both Sita and his mount are vigorous and naturalistic and their modelling is far from incompetent. Sita has now, it is true, a somewhat naked look, but possibly the details of his dress and body-armour were carried out in paint, and the rendering of the helmet, the hexagonal shield, the long sword with heavy pommel, and the spear is very careful. The most unsuccessful features of the stone are the squat, clumsy, almost barbaric figures of the central Sphinx and flanking lions that top the niche. These were, perhaps, consigned to the hands of an inferior workman.

The inscription reads: *Rufus Sita eques c(o)ho(rtis) VI T(h)racum ann(orum) XL stip(endiorum) XXII heredes exs test(amento) curave(runt) h(ic) s(itus) e(st).*

Archaeological Journal, lxxxii, 1925, pl. 1 (upper fig.); I. A. Richmond, *Roman Britain*, 1955, pl. 1; *Transactions of the Bristol and Gloucestershire Archaeological Society*, lxxvii, 1959, pp. 32–3, 40–1.

83. CAVALRYMAN Plate 92
From Colchester (Camulodunum), Essex. A.D. 43–9.

1. The Roman continental examples come almost exclusively from the Rhineland; *Germania Romana*, ed. 2, iii, 1926 (*passim*).
2. G. M. A. Richter, *Sculpture and Sculptors of the Greeks*, 1950, p. 44, fig. 215.
3. E.g. F. Cumont. *Recherches sur le symbolisme funéraire des Romains*, 1942, pl. 44, figs. 2–3.
4. E.g. the Monument of the Julii, Saint Remy, Provence, north panel: *Mitteilungen des Deutschen Archäologischen Instituts, Römische Abteilung*, lii, 1937, pl. 2.

British stone. Height: 6 feet; width, 2 feet, 6½ inches. *Colchester and Essex Museum, Colchester.*

The person here commemorated is another Thracian trooper (*cf.* no. 82), Longinus, a *duplicarius* (petty officer). The stone was found in the same cemetery as was no. 81 and must, like it, date from the very early, pre-*colonia* phase of Roman Colchester, since the man was a serving soldier when he died.[5] It, too, had been hurled down, unweathered, at the time of the Boudicca rising, but the face of Longinus and the muzzle of his horse have been smashed away, a small portion of the curved and round-headed niche, in which he is displayed, has been lost, and the inscription panel below the carving is cracked across diagonally.

In contrast to no. 82 and to the great majority of continental versions of the theme, the horse here is neither galloping nor rearing, but stands stock still, with three hooves planted firmly on the ground, while it paws the air with its left foreleg. Longinus, too, is seated placidly on his fringed saddle-cloth, with his right arm akimbo, making no attempt to spear his enemy and flourishing his oval shield in his left hand. It is clear that his face was turned full to the spectator; and indeed both mount and rider have the air of consciously posing for their portraits after the fight was over, instead of being caught by the artist at the height of the contest. Of that contest the only visible indication is the crumpled form of a naked barbarian with streaming hair and beard and animal-like ears and features, who is doubled up on his shield between the horse's legs. Longinus wears a scale-cuirass and his horse has elaborate harness decorated with *phalerae* (metal roundels). The niche is crowned by a crouching Sphinx between two lions, each of which holds a snake by the tail in its paws. All the figures are plastically modelled, well-proportioned, on the whole, and very competently carved by a sculptor well versed in the traditions of classical representational art. Since the stone was worked for a Thracian auxiliaryman it is likely that the sculptor was himself a provincial. But, if so, he must have learnt his craft in an army workshop of high standing, perhaps in the legionary workshop which produced no. 81. Only in the treatment of the lions' manes and beards and of the hair and beard of the fallen barbarian is the carver's Celtic origin betrayed.

The inscription reads: *Longinus Sdapezematygi f(ilius) duplicarius ala(e) prima(e) T(h)racum pago Sardi(ca) anno(rum) XL aeror(um) XV heredes exs testam(ento) f(aciendum) c(uraverunt) h(ic) s(itus) e(st).*

Journal of Roman Studies, 1928, pp. 212–3, pl. 23; M. R. Hull, *Roman Colchester*, 1958, pl. 1, b.

84. MALE MEDUSA HEAD Plate 91
From Chester (Deva). Second or third century A.D. British stone. Height: 2 feet, 2 inches; width: 4 feet, 11 inches. *Grosvenor Museum, Chester*

Gaulish analogies suggest that bodiless and neckless heads carved on funerary monuments represent Other-World

5. *Cf. Archaeological Journal*, cxv, 1958 (1960), p. 61.

Divinities. On this pediment, which topped a tombstone, is depicted such a head, bearded and moustached, with severely patterned hair and eight writhing snakes framing the face. It is, in fact, a kind of male Medusa; and it presents one of the only two certain British parallels that the present writer knows to the Bath Medusa's most obvious and most un-classical feature, namely its masculinity (nos. 90-1).[1]

R. P. Wright and I. A. Richmond, *Catalogue of the Roman Inscribed and Sculptured Stones in the Grosvenor Museum, Chester*, 1955, p. 54, no. 163, pl. 39.

85. FUNERARY BANQUET   Plate 89

From South Shields (Arbeia), County Durham. Third century A.D. British stone. Height: 3 feet, 3 inches; width: 1 foot, 11 inches. *South Shields Museum*

The so-called funerary banquet type of provincial grave-relief shows the deceased man or woman reclining on a couch, most commonly with a small three-legged table in front of it, and sometimes accompanied by members of his or her family or by attendants. The type has its counterparts on sepulchral altars from Rome and Italy[2] and on Hellen-istic tombstones,[3] while the feasting of the dead had, of course, been a favourite topic of Etruscan art. These Hellen-istic, Roman, and Italian scenes, ultimately based on the symposium of the living, would represent either the funerary meals eaten at the tomb, in which the unseen departed were believed to share, or the soul's celestial banquet in the other world. We need not suppose that the provincial versions of the theme dating from imperial times were 'mostly quite conventional',[4] that is, unrelated to actual faith and practice. As regards the northern and western continental provinces, the banquet relief was almost exclusively confined to the Rhineland,[5] the region from which the type in general is most likely to have made its way to Britain. But the British piece now before us was most probably derived from a far more distant place of origin.

There can be few archaeological monuments that speak more eloquently of the Roman Empire's international character than do the two sculptured grave-reliefs, this and no. 87, from South Shields. That the same hand, or hands from the same workshop, carved both reliefs there can be little doubt; but to judge from the fact that the 'Ms' in the two inscrip-tions are differently formed (although both forms could well be contemporary) and that one inscription is superior to the other in the general competence of its execution, the same letterer was not employed for both stones. The circumstance that no. 87 was erected to Regina, a British woman, by her

Palmyrene husband, carries a Palmyrene, as well as a Latin, inscription, and shows, as we shall see, certain eastern features, is of particular interest in view of the close Palmyrene affinities of the piece with which we are here concerned.

The dead man, Victor, a Mauretanian, who was the freed-man of a trooper of the First Asturian (Spanish) Horse, stationed at Benwell (Condercum) on Hadrian's Wall, is shown reclining in a pedimented recess. He lies, as usual, towards the left, on a couch with elaborately carved frame and legs, the latter raised on blocks, and on a thick mattress with three embroidered transverse bands. With his left elbow he props himself against a round bolster on which is spread a fringed cloth. He wears a long tunic with sleeves to the elbows and a heavy mantle swathing his legs and back. His right knee is drawn up and on it rests his right hand, which holds a bunch of leaves. In his left hand is a cup. Victor's face, parts of which are smashed, is turned fully to the front. He has a mass of short, curly hair confined by a narrow fillet and his chin is beardless. On the wall behind him is incised a stylised tree, a symbol of paradise. Beside the couch stands a tiny slave handing up to his master a wine-jar, which he has, it seems, just filled from the two-handled mixing-bowl to the right of him. The three-legged table is omitted here. In the centre of the pediment is carved in high relief a lion's head, while incised spirals fill its corners and a human bust emerging from a roundel occupies each of the spandrels outside it. We have only to compare the treatment of the drapery, the details of the accessory orna-mentation, and Victor's attributes in this relief with what we find in similar sepulchral banquet-scenes on Palmyrene tombstones[5] in order to be convinced that a Palmyrene sculptor had either visited South Shields or established his workshop in the district. The lettering suggests the third century; and that was, indeed, the period of the fort's maxi-mum prosperity, when there developed outside its walls the busy civil settlement in which Victor would have carried on business activities on his patron's behalf, until death claimed him at the early age of twenty.

The inscription reads: *D(is)M(anibus) Victoris natione Maurum annorum XX libertus Numeriani eqitis* [sic] *ala(e) I Asturum qui piantissime* [sic] *pr[ose]qutus* [sic] *est* [= 'who most devotedly conducted him to his tomb'].

Journal of Roman Studies, ii, 1912, pp. 144-7, pl. 6; J. Liver-sidge, *Furniture in Roman Britain*, 1955, fig. 2; *Archaeologia Aeliana*, ser. 4, xxxvii, 1959, pl. 31, fig. 2.

86. BOY-CHARIOTEER   Plate 88

From Lincoln (Lindum). Second or third century A.D. British stone. Height: 7½ inches; width: 8 inches. *1 Lee Road, Lincoln (Mrs. K. Harding)*

Very classical in workmanship and perhaps by a Gaulish sculptor is this fragment, which shows a boy in high relief standing three-quarters towards the right, while his head,

1. The other example is the terracotta antefix showing a bearded Medusa head from Dorchester (Durnovaria), in Dorset: *Journal of Roman Studies*, xlvi, 1956, pl. 16, fig. 2 (Dorset County Museum, Dorchester).
2. F. Cumont, *Recherches sur le symbolisme funéraire des Romains*, 1942, pl. 44, figs. 1-4.
3. *Jahrbuch des Deutschen Archäologischen Instituts*, xx, 1905, pp. 47-96, 123-55.
4. R. P. Wright and I. A. Richmond, *Catalogue of the Roman Inscribed and Sculptured Stones in the Grosvenor Museum, Chester*, 1955, p. 7.
5. E.g. *Germania Romana*, ed. 2, iii, 1926, pls. 10, figs. 2, 4; 11, figs. 1-4; 12, fig. 2.

5. E.g. M. Rostovtzeff, *Caravan Cities*, 1932, pl. 23, fig. 1; *Berytus*, ii, 1935, pls. 26, 32; *Syria*, xxviii, 1951, pls. 7, fig. 1; 8, fig. 2. *Cf. Archaeologia Aeliana*, ser. 4, xxxvii, 1959, p p.207-10, pl. 34.

with its delicately drawn facial features, is in profile. He wears a circlet in his hair and is enveloped in a cloak, which is fastened on the right shoulder by a round brooch and flutters about him in easy, naturalistic folds. From the waist of the figure downwards all is lost, but the boy is clearly standing in a chariot, the left arm (of which a stump only now survives) extended to grasp the reins, the right arm drawn back, with the hand open in a gesture of tension or excitement. It has been suggested that the child belonged to the local aristocracy of Lindum and was a member of a species of 'Youth Organisation' (*iuventus*), whose sports-programme included chariot-races. There is no proof that this relief is funerary; but that is the most likely explanation of it.

Archaeological Journal, ciii, 1947, p. 54, pl. 7, a; I. A. Richmond, *Roman Britain in Pictures*, 1946, fig. on p. 27; *Roman Lincoln 1945–6 (Report of the Lincoln Archaeological Research Committee, 1946)*, p. 19, pl. 7; *Catalogue of an Exhibition of Romano–British Antiquities in the Castle Museum, Colchester, July, 1950*, p. 29, no. 88, pl. 20.

87. SEATED WOMAN   Plate 85

From South Shields (Arbeia), County Durham. Third century A.D. British stone. Height: 4 feet, 1½ inches; width: 2 feet, 4¼ inches. *South Shields Museum*

This relief has been already cited as coming from the hand of the same Palmyrene sculptor, or from the same Palmyrene sculptor's workshop, as no. 85. The treatment of the architectural details in both reliefs is very similar; and in this case the broken pediment interrupted by a rounded niche in which Regina is seated, although found elsewhere in the West, is a typically east-Roman feature.[1] Regina, a Catuvellaunian woman from southern Britain, is enthroned to the front in a high-backed wicker chair and is warmly dressed in a long-sleeved tunic reaching to the feet and a heavy mantle; and she has a necklace and bracelets. Behind her head, which is unfortunately badly broken and defaced, there is an oval object traced in low relief on the semi-dome of the niche – possibly the outline of a shell-canopy, the details of which were never worked or completed in paint. On the ground to her right is a metal box or casket, with a lock, on which her right hand rests. It is balanced on her left side by a wicker basket in which large balls of wool are piled high. The attribute in Regina's left hand may be a distaff, which, together with a box and a basket, frequently accompanies women on Palmyrene grave-reliefs.[2] The plastic modelling of the body and the linear, but naturalistic, handling of the drapery are those found on no. 85. If the carver of the scene was indeed a Palmyrene, the secondary, Palmyrene text would presumably have been cut by him; and if he cut the Latin text on this stone (but not on no. 85) as well, its odd grammar and spelling would be readily explained.

1. E.g. K. Lanckorónski, *Städte Pamphiliens und Pisidiens*, ii, Pisidien, ii, 1892, pl. 4 (temple at Termessos); H. C. Butler. *Syria*, ii, Architecture, A, Southern Syria, v, 1915, p. 318 (Iṣ-Ṣanamēn); D. S. Robertson, *Greek and Roman Architecture*, 1943, pl. 13 and fig. 97 (Baalbek); pl. 24, a (Spalato).
2. *Archaeologia Aeliana*, ser. 4, xxxviii, 1959, pp. 203–7, pls. 32–3.

The inscription reads: *D(is) M(anibus) Regina liberta et coniuge* [sic] *Barates Palmyrenus natione Catuallauna an(norum) XXX.* The epitaph of Barates himself came to light at Corbridge. It reads: [*D(is)*] *M(anibus)* [*Ba*]*rathes Palmorenus vexila(rius) vixit an(n)os LXVIII.*[3] Barates was probably a standard-maker (rather than a standard-bearer) for the Roman army.

Journal of Roman Studies, ii, 1912, pp. 144–7, pl. 7; J. Liversidge, *Furniture in Roman Britain*, 1955, fig. 30; *Archaeologia Aeliana*, ser. 4, xxxvii, 1959, pl. 31, fig. 1; E. Birley, *Roman Britain and the Roman Army*, 1953, pp. 81–2.

88. FAMILY GROUP   Plate 90

From York (Eburacum). Second or third century A.D. British stone. Height: 5 feet, 8 inches; width: 2 feet, 10½ inches. *Yorkshire Museum, York*

In the family quartet the figure of the woman is the tallest and the most impressive; and in the inscription her name, Flavia Augustina, comes first. The text informs us that her husband was a veteran of the Sixth Legion, C. Aeresius, who had the stone put up in commemoration of her, of her two infants, Saenius Augustinus and a daughter (her name is lost), both of whom died before they were two, and of himself. The niche in which the group is contained terminates above in a pair of half-arches; and inside each of these stands one of the parents, Augustina on the left, wearing a high coronal of hair and holding either a scroll or a long purse, Aeresius on the right, grasping a scroll. In front of their mother stand the two babies, depicted as much older than they really were (the family group relief may have been a stock one) and as clutching each a ball, the nameless daughter, who has long hair reaching to the shoulders and survived to one year, nine months, being represented as taller than her brother, who lived only three days beyond his first birthday. All four figures are rigidly frontal and look as though they were waiting for the artist to take their picture in the places in which he had posed them. Unfortunately all the facial features have vanished. But the details of the costumes are very clear – sleeved tunics and thick, muffling cloaks which, in the cases of the father and daughter, hang down in front in a tapering fold. And it is the richly patterned quality of all the folds of these voluminous garments that make this scene one of the most attractive to the eye of all Romano-British tomb-reliefs. It is, indeed, a particularly fine example of native carving, perhaps of the second century, if the hairstyle of Augustina (who appears to have a veil above her coronal of plaits) can be regarded as modelled on that of the Elder Faustina. There are, unfortunately, now no indications of the nature of Aeresius' beard, if he had one.[4]

3. *Ephemeris Epigraphica*, ix, 1913, p. 578, no. 1153a.
4. Another stone from York, commemorating Julia Brica and her little daughter, Sempronia Martina, shows the same style of drapery and undoubtedly came from the same workshop as the Flavia Augustina stone. There the mother holds a vase or basket, the child, her pet. The inscription reads: *D(is) M(anibus) Iuli(a)e Bric(a)e an(norum) XXXI Semproni(a)e Martin(a)e an(norum) VI Sempronius Martinus f(aciendum) c(uravit)*: Yorkshire Museum, York: *Ephemeris Epigraphica*, ix, 1913, p. 561, no. 1117; *Royal Commission on Historical Monuments (England): York i (Roman)*, 1962, p. 124, no. 80, pl. 54. Plate 246.

The inscription reads: *D(is) M(anibus) Flaviae Augustinae vixit an(nos) XXXVIIII m(enses) VII d(ies) XI filius Saenius Aug(u)stinus vixit an(num) I d(ies) III . . . vixit an(num) I m(enses) VIIII d(ies) V C(aius) Aeresius Saenus vet(eranus) Leg(ionis) VI Vic(tricis) coniugi cari[s]simae et sibi f(aciendum) c(uravit).*

G. Home, *Roman York*, 1924, pl. opp. p. 54; *Royal Commission on Historical Monuments (England): York i (Roman)*, 1962, pp. 122, 124, no. 77, pl. 54.

89. MOTHER AND CHILD   Plate 86
From Murrell Hill, Cumberland. Second or third century A.D. British stone. Height: 4 feet, 3 inches; width: 3 feet. *Carlisle Museum, Tullie House*

This relief shows a woman seated to the front on a high-backed chair and nursing a pet bird, which a child, standing at her left knee, is fondling. The head of the woman is defaced; but the main charm of the piece must always have resided in the ornamental black-and-white effect produced by the deeply gouged-out lines of the trailing tunic, with an overfold and wide, hanging sleeves, and of the mantle wrapped about the shoulders – an effect that is further carried out by the firmly incised, radiating spokes of the large, round fan held in the woman's right hand. The style and technique are thus characteristically Romano–British, while the scheme of the design is classical.[1] Incidentally, the figures crowning the rounded pediment, the central Sphinx, protecting a human head, and the flanking lions, each of which is devouring a head, dispose of the notion, sometimes aired,[2] that these creatures, when carved on grave-reliefs, have Mithraic connotations, since no women were admitted to Mithraic initiation. There is no inscription.

F. Haverfield, *Catalogue of the Roman Inscribed and Sculptured Stones in the Carlisle Museum, Tullie House*, 1922, no. 103, pl. opp. p. 37.

Architectural Features

90. SCULPTURED PEDIMENT ON TEMPLE OF SULIS-MINERVA AT BATH   Text ill.
From Bath (Aquae Sulis), Somerset. Second or third century A.D. Bath stone. Height, at greatest extent: *c.* 8 feet; width, along bottom: *c.* 26 feet. *Roman Baths Museum, Bath*
Of the shrine of the local goddess, Sulis-Minerva, which, together with the neighbouring hot springs and thermal establishment, gave Bath its European reputation in Roman times, no structural vestiges survive *in situ*. But its reconstruction as a tetrastyle temple purely classical in type is securely grounded on the evidence of the fragments of architectural ornament that have come to light – a composite capital, an Attic column-base, some sections of fluted column-shaft, some portions of cornice, and parts of a sculptured pediment, the overall width of which, including

the lower angles of the raking cornice, can be estimated at about thirty feet, sufficient to accommodate a four-columned porch. The reliefs which adorned that pediment are probably the best-known of all extant works of Romano-British plastic art.

Of the carved slabs of which the pediment (exclusive of the raking cornice) was composed, one complete slab and the major parts of five other slabs remain. These six slabs suffice both to disclose the size of the angle at the apex (*c.* 115 degrees) and the dimensions of the whole triangular field and also to suggest that they are the survivors of an original total of eighteen slabs, eleven rectangular and seven triangular, rather than of a total of twelve slabs, as Haverfield and Stuart Jones calculated.[3] It may even be that the triangular space at the apex was occupied by four slabs, one large and hexagonal and three quite small and triangular, instead of by one very large triangular slab. Furthermore, it was obvious at the time of the stones' discovery in 1790 that a kindly fortune has preserved for us just those slabs which enable us to reconstruct the basic elements of the design.

The slabs show an eminently classical scheme of composition – a great circular shield upheld on either side by a flying Victory. On the central boss of the shield is the famous Medusa (no. 91), encircled by two concentric oak-wreaths, of which the larger adorns the shield's rim. The feet of the Victory on the right rest upon a globe, and although the corresponding slab on the left has disappeared, we cannot doubt but that it carried an identical foot-rest for the left-hand Victory. Victories on globes symbolise Sulis-Minerva's universal conquest of sickness and death, just as Minerva features as conqueress of death in Roman funerary contexts. A short distance below the right hand of the Victory on the left is an oddly designed helmet, presumably Minerva's, and just below the left hand of the Victory on the right are an owl, Minerva's emblem, and a human left hand, the fingers of which are bent inwards towards the palm. Immediately to the right of the right-hand globe there remains a considerable portion of a male, seaweed-skirted torso; and again we cannot doubt but that the left-hand globe was neighboured by a corresponding figure. Classical canons, in which the carver of the pediment was clearly well versed, demanded that the two sides of a decorative design of this type should be symmetrical. In the new reconstruction of the pediment, drawn for them by Mr. Austin Child, I. A. Richmond and the present writer tried to keep this principle in mind,[4] thereby correcting certain slight errors in the arrangement of the slabs as erected in the Roman Baths Museum[5] and superseding the reconstruction published by S. Lysons in his *Reliquiae Britannico-Romanae*, i, 1802, pl. 5.[6] The oval shields and the cuirasses, which Lysons placed in the two lower angles of the pediment, are purely imaginary and can be discarded. Long, pronged tails emerging from the seaweed skirts of the two male figures would fit the lower portions of

1. *Cf.* the Chatsworth statuary group of mother and child, found at Apt in Provence and dating from the Flavian period (E. Strong, *La scultura romana*, ii, 1926, p. 381, fig. 227).
2. E.g. *Archaeological Journal*, lxxxii, 1925, pp. 1–24.

3. *Journal of Roman Studies*, ii, 1912, p. 132.
4. *Journal of Roman Studies*, xlv, 1955, pl. 27, fig. 1.
5. A. J. Taylor, *The Roman Baths at Bath*, 1954, p. 26.
6. *Journal of Roman Studies*, xlv, 1955, pl. 23.

Key: existing stones are shaded.

Scale of   0   1   2   3   4   5   6   7   8   9   10   11   12   13   14   15   16   17   18   19   20   Feet.

F.A.C.

the lateral angles of the pediment much more naturally. If, as seems almost certain, these personages were Tritons, it would be possible to think of them as turning their heads towards the bottom corners of the pediment and blowing each a conch, which followed the line of the pediment's downward slope. Tritons would clearly be appropriate in the context of sacred waters.

We may also, on the score of symmetry, discard another fruit of Lysons's imagination, a naked, crouching figure, holding in its left hand the owl below the right-hand Victory. Haverfield's and Stuart Jones's suggestion that the owl and hand topped a helmet has much more to commend it, since a second helmet is needed in this place to match the helmet on the left. The owl and the hand, which seems to be clutching the under part of the outspread wing of the bird, would, then be the right-hand helmet's crest; and indeed the left-hand helmet's crest must have once occupied the space on the left, between the legs of the left-hand Victory and the shield, corresponding to that which the owl and hand occupy on the right. If the right-hand helmet was also, as seems very probable, shown in profile, we must assume that the sculptor was copying in stone a metal crest on either side of which an owl and hand were shown frontally, at right-angles to the face of the helmet's wearer. Such an arrangement would, admittedly, be unusual: so also is the combination of owl and hand. But for an owl perched on Minerva's helmet several parallels can be adduced.[1] What the rest of the right-hand helmet was like we have no means of knowing. But it cannot have repeated the left-hand helmet quite precisely. For the top of the bonnet of the latter is flush with its slab's upper edge, while on the right the legs of the owl must have occupied a shallow space between the upper edge of the helmet's slab and the bonnet of the helmet. It is, in view of this, unlikely that the crest of the left-hand helmet took the form of a frontal owl.

This helmet, quite apart from its crest, constitutes a problem.

At present it appears to be *sui generis*, without a fellow. It has an undulating brim, cheek-pieces, false ears such as are found on decorated 'sports-helmets' (*cf.* nos. 98–104), and a bonnet shaped like an animal's head, with a snub nose, small, round eyes, and curved, incised lines running back from the eyes and suggestive of fins or whiskers. It seems to be a sea-creature – a dolphin, sea-lion, seal, or otter – appropriate to the goddess of the healing waters, an otter, as an inland beast, being the most likely.[2] No. 124 provides a parallel instance from southern Britain of beast-shaped headgear in close association with Minerva.

Mediterranean parallels help us to envisage what the Tritons of the Bath pediment originally looked like.[3] The combination of a central Medusa head, or Medusa head on a shield, with flanking Tritons, in a pediment occurs on two well-known late-Hellenistic reliefs, the so-called 'Icarus' and 'Citharoedus' reliefs, of each of which several replicas exist.[4] The Bath Victories share their classical dress and anatomical distortion with the spandrel Victories on the great Severan Arches of Lepcis Magna, in Tripolitania,[5] and of the Roman Forum.[6] There are, however, marked and significant divergencies between the British and the Mediterranean Victories in the style and treatment of their draperies. In the case of the left-hand Bath Victory, the legs are swathed in the skirt of the tunic and the latter's folds are linear, two-dimensional, and schematic, rendered in a highly patterned, energetic, flowing manner that is typically British. The sculptor has cut deep into the surface of the stone, producing

1. E.g. relief on the Arch of Marcus Aurelius and Lucius Verus at Tripoli: *ibid.*, pl. 30, fig. 3; bronze statuette of Minerva at Avenches: W. Deonna, *L'art romain en Suisse*, 1942, fig. 28; bronze statuette of Minerva in the Louvre: S. Reinach, *Répertoire de la statuaire*, ii, 1897, p. 293, no. 2; bronze statuette of Minerva at Agram (Zagreb): *ibid.*, v, 1924, p. 120, no. 9.

2. A small carved marble sarcophagus in the Ashmolean Museum, Oxford, shows a Cupid carrying on his shoulders a helmet in the form of an animal, probably a dog: *Journal of Roman Studies*, xlv, 1955, pl. 31, fig. 2. A relief at Trier shows Minerva wearing what may be an animal mask on her helmet: E. Espérandieu, *Recueil général des bas-reliefs, etc., de la Gaule romaine*, vi, 1915, no. 4931 with fig.

3. E.g. frieze at Munich from the so-called 'Altar of Ahenobarbus': E. Strong, *La scultura romana*, i, 1923, p. 11, fig. 5; figures from the Odeion of Agrippa in the Athenian Agora: *Hesperia*, xix, 1950, pl. 62.

4. M. Bieber, *Sculpture in the Hellenistic Age*, ed. 2, 1961, fig. 656 ('Icarus'); *Memoirs of the American Academy in Rome*, iii, 1919, pl. 75 ('Citharoedus').

5. *Journal of Roman Studies*, xlv, 1955, pl. 30, fig. 4.

6. *Ibid.*, pl. 32, fig. 2.

an effect of black-and-white sharply contrasted, as on nos. 88 and 89. On the pediment, the slender arms and hands, with their jewelled armlets, are sensitively modelled, but drapery rather than flesh was the artist's leading interest. The African Victories, on the other hand, are naked save for cloaks, while the tunics of their Roman sisters gape apart to expose one shapely leg; and both African cloaks and Roman tunics are richly plastic, three-dimensional, and naturalistic. The Bath Victories offer, in fact, a vivid instance of the translation, in British art under Roman tutelage, of classical content into a native vocabulary.

Journal of Roman Studies, xlv, 1955, pp. 97–105, pls. 23–36.

91. CENTRAL SHIELD FROM BATH PEDIMENT Plate 96
From Bath (Aquae Sulis), Somerset. Second or third century A.D. Bath stone. Diameter: 6½ feet. *Roman Baths Museum, Bath*

That the glaring mask on the boss of the central, dominating shield of the Bath pediment is, to some extent, at any rate, intended, despite its masculinity, to depict the Medusa of Minerva is certain. Of this the wings and snakes in the hair are clinching evidence; the owl beside the shield was specifically Minerva's bird (*cf.* no. 90); the temple was dedicated to her as conflated with the Celtic Sulis; and to Minerva, as the child of Jupiter, oak-wreaths are appropriate.[1] The Bath face, with its trap-like mouth, lined, scowling brows, and huge, deeply drilled, and penetrating eyes, is, indeed, very different from the normal, feminine Medusas of Hellenistic and Roman art. All the same, wild, glowering, frowning faces, sometimes set on round shields, were not unknown in Roman art in Mediterranean lands. We find them, for example, on the Hadrianic Baths at Aphrodisias, in Caria, and in the Severan Forum at Lepcis Magna, in Tripolitania. A corbel from the Aphrodisian Baths carries the wild-looking head of a horned bull-god, probably not the Minotaur, to cite the usual interpretation,[2] but the Syrian bull-god Hadad.[3] The spandrels of the internal arcade of the Severan Forum at Lepcis bear frontal heads of two categories. Those of the first category are Medusas of the normal type, although some of them, with their staring eyes and contracted foreheads, almost rival the Bath mask in ferocity.[4] The other heads portray a Sea-Divinity,[5] not a Nereid, as has been supposed,[6] but a Sea-Medusa, or possibly the Syrian Fish- and Nature-Goddess, Atargatis Derkéto (*cf.* no. 73).[7] She has fins for eyebrows and seaweed-like scallops on her cheeks; and from her hair emerge six water-creatures, two sea-hounds below, two sea-lions above, and between, what appears to be a pair of dolphins. These heads, found in close association with Medusas, link the latter directly with Water-Deities; while Sea-Medusas are a well-known species, of which it will suffice to quote one instance from Roman Britain, the head with snaky, lank, upstanding hair and seaweed collar set at the base of a bronze jug-handle from Cairnholly, in Kirkcudbrightshire.[8] But the nearest parallel to the Bath Medusa known to the present writer is a remarkable stone head in relief built into the façade of the great central temple at Hatra, in Mesopotamia, and dating from the third quarter of the first century A.D. This shows a moustached personage with seaweed sprouting from his chin and cheeks and snakes twisting in his hair – almost certainly a male Sea-Medusa.[9]

The Lepcis heads, for all their wildness of mien, are technically orthodox – plastic and three-dimensional: their sculptural tradition is wholly classical. The Bath mask, on the other hand, is, as has often been noted, flat, linear, and two-dimensional in treatment. Its technique is that of drawing or engraving, rather than of carving in the full sense.[10] The fine lines etched in the individual locks of the hair, moustache, and beard recall those on chased metal-work; and, indeed, the general effect is that of a beaten gold, silver, or bronze sheet applied to the surface of a shield, or of a device incised directly on it. Here the impression of unbroken flatness is enhanced by the set of the elephantine ears, which are flush with the plane of the face, and by the halo of shooting snakes and locks, which radiate in all directions from the brow, cheeks, and chin. Again, we might compare the mask to a huge, wide-open sunflower. The Medusa states in the clearest terms that these pedimental sculptures were the work of a Celtic artist, trained in a classical school, but transposing the themes that he had learnt there into the native idiom of his race. Part of that idiom is the subtle blending in the mask of the snakes, locks, and wings – so subtle that it is by no means easy, at first glance, to pick out the six un-crested heads of the female snakes. And it takes some thought to disentangle the two crested males, which are knotted together below the Medusa's chin. In fact, we cannot be absolutely certain how they go; and possibly the sculptor himself was not quite clear on this point when he came to rendering in relief what he would have originally conceived as a flat, linear pattern. All the same, the more we study the Bath Medusa, Celtic as it is, the more are we aware of its largely classical ancestry, the more intellectually controlled and civilised, the less barbaric, does it appear. It is, moreover, difficult to hold that so competent, so masterly, and so well-educated a sculptor, as was the Bath artist, suffered from confusion of ideas and misunderstood what he was doing. This conflation of Medusa

1. A tomb-painting, probably of the second century B.C., from Gnathia in southern Italy and now in the Naples Museum, shows a conventional female Medusa in the centre of a shield rimmed by an oak-wreath (*Mitteilungen des Deutschen Archäologischen Instituts, Römische Abteilung*, xxvii, 1912, pp. 109–10, pl. 4, fig. 2).
2. M. Squarciapino, *La scuola di Afrodisia*, 1943, p. 68, pl. N, a.
3. C. Picard, *Revue Archéologique*, 1951, pp. 231–3, fig. 11; *cf. Collection Latomus*, ii, 1949, pp. 257–64, pl. 16.
4. *Journal of Roman Studies*, xlv, 1955, pl. 36, fig. 1.
5. *Ibid.*, pl. 34, fig. 1.
6. Squarciapino, *op. cit.*, p. 83.
7. C. Picard, *Revue Archéologique*, 1951, p. 231–2, fig. 11.

8. *Proceedings of the Society of Antiquaries of Scotland*, lxvi, 1931–2, pp. 297–8, fig. 8.
9. Unpublished. Plate 248.
10. *Cf.* the technique of a much inferior piece, part of a temple pediment, found in the civil settlement outside the legionary fortress of Caerleon and showing an excessively ill-favoured female Medusa in its centre (*Journal of Roman Studies*, xlv, 1955, pl. 36, fig. 3).

and Water-God was surely deliberate. The Medusa belongs to Sulis-Minerva, presiding goddess of the local shrine of healing. The Water-God is that of the actual springs or of the River Avon that flows past the Roman city – possibly of both, although the role of the former would have been by far the more important. After all, Fons was a male deity, as was also Nemausus, the Gaulish god of the healing springs at Nîmes; and it may be that at Bath the medicinal springs themselves were conceived of as male, personified by a Genius, who was subordinate to Sulis. Alternatively, Sulis-Minerva may have been believed to be a daughter of a Water-God, just as the classical Nymphs of sea and springs were reckoned to be daughters of Oceanus. And in this connection it is worth remembering that a fragment, in the Roman Baths Museum, of a handsome, carved stone cornice, which may have been part of the temple decoration or of some building in its vicinity, carries the vigorous head, now sadly mutilated, of a bearded Water-God.[1]

At all events, the sculptor of the pediment has harmonised both aspects of the local cult, the Roman and the Celtic, in a work of consummate power and originality. It represents the perfect marriage of classical standards and traditions with Celtic taste and native inventiveness. As R. G. Collingwood reminded us, the pediment must once have stood 'blazing with colour, like a Celtic enamel'.[2] Yet the paint was never needed to make good shortcomings on the carver's part. Weathered and damaged as the sculpture is, we can still appreciate today the subtlety and finish with which it was executed. In this case certainly the Roman master has not stultified, but perfected, stimulated, and fertilised, the genius of his Celtic pupil.

We do not know whether this Celtic artist was a Briton or a Gaul. If the former, was he the *scultor* Sulinus, son of Brucetus, who left a record of himself at Bath,[3] of which he was, presumably, a native, and also dedicated an altar at Corinium?[4] If the latter, as would seem to be more likely, was he the *lapidarius* Priscus, son of Toutus, described as *civis Car[nu]tenns*, who came to Bath possibly from Autricum (Chartres)?[5] Did the artist of the pediment also carve the Sea-God cornice? On what occasion was this grandiose façade erected? When the Romanised version of the cult was first inaugurated? Or when an original Celtic shrine was remodelled and perhaps enlarged on classical lines at a later period? Finally, what is the date of the pedimental sculptures? No answers can at present be offered to these questions, in view of the absence of external evidence. Attempts to date provincial works on the internal evidence of style alone must always be very tentative. All that can be said is that many of the nearest sculptural parallels from Mediterranean lands are of the second or early-third century.

Journal of Roman Studies, ii, 1912, pp. 132–6, pl. 4; xlv, 1955, pp. 102–5, pls. 33, 35.

1. *VCH Somerset*, i, 1906, p. 242, fig. 22.
2. *Roman Britain*, 1932, p. 115.
3. *Corpus Inscriptionum Latinarum*, vii, no. 37.
4. *Archaeologia*, lxix, 1917–8, pp. 180–2, fig. 7.
5. H. Dessau, *Inscriptiones Latinae Selectae*, ii, 1902, no. 4661.

92. PART OF FRIEZE FROM TEMPLE OF JUPITER DOLICHENUS   Plate 95
From Corbridge (Corstopitum), Northumberland. Third century A.D. British stone. Height: 1 foot, 9½ inches; length: 5 feet. *Corbridge Museum*

This frieze was evidently broken up at the time of the destruction of the site in A.D. 297 and it has been convincingly assigned by I. A. Richmond to the shrine of Jupiter Dolichenus which the Roman station is known to have possessed.[6] The surviving fragment consists of four adjoining carved portions, three found in 1908 and one in 1938; and the flat, two-dimensional relief of its figure-work reveals the hand of a native, or north-west continental, sculptor. The scene, so far as it remains, displays, from left to right, Sol radiate, riding towards the right on a winged and prancing horse; a Dioscurus, standing to the front and holding his mount by the bridle within a L-shaped, bewreathed building, of which the pediment and roof rest on Corinthian columns; a tree; and the nude figure of a long-haired youth, possibly Apollo, standing towards the right. Dolichenus himself does not appear in the existing portion of the scene. But since Sol and Luna and the Dioscuri are frequently depicted in his company,[7] his one-time presence as the central figure of the frieze, together with that of the second Dioscurus and of Luna to balance Sol, can be assumed. I. A. Richmond would restore the missing figures to the left of Sol. But it would be strange to represent the latter as riding away from, instead of towards, the presiding deity; the tree could be a landscape feature, not a line of demarcation between two separate scenes; and it seems more probable that Dolichenus, the second Dioscurus, and Luna (who is normally shown to the right of Sol on cult-reliefs of this kind) are to be thought of as having occupied lost blocks that completed the composition to the right of the surviving parts.

Journal of Roman Studies, ii, 1912, pp. 135–8, fig. 11; *Archaeologia Aeliana*, ser. 4, xxi, 1943, pp. 179–96, pl. 7, fig. 3.

93. ARCH WITH MARS THINCSUS, ETC.   Plate 94
From Housesteads (Vercovicium), on Hadrian's Wall, Northumberland. Second or third century A.D. British stone. Height: 3 feet, 8 inches; Diameter of arch: 5 feet, 6 inches. *Chesters Museum*

Probably, although not necessarily, part of a shrine is this round-headed arch, the face of which is decorated with three panels, each containing a human figure in relief. In the central panel, which projects well above the others, is Mars Thincsus, a Germanic deity, whose worship at Housesteads, in association with that of the two goddesses Alaisiagae, is

6. The existence of the temple is attested by an altar dedicated to Dolichenus in association with Caelestis Brigantia and Salus (*Archaeologia Aeliana*, ser. 4, xxi, 1943, pl. 10H: *cf*. no. 80, note 3) and by the stone body of a bull, on the back of which the figure of the god once stood (*ibid.*, pl. 8, fig. 3).
7. As in the temple of Dolichenus on the Aventine in Rome (*Bullettino della Commissione Archeologica Comunale di Roma*, lxiii, 1935, p. 153, fig. 9; pl. 4).

attested by inscriptions.[1] The god stands to the front, helmeted and armed, a spear in his right hand and his left hand resting on his shield, while on the left is seen his adjunct, a large, plump bird, probably a goose. In each of the lateral panels is a naked, floating, female figure, holding a wreath and a pointed, stick-like object. If these figures are the Alaisiagae they are shown in the guise of Victories,[2] the stick-like object being the carver's misunderstanding of a torch, or even of a palm-branch. The work is crude, but vigorous, and bravely tries to carry on the classical tradition.

E. A. Wallis Budge, *An Account of the Roman Antiquities Preserved in the Museum at Chesters, Northumberland*, 1907, p. 326, no. 126, fig. on p. 193; J. Werner, *Die beiden Zierscheiben des Thorsberges Moorfundes*, 1941, pl. 19, fig. 1.

94. CAPITAL WITH WATER-NYMPHS   Plate 101
From Corbridge (Corstopitum), Northumberland. Second or third century A.D. British stone. Height: 11½ inches; width: 13 and 10 inches (top edges); 9 and 8 inches (bottom edges). *Corbridge Museum*

Columns decorated with human figures in relief are a not uncommon feature of Hellenistic and Roman architecture.[3] Among the best known examples from Italy are the pilaster-caps at Pompeii[4] and the column-capitals from the Baths of Caracalla in Rome.[5] From Roman Britain we have several such pieces. This one is a capital originally carved on all four sides, but bereft of its reliefs on two sides, owing to the re-use of the piece first as a gully and secondly as a paving-stone. The compositions on the two surviving faces are identical; on one of the defaced sides there are traces of the same design; and we may assume that this design was again repeated on the fourth side. A Water-Nymph, draped in a long, high-girt tunic, reclines towards the left, facing the spectator, on the steep bank of a stream, the top of which is crowned by a tree. She holds a water-plant in her right hand and beside her left hand is an overturned urn, from which water is gushing. On the left of this idyllic scene is a goat, resting its forepaws on the Water-Nymph's right shoulder. The execution is that of local work, but the art-type is purely classical.

Archaeologia Aeliana, ser. 4, xxi, 1943, pp. 204–6, pl. 10, figs. 1–2.

95. CAPITAL WITH NATIVE GODS   Plates 97–100
From Cirencester (Corinium), Gloucestershire. Third century A.D. Cotswold stone (oolite). Height: 3 feet, 5 inches; width at top: 3 feet, 6 inches. *Corinium Museum, Cirencester*

More completely Celtic both in style and feeling than the Water-Nymphs of no. 94 are the four half-figures that emerge, one on each side, from the acanthus-foliage of this well-known composite capital. The piece, which has a dowel-hole in the centre of its upper surface, may well have topped a 'Jupiter'- or 'Giant'-column, of which the shaft and crowning statuary group have disappeared; for we know from an inscription on a base, which has a socket for a shaft on its upper surface, that a small column of this class dedicated to Jupiter was erected in the Roman city.[6] The four busts depict (i) a woman wearing a sleeveless tunic, with fruit in her hair and holding in her left hand an oval shield or tray; (ii) a Maenad-like woman, with a slipped tunic leaving the right breast exposed, two heavy clusters of grapes on either side of her face, an ornamental wand (?) appearing from behind her left shoulder, and a small, round object in her left hand; (iii) a nude male personage with curly hair and beard, holding in his right hand a double-axe and a vine-branch in his left hand; and (iv) a wild, Silenus-like nude man, with a snub nose, round eyes, straggling hair and beard, blowing on a conch held in his right hand, and grasping a knotted stick in his left hand. These busts have been interpreted as Seasons.[7] But while (ii) could possibly be Autumn, the other three lack the normal seasonal attributes as found in Roman provincial art; and it seems more likely that all of them represent Celtic Fertility-Deities, whose names at present elude us. The careful carving of the acanthus-leaves and the boldness and vigour with which the busts are treated reveal the hand of a gifted and original craftsman of British or Gaulish origin.

Archaeologia, lxix, 1917–8, pp. 191–3, fig. 16, pls. 9–10; I.A. Richmond, *Roman Britain in Pictures*, 1947, fig. on p. 25.

96. ANTEFIX   Plate 103
From Gloucester (Glevum). Late-first or early-second century A.D. Cotswold stone (oolite). Height: 2 feet, 3 inches. *City Museum, Gloucester*

This handsome piece must once have decorated some important building in the colony. It displays a human head carved in high relief against a flat background, which is shaped so as to follow the lines of the inward-curving spirals of the frond-like objects – probably intended for the leaves of a palmette with curled-up tips – that flare up above the crown of the head and frame the temples on either side. The hair, which shows no drilling, is waved in feminine fashion on either side of a central parting; and there is a large, spherical pendant-earring. But the face looks male and rather elderly, with its furrowed forehead, beetling eyebrows, and large, round, plain eyes. The protruding upper lip might be moustached, while the very square chin appears to be beardless. The non-plastic eyes are suggestive of an early date. A narrow, tapering ornament shoots up from above the central parting; and below each ear fly out what seem to be the clustered ends of *taeniae* (ribbons), perhaps attached behind

1. E.g. J. Collingwood Bruce, *Handbook to the Roman Wall*, ed. 11 (I. A. Richmond), 1957, fig. on left on p. 129.
2. *Ibid.*, p. 131.
3. I. A. Richmond's statement (*Archaeologia Aeliana*, ser. 4, xxi, 1943, pp. 204–6) that figured capitals are essentially foreign to classical art and express distinctively Celtic feeling cannot, of course, be maintained. For classical figured capitals in general, see E. von Mercklin, *Antike Figuralkapitelle*, 1962.
4. A. Maiuri, *Pompei (Itinerari dei Musei e Monumenti d'Italia, No. 3)*, 1931, pl. 32. *Cf.* also the figured capitals, each carrying a Victory in relief, on the Casa del Gran Portale at Herculaneum (E. Nash, *Herculaneum*, 1960, pls. 14–5).
5. E. Strong, *La scultura romana*, ii, 1926, pp. 367–8, figs. 185–6.
6. *Archaeologia*, lxix, 1917–8, pp. 188–91, fig. 15.
7. *Ibid.*, p. 192; I. A. Richmond, *Roman Britain*, 1955, pl. 8.

to the tapering ornament – unless they are the ends of hanging tresses. The personage's identity remains a mystery. Unpublished.

97. DISTANCE-SLAB

Plate 102

From Bridgeness, the eastern terminus of the Antonine Wall, Linlithgowshire. Mid-second century A.D. British stone. Height: 3 feet, 11 inches; width: 9 feet, 2 inches. *National Museum of Antiquities of Scotland, Edinburgh*

The most distinctive monuments of army art in Roman Britain are series of reliefs, from frontier areas of the province, which form decorative adjuncts to inscriptions that record the building activities of legionary and auxiliary units. The richest series of reliefs of this type is that of the 'distance-slabs' from the Antonine Wall, worked by legionary carvers, for which no exact parallels exist elsewhere in the Roman world. This is the best-known and most elaborate specimen of the group. Here the inscription panel, recording the work of the Second Augustan Legion, with *ansae* (handles) formed by Griffin-headed *peltae* (crescent-shaped shields), is flanked on either side by figure-scenes in high relief, each contained within a colonnaded framework.

On the left a helmeted Roman cavalryman, with portrait-like features, stern and resolute, rides triumphant over a group of five barbarians, one of them decapitated. The right-hand scene shows the familiar Roman *suovetaurilia* sacrifice. In the foreground the three victims, pig, sheep, and ox, advance towards a seated figure on the left, while in the background are a *tibicen* (piper) playing on a double-pipe and five male standing figures, of whom the foremost is sacrificing at an altar. In the case of both panels the sculptor has employed the high horizon and the 'map-technique' of raising the background figures above the heads of those in the foreground. The execution of these carvings is crude and naïve in the extreme – wholly unlike the accomplished, mid-first-century legionary sculpture of no. 81. Yet their content is obviously derived from classical models.

The inscription reads: *Imp(eratori) Caes(ari) Tito Aelio Hadri(ano) Antonino Aug(usto) Pio P(atri) P(atriae) Leg(io) II Aug(usta) per m(illia) p(assuum) IIIIDCLII fec(it)*. On the banner in the right-hand scene is *Leg(io) II Aug(usta)*.

Journal of Roman Studies, ii, 1912, pp. 128–30, fig. 9; G. Macdonald, *The Roman Wall in Scotland*, 1934, no. 1, pp. 362–5, pls. 3, fig. 2; 61.

DECORATED ARMOUR

98. HELMET

Plate 106

From Newstead (Trimontium), Roxburghshire. Late-first century A.D. Brass. Height: 11 inches. *National Museum of Antiquities of Scotland, Edinburgh*

This piece and nos. 99–104 are examples of the 'sports-helmets' worn by auxiliary horsemen in the Roman army for tournaments and exercises – the ἱππικὰ γυμνάσια described by Arrian as taken over by the Romans from the Iberians and Celts.[1] The helmets used on those occasions were, he says, made of iron or bronze and gilded; and, unlike battle-helmets, 'did not protect the head and cheeks alone, but conformed in every way to the rider's face, with openings for the eyes.' With that literary account, published in A.D. 136, many of the helmets of this class found on Roman sites in Britain and throughout the Empire tally closely.

Nos. 98–100 were found in a rubbish-pit outside the Roman fort. The material in the pit indicates that it was filled in *c.* A.D. 100. Nos. 99 and 100 show the face-mask visor to which Arrian alludes; and we may be reasonably certain that although no. 98 now consists of a bonnet only, it, too, was once completed with a mask. It is true that its neck-guard has no rivet-holes for the mask's attachment, as has that of no. 99. But the neck-guard of no. 101, which has

its mask surviving, also lacks such holes; and it may be that the nick on either side of the Newstead helmet, at the junction of the pointed, upstanding peak and the ear-guard, served for the attachment of the mask. On the inside of the bonnet are relics of a leather lining.

Both the top and the back of the bonnet are richly embossed. On the back is a Cupid in a boat-shaped, two-wheeled chariot, driving a pair of leopards; behind the Cupid we can identify a large palm-leaf; but the two ribbed, cone-like objects that flank the group defy explanation. On the crown is another Cupid flying along with arms outstretched and with his legs and feet towards the peak. The neck-guard has no ornamentation, but carries an inscription of eight pounced letters ending in T G E S. So closely does the Newstead helmet resemble, in style and shape, the gilt-bronze helmet discovered at Nicopolis, in Moesia, an early-Trajanic foundation, that it is tempting to assign both pieces to the same workshop. The Moesian piece likewise lacks its face-mask; and there, too, the crown is covered with embossed figure-scenes – a sacrifice, groups of captives, and swags upheld by flying Cupids.[2]

J. Curle, *A Roman Frontier Post and its People: the Fort of Newstead*, 1911, pp. 166–8, pls. 27–8.

1. *Tactica* 34 ff.

2. Kunsthistorisches Museum, Vienna: O. Benndorf, *Antike Gesichtshelme und Sepulchralmasken*, 1878, pl. 12, fig. 3, a–c. Plate 249.

99. FACE-MASK HELMET   Plate 104

From Newstead (Trimontium), Roxburghshire. Late-first century A.D. Iron, silver-plated. Height: 9½ inches. *National Museum of Antiquities of Scotland, Edinburgh*

Of the Newstead trio of helmets this is the most important inasmuch as its remains consist of the major portion of both face-mask and bonnet, although their line of junction is unfortunately lost. Of the mask, the right of the face is badly damaged; but the left side is well preserved and presents clear-cut, youthful features, with a cluster of spiral locks hanging down each cheek, in front of the ear. The idealised, somewhat effeminate cast of countenance shown here, and in nos. 100 and 101, could be explained by the supposition that these face-masks represented quasi-dramatic types and characters impersonated by the horsemen in displays which were not merely feats of skill, but contained ceremonial, commemorative, and even religious and funerary elements. On this Newstead helmet tight, spiral curls, radiating from a central 'star-fish', cover the crown and back of the head and are confined by a laurel-wreath, which bears a round, decorated ornament in front, at the apex of the crown, and is tied behind with ribbons (*taeniae*). Comparable imitation hair occurs on a silvered bronze face-mask visor-helmet from Vize (Bizye) in Thrace.[1] On the neck-guard of the Scottish piece is a pattern of dots and zig-zags. From the top of the bonnet, above the brow, projects a small ring, perhaps an attachment for a 'mane' or streamer such as Arrian connects with helmets of this kind; and there are two tubular plume-holders, one on top, in front of the ring, and one on the left side of the head; two hooks, one riveted onto the centre of the 'star-fish' and one at the base of the neck; and various small round rivets, some securing ancient patchings, others serving for the onetime attachment of mask and bonnet. On the inner surfaces of both mask and bonnet traces of a woollen lining or padding can be detected.

J. Curle, *A Roman Frontier Post and its People: the Fort of Newstead*, 1911, pp. 168-70, pl. 29.

100. FACE-MASK FROM HELMET   Plate 105

From Newstead (Trimontium), Roxburghshire. Late-first century A.D. Bronze. Height: 8½ inches. *National Museum of Antiquities of Scotland, Edinburgh*

This is a complete and very well preserved face-mask, found without any vestige of the bonnet with which it had been worn. Here, again, the face is young and idealised, but somewhat heavier than that of no. 99. The most notable feature of this object is the thick roll of hair above the brow, divided, in a very complicated fashion, into four segments, two of superimposed bands of horizontal, waved tresses and two of tiers of horizontal, sinuous locks ending in spirals, with three vertical plait-bands parting the segments from one another. From each end of this roll four neat, wavy locks escape down

either cheek, in front of the imitation ears, below each of which is a rivet-hole for attachment to the bonnet.

J. Curle, *A Roman Frontier Post and its People: the Fort of Newstead*, 1911, pp. 170-1, pl. 30.

101. FACE-MASK HELMET   Plate 108

From Ribchester (Bremetennacum), Lancashire. Late-first century A.D. Bronze. Height: 11 inches. *British Museum*

This is the most impressive face-mask visor-helmet so far found in Britain. It is worked in very thin metal; and is virtually intact, apart from a few gashes in the bonnet and the loss of the central portion of the upper section of the mask. Mask and head-piece fit together perfectly; and there can be little doubt but that this example belongs to the same school of decorated armour as nos. 98-100. Once again the visor consists of a youthful, idealised face, with almond-shaped eyes, a small mouth, and a pointed chin, girt by an imitation strap. The hair takes the form of a fringe of small, horizontal, wavy curls above the brow, and then escapes down either cheek in a thick, flowing lock, mainly in relief, but with some engraved details, and entwined with serpent-heads. There are imitation ears; above the hair is a mural crown; and above that again is a frieze, incomplete and damaged, consisting of seated human figures, sea-monsters, and frontal heads. The bonnet of this helmet is of the same general type as are the bonnets of no. 98 and its counterpart from Nicopolis. It, too, has an upstanding peak, but rounded instead of pointed, and carrying along its upper edge five projecting knobs which give it a diadem-like appearance. The crown and back of the bonnet are embossed with groups of fighters, foot-soldiers and cavalrymen, all armed with short, broad swords; and in the field, above each ear, are the same two ribbed, cone-like objects as on no. 98. Behind, at the base of the bonnet, just above the neck-guard, is a kind of frieze containing a small, round shield in relief with incised crossed spears behind it. Two rings, one on the top of the crown, the other at the back, low down in the combat-scene, project from the surface of the head-piece. There are punched *graffiti* – CARAVI and CARAV.[2]

Guide to the Antiquities of Roman Britain in the British Museum, 1922, pl. 5; 1951, p. 67, no. 4, pl. 25; 1958, p. 67, no. 4, pl. 26; H. B. Walters, *Select Bronzes in the British Museum*, 1915, pl. 72.

102. HELMET   Plate 109

From the River Wensum, Worthing, Norfolk. Third century A.D. Bronze. Height: 10 inches. *Castle Museum, Norwich*

Different in type from the helmets of the Newstead-Ribchester group is the present piece, found in 1947 in river-dredging operations fifteen miles north-west of Norwich. Its remarkably good state of preservation is due to its having been sealed in a bed of peat under several feet of shingle. Above the brow is a false, upturned peak, triangular in shape, of which the sides are each adorned with a bird-

---

1. National Museum of Antiquities, Istanbul: *Jahrbuch des Deutschen Archäologischen Instituts: Archäologischer Anzeiger*, 1941, cols. 169-75, figs. 31, 33. Plate 250.

2. *Journal of Roman Studies*, l, 1960, p. 240.

headed, long-billed snake. The heads of these fantastic creatures, turned back upon their bodies, are at the lower angles of the triangle, while their bodies merge into one another at the upper angle. The field of the peak is empty; but on either side of the bonnet, facing towards the front, is a sea-dragon rampant, with wings, fins, curling body, huge, splayed paws, and long, three-pronged tail. The helmet also has a crest, decorated with stylised feathers and terminating in an eagle's head just above the brow,[1] while below, at the base of the skull, it is finished off in a large, round, ornamental knob. Lateral holes for fastening on cheek-pieces are lacking; and there was probably a separate skull-cap of leather, cloth, or woollen padding, secured beneath the chin, by which the helmet could be held in place when worn. On the upper surface of the neck-guard is scratched XII, a reference to *turma* (squadron) XII, proving that the helmet belonged to cavalry not to mounted infantry, whose cohorts did not contain as many as twelve *turmae*. In the centre of the peak's lower edge, just above the brow, there is a rivet, securing on the inside a narrow metal plate, the lower end of which is broken off. This probably represents the upper portion of a nose-guard. There is no evidence for there ever having been a face-mask visor.

All the figure-decoration of the Worthing helmet is classical, in the sense that its content is representational, not abstract; and the sea-dragons, in particular, are based on a well-known Graeco–Roman type. But in these dragons, in the uncouthness of the bird-headed snakes, and in the grim and sinister appearance of the eagle there is a note of violence and wildness that engenders a strange, unconventional, unnaturalistic, and almost barbaric atmosphere. The work suggests the hand of a provincial craftsman who had seen, and was consciously copying, classical models, but was more interested in exploiting their possibilities as arresting patterns than in imitating 'Nature'.

It seems not unlikely that this helmet had belonged to someone from the 'Saxon Shore' coastal fort at Brancaster (Branodunum), about eighteen miles north-west of Worthing – a fort that was established in the middle of the third century[2] and was manned by a static unit, a detachment of Dalmatian cavalry. From the absence of any trace of a face-mask on the piece, and on the two pieces which resemble it most closely, found respectively at Guisborough, in Yorkshire,[3] and in the River Saône at Châlon,[4] it would appear that this type of 'sports-helmet' came into fashion after Arrian's time, during the late-second, or early-third, century.

Journal of Roman Studies, xxxviii, 1948, pp. 20–7, pls. 2–4.

1. For the eagle's head, compare that on the crest of a bronze 'sports-helmet' found at Heddernheim, near Frankfurt-am-Main, dating from the second half of the second century (Historisches Museum, Frankfurt-am-Main: *Mittheilungen über römische Funde in Heddernheim*, i, 1894, pp. 21–50, pl. 4).
2. *Journal of Roman Studies*, xxvi, 1936, pp. 250–1.
3. *Guide to the Antiquities of Roman Britain in the British Museum*, 1922, p. 81, fig. 101, pl. 4 (right-hand fig.); 1951, p. 66, (viii, a), no. 3, pl. 25; 1958, p. 67, no. 3, pl. 26.
4. J. Dechelette, *La collection Millon: antiquités préhistoriques et gallo-romaines*, 1913, pp. 253–8, pls. 43–4.

103. VISOR-MASK FROM HELMET   Plate 107

From the River Wensum, Worthing, Norfolk. Third century A.D. Bronze. Height: 8 inches. *Castle Museum, Norwich*

The helmet from Heddernheim (*cf.* no. 102, note 1) has attached to its bonnet a separately made visor-mask, protecting brow, cheeks, and chin. On that piece there are no indications that another, inner portion, covering the eyes, nose, and mouth, was ever fastened to the mask. On other helmets, however, just such an inner mask is actually in position, for instance on that from Pfrondorf, near Stuttgart, where the two parts are connected by 'hook and eye'.[5] Sometimes only the inner mask has survived.[6] In the case of the present visor-mask, found in 1950 close to the spot on which no. 102 came to light, there are traces of soldering round the inner edge of the T-shaped aperture, suggesting that an inner mask had once been attached in this way. Along the upper edge of this outer mask (which was certainly not made for no. 102) are two rows of small, round, conventionalised curls; a Medusa head, with snakes flying out from it to right and left, screens the chin; while on the cheeks are standing figures – Mars, with a helmet, shield, and spear, on the right cheek and Victory, with a wreath and palm, on the left cheek. The best parallel in shape and general character to the Worthing mask is one from Rodez (Aveyron), which also has stylised hair above the brow and figures on the cheeks – a bust of Hercules on the right cheek and one of Mars on the left cheek.[7] But of the Worthing confronted figures of Mars and Victory the most impressive counterparts are on a bronze horse-chamfron from the famous hoard of 'sports-equipment' found at Straubing, on the Danube, in 1950.[8] In the lower corner of each cheek of the Worthing mask is a round knob for attaching it by wires or leather thongs to the now vanished head-piece.

Journal of Roman Studies, xli, 1951, pp. 131–2, fig. 20, pl. 11.

104. CHEEK-PIECE FROM HELMET   Plate 110

From South Shields (Arbeia), County Durham. Late-second or third century A.D. Bronze. Height: 7½ inches. *Museum of Antiquities of the University of Durham and of the Society of Antiquaries of Newcastle upon Tyne (King's College, Newcastle upon Tyne)*

The four isolated cheek-pieces with figured ornament found in Roman Britain must have belonged either to a class of helmet with cheek-pieces known from a number of examples from Holland, or to helmets of the Guisborough-Châlon-Worthing group, two of which, those from Guisborough and Châlon, have rivet-holes for such appendages. The South Shields piece, dredged from the River Tyne, is the most elegant of the quartet, its whole decoration, an

5. Württembergisches Landesmuseum, Stuttgart: *Mittheilungen über römische Funde in Heddernheim*, i, 1894, p. 37, fig. 39.
6. *Ibid.*, p. 36, figs. 36–7.
7. Rodez Museum: *Germania*, xvi, 1932, p. 56, fig. 3.
8. Straubing Museum: J. Keim and H. Klumbach, *Der römische Schatzfund von Straubing*, 1951, pls. 21, fig. 1; 29. Plates 252–3.

exquisite piece of drawing, being pricked out in very fine pounced lines. It shows a Dioscurus (*cf.* nos. 61 and 92), whose flowing curls are topped by a *pilleus* with a star above its peak, wearing a mantle and standing three-quarters towards the spectator's left in front of a horse, which also faces leftwards. His spear is in his left hand, his bridle in his right hand. Below the group is a dolphin, likewise turned towards the left, above it, a frieze of trefoil leaves; and an eight-petalled rosette, rendered in the same technique, takes the place of the usual imitation ear. A cheek-piece which includes such an imitation ear and displays a much more stockily built Dioscurus with his mount, worked in *repoussé*, was discovered at Brough (Crococalana) on the Foss Way.[1] The two lost cheek-pieces that went respectively with the South Shields and Brough examples would presumably have each displayed the other Dioscurus.

Archaeologia Aeliana, ser. 2, x, 1885, pp. 262–3 with woodcut.
1. Newark Museum: *Archaeologia*, lviii, 1903, p. 573, pl. 55.

METAL TABLE-WARE

Figured Silver-Ware

105. SKILLET-HANDLE   Plate 122
From Capheaton, Northumberland. Late-second or early-third century A.D. Height of figure-work portion: 7¾ inches. *British Museum*

The Capheaton silver hoard comprises a figured *emblema*, or circular medallion, from the centre of the interior of a skillet (casserole or pan) and four flat, richly decorated skillet-handles, of which this is one. On the present piece the most arresting motif is a large, draped female bust in the centre of the terminal. This woman, who wears a high diadem and a cross-strap passing over the right shoulder and whose body emerges from a cup of leaves, has been identified as Juno or as an Empress. But neither of these explanations would appear to suit the miniature figure-groups beside the bust – on the left, a pedlar trudging along with pack on back and a staff, on the right, a shepherd lying on the grass as he minds his flock. The central figure is, indeed, more likely to be Diana with a quiver-strap, in her role as guardian of the countryside and of those who work in it or travel through it. On the stem is Mercury, giver of wealth, seated beneath a canopy and naked save for a cloak thrown about him, with wings in his hair, a purse and a *caduceus* in his hands, and his cock beside him. On the base of the handle are further emblems of prosperity – in the centre, Bacchus with a *thyrsus* (Bacchic staff), a bunch of grapes, and a wine-jar, and Ariadne or a Maenad with a *thyrsus* and a panther; on the left a reclining Water-Nymph with water gushing from an overturned urn at her feet; and on the right a bearded River-God, also reclining, with a dolphin beneath his elbow. Rural well-being would seem to be the underlying theme of the decoration on this handle.

The style of the Capheaton pieces is wholly classical; but there are a slight coarseness, clumsiness, and provincialism, on occasion, in the workmanship. The content of one of the handles, dominated by Minerva as goddess of fertility and healing springs, is strongly suggestive of a Celtic workshop, probably not British, but Gaulish. The religious character of the subject-matter of all the Capheaton pieces would seem to indicate their use as ritual 'table'-ware.

Archaeologia, xv, 1806, pp. 393–4, pls. 30–2; H. B. Walters, *Catalogue of the Silver Plate (Greek, Etruscan and Roman) in the British Museum*, 1921, pp. 48–51, nos. 189–93, figs. 49–53; *Journal of Roman Studies*, xiii, 1923, pp. 99–101, pl. 5; *Guide to the Antiquities of Roman Britain in the British Museum*, 1922, pp. 90–3, figs. 111–2; 1951, p. 41, nos. 49–50, pl. 10; 1958, p. 41, nos. 49–50, pl. 10; M. Rostovtzeff, *Social and Economic History of the Roman Empire*, 1957, p. 230, pl. 40, fig. 3.

106. MILDENHALL TREASURE   Plates 113–9, 124
From Mildenhall, Suffolk. Fourth century A.D. *British Museum*

This hoard of thirty-four silver objects was disclosed to the British public in the summer of 1946. The treasure reached the national collection as the result of an inquest held in July 1946, when the jury declared it to be 'treasure-trove' and 'seized it for the Crown'. At the inquest it was stated that the silver had actually been found four years earlier, during the ploughing of a field, the plough having been set to work four inches deeper than had formerly been the case; that the ploughman's employer, at first believing the articles to be of lead or pewter, had kept them in his house; and that the rich designs on the bowls and dishes, which form the major portion of the hoard, had, at the time of discovery, been completely obscured by incrustation and were only gradually revealed by cleaning.

It was at once obvious that close analogies exist between the Mildenhall objects and those in the Traprain Law hoard (no. 107), the limiting upper date for the deposition of which is fixed by the associated coins, the latest being of Honorius and Constantine III (A.D. 407–411). For instance, borders of large, round, hollow beads are common to both deposits and there are no known pre-fourth-century works on which they occur. Flanged bowls, fluted bowls, and scalloped bowls are common to both collections; and in the decoration of objects belonging to both some of the same types of figure-subjects and the same patterns, as well as the same technical processes, can be discerned. There can be little doubt but that the bulk of the pieces in both hoards are of fourth-century date. Sixteen items from the Mildenhall treasure were included in the Exhibition.

The most arresting piece in the collection is, of course, the superb round dish with heavily beaded rim, nearly two feet in diameter, weighing eighteen-and-a-quarter pounds, magnificently preserved, and covered all over with figure-relief

The central feature is a mask of Oceanus, with large, staring eyes, broad nose and cheeks, heavy moustache, and seaweed beard, while four dolphins emerge from between the wild locks of his hair, which flaps in the wind. The rest of the dish is filled by two concentric zones of figure-scenes, separated from one another by a border of scallop-shells. The inner and narrower zone shows a sea-*thiasos* of Nereids with Sea-Centaurs and marine beasts. The outer and broader frieze contains a Bacchic *thiasos* flowing round the dish and throbbing with movement. It is carried out in a vigorous, free, and naturalistic style and so fully in the classical tradition that the possibility of its execution in a British workshop, as was once suggested, seems to be wholly excluded. The protagonists are Bacchus, standing with his foot on the back of a panther and holding a *thyrsus* and a bunch of grapes, while a Silenus approaches with a wine-cup, and Hercules, dead-drunk and only saved from collapse in an amorphous heap upon his lion-skin by two young and helpful Satyrs, one of whom buttresses him up in front, while the other clasps him round the middle from behind. The latter Satyr has, incidentally, no body below the shoulders and no legs: the artist must have felt that, had he completed the figure, he would have confused and overweighted his design at this point; and a somewhat similar omission occurs on no. 108. The remainder of this frieze is peopled by Maenads, Satyrs, and a bearded Pan, all whirling in the dance, with a panther and various Bacchic objects in the field. The garments of the Maenads carry very delicately stippled borders representing embroidery. The upper part of the *thyrsus* of one Maenad, which passes behind a Satyr's pipes, and the legs in the second plane of some of the animals in both friezes, are merely engraved – a conventional device for indicating depth in the picture, which is also to be noted on no. 108.

Despite their general swing and liveliness, both Bacchic and marine scenes show an oft-recurring clumsiness, a distortion, and a misunderstanding in the drawing of the details of human and animal forms which betray the late-antique craftsman's hand. Furthermore, one of the Maenads in the outer frieze has her hair dressed in a thick plait or roll which is brought forward from the nape of the neck in a kind of crest across the crown of the head to a point on the centre of the brow – a coiffure in vogue throughout the fourth century, as we know from the coin-portraits of Empresses. The three sets of motifs that adorn the great Oceanus dish all occur together so persistently on pagan funerary monuments, such as Bacchic and other sarcophagi, that it is hard to believe that the juxtaposition of Oceanus and the marine *thiasos* with the Bacchic *thiasos* was merely decorative or purely fortuitous and had no inner, symbolic meaning. Oceanus recalls the situation, according to one version of Graeco–Roman other-world topography, of the Islands of the Blessed; the Nereids riding over the waves on sea-beasts could represent here, as on sarcophagi, the journey of the souls of the departed across the Ocean to the after-life; and the Bacchic revel-rout could, again as on sarcophagi, be an allegory of souls in bliss in paradise – worked out here in the terms of the well-known story of the

drinking-contest between Hercules and Bacchus. This splendid object is, in fact, very likely to have served a ritual or religious purpose, perhaps in connection with some 'mystery-cult'.

Very similar in style and content to the large dish, and possibly produced in the same workshop, is a pair of small round dishes or platters, seven-and-three-eighths and seven-and-a-quarter inches in diameter respectively, edged with heavy beading, and adorned with Bacchic scenes in relief. One displays a dancing Maenad, playing on a double-pipe, and a dancing Pan, with a *syrinx* and a *pedum*, while in the field are a reclining Water-Nymph, a fawn and a snake, a covered bowl, and a tambourine. The other platter carries a dancing Maenad, with a *thyrsus* and a tambourine and exquisite vertical borders of scroll-work on her robe, and a dancing Satyr, while in the field are a covered bowl, a *syrinx*, five cymbals, and a cloth filled with grapes and knotted to a *pedum*. The artist of these platters has surpassed the designer of the great dish in his mastery both of drapery and of human forms. The grace, the verve, and the skilful drawing that his figures show are not only wholly classical in spirit, but also devoid of any vestige of degeneration in technique and style. Both the great dish and the platters were undoubtedly the products of a Mediterranean, possibly Roman, studio.

The relief-work of these three Mildenhall pieces, and that of the lower zone of ornament on the domed lid from Mildenhall described below and that of no. 108, was probably produced as follows. The design was first drawn upon the surface of a cast silver sheet, which was then laid on the anvil and the background of the design hammered down. Concurrently with the lowering of the background the modelling of the figures with chasing-tools proceeded, always from the front of the sheet: no work at all was done at any time from the back.[1]

Another remarkable object in the Mildenhall hoard is a hemispherical, flanged bowl, nine inches in diameter, over the vertical rim of which, above its flange, a domed lid fits very roughly – an indication that the two pieces were not originally made for one another. Furthermore, the clumsy, cast figure of a Triton blowing on a conch, loosely riveted onto the apex of the lid to form its handle, was obviously added at a later stage. The bowl, of which the flange has a bead-and-reel edging and is incised on its upper surface with a very stylised running floral scroll, recalls in type the second-century flanged bowls from Chaourse[2] and Graincourt-lès-Havrincourt[3] in northern Gaul. Bead-and-reel edgings occur on bowls on both of these Gaulish treasures[4] and on a bowl in the Chatuzanges treasure.[5] But the scroll-work on the Gaulish pieces is in relief and much more freely naturalistic;

1. *Man*, xlviii, 1948, pp. 25–7, pl. C; pp. 38–41, figs. 1–5; *American Journal of Archaeology*, liii, 1949, p. 123.

2. H. B. Walters, *Catalogue of the Silver Plate (Greek, Etruscan, and Roman) in the British Museum*, 1921, p. 44, nos. 170–2, pls. 24–6.

3. Louvre: *Trésor d'argenterie romaine: Galerie Charpentier*, 10 Juin, 1958, no. C.

4. Walters, *op. cit.*, p. 43, no. 164, pl. 30; Louvre: *Trésor*, etc., no. B.

5. Walters, *op. cit.*, p. 34, no. 133, pl. 13.

and the bead-and-reel edging is also found on fragments from the Traprain Law hoard (no. 107) with late-looking niello inlay.[1] The Mildenhall bowl need not, indeed, be earlier than the second half of the third century and could well be later. The cover shows, below, a zone of figured relief-work – six profile Bacchic heads alternating with six groups of a Centaur in combat with a wild beast against a background of trees and shrubs. A similar design, showing wild-beast combats, occurs on a dish from Graincourt-lès-Havrincourt.[2] But the style and technique of the Mildenhall frieze are definitely late in character and its content is paralleled on two bowls with heavily beaded rims from Mildenhall[3] and on two late bowls from Carthage.[4] Moreover, the gouged and stylised leaf-, or possibly shell-, pattern on the upper portion of the lid is very close to that on a fragment of a late rectangular tray or dish from Balline, County Limerick, in southern Ireland.[5] Both the bowl and the domed lid from Mildenhall may well be of provincial, probably Gaulish, origin.

Two more vessels from the Suffolk treasure, shown in the Exhibition, could be Gaulish work. The first is a circular scalloped bowl, just over sixteen inches in diameter, with alternating straight and curving conventionalised palm-like leaf-designs on the depressions between the flutes, which radiate from a central roundel that contains two interlaced triangles resembling a 'Shield of David', set against an 'allover' background of groups of elongated leaves – all engraved and gouged.[6] Two drop-handles probably belonged to it. That scalloped bowls of this type were made in fifth-century A.D. Gaulish workshops we know from a letter of Sidonius Apollinaris.[7] The second of these provincial-looking pieces in the Exhibition is one of two fluted bowls, six-and-three-eighths inches in diameter, each with a central rosette in the interior and a heavily beaded flange that is adorned with a stylised running floral scroll inhabited by birds and a crouching hare.

The remaining objects exhibited were one of four ladle-handles, three-and-three-quarters inches long, each of which takes the form of a stylised, but very effective, dolphin, with a knot in the middle of its body; and six spoons, varying in length from six-and-a-half to eight-and-a-quarter inches. One spoon, from a group of four, has a foliate pattern on the inside of its bowl, recalling the design on the round scalloped bowl described above. Five spoons are of special interest in view of their Christian inscriptions – *Papittedo vivas* (1), *Pascentia vivas* (1), Chi-Rho

between A and Ω (3). From these, which could well be Christening-spoons, we may deduce that the person who deposited the Mildenhall hoard in the late-fourth century,[8] or at least some members of his family, had embraced the Christian faith; and it would have been completely normal for the owner, or owners, of the Christian spoons to preserve the great Oceanus dish, the Bacchic platters, and the bowl with Bacchic heads and Centaurs, for all their pagan content, either as heirlooms from a pagan ancestry, for family reasons, or as art-treasures, for aesthetic reasons. Such a person, or persons, might even have been able to regard such motifs as symbols of the Christian after-life.

From the find-spot we may guess that the owner, or owners, of the Mildenhall hoard were civilian members of a wealthy and highly cultivated family. Of their residence we have as yet no knowledge; nor can we tell whether they were Romanised natives or immigrants from the Continent. At all events, it is clear that the find is of great significance, not only from the artistic standpoint, but also for the light that it throws on the social and economic life of southern Britain in the latter days of the island's history as a Roman province.

The Mildenhall Treasure: a Handbook, ed. 2, 1958; *Guide to the Antiquities of Roman Britain in the British Museum*, 1951, pp. 38, 40, nos. 9–42, frontispiece and pls. 7–8; 1958, pp. 38, 40, nos. 9–42, frontispiece and pls. 7–8; *Mitteilungen des Deutschen Archäologischen Instituts*, ii, 1949, pls. 14–5, 18–9, 22–9; *Forschungen zur Kunstgeschichte und Christlichen Archäologie*, ii: *Wandlungen Christlicher Kunst im Mittelalter*, 1953, pp. 41–55, figs. 1–4, 6; *Catalogue of an Exhibition of Romano–British Antiquities in the Castle Museum, Colchester, July, 1950*, p. 18, nos. 45–51, pls. 10–2; H. Schoppa, *Die Kunst der Römerzeit in Gallien, Germanien, und Britannien*, 1957, p. 61, pls. 133–6.

107. TRAPRAIN LAW TREASURE   Plates 120, 123
From Traprain Law, East Lothian. Fourth century A.D.
National Museum of Antiquities of Scotland, Edinburgh

All the other finds of Roman silver in the exhibition (nos. 105–6, 108–10) were made within the boundaries of the province and all would appear to have been deliberately concealed by their rightful owners to save them from theft or destruction. The Traprain hoard came to light beyond the imperial frontier and was undoubtedly pirates' loot, the sources of which are hidden from us. The claim of the decorated objects comprised in it to rank as works of art derived from Roman Britain is thus uncertain: the pirates could have stolen them from Gaul. All the same, the Mildenhall discovery has shown that large and varied collections of silver-ware were not unknown in late-antique Britain; and the robbers who occupied this stronghold in southern Scotland in the early-fifth century might have obtained their treasure from a British source. Nor does the presence in the hoard of Teutonic objects necessarily imply a continental origin, now that we know that some decorated works of a

1. A. O. Curle, *The Treasure of Traprain*, 1923, pp. 56–7, nos. 68–9, figs. 36–7, pl. 24.
2. Louvre: *Trésor, etc.*, no. F.
3. See bibliography.
4. British Museum: O. M. Dalton, *Catalogue of Early Christian Antiquities in the British Museum*, 1901, p. 79, nos. 356–7 with fig.
5. National Museum, Dublin: *Proceedings of the Royal Irish Academy*, li, C, 3, 1947, pl. 1, fig. 4.
6. For the alleged Jewish origin of these motifs on this piece, see *Forschungen zur Kunstgeschichte und Christlichen Archäologie*, ii: *Wandlungen Christlicher Kunst im Mittelalter*, 1953, pp. 51–4.
7. *Epp.* iv, 8, 4–5.

8. For the possible occasions of the deposition of the treasure, see *Forschungen, etc.*, ii, pp. 54–5.

Germanic character (e.g. no. 129) were reaching this country during the Roman epoch.

Two figured items from Traprain were shown at the Goldsmiths' Hall – one of the five flagons[1] and one scalloped bowl.[2] The flagon, eight-and-a-half inches high, is virtually whole and carries two superimposed freizes, both of Christian content. The lower and larger zone contains four Biblical scenes – the Fall, the Betrayal (?), the Adoration of the Magi, and Moses bringing Water from the Rock; while the upper and narrower frieze depicts the pastoral paradise. These scenes, which are executed in *repoussé*, recall those on Romano–Christian carved sarcophagi and the piece is very likely to have come from a Mediterranean workshop.

The scalloped bowl, twelve inches in diameter, is likewise complete. It has gouged 'palms' in the depressions between the flutes and in its central roundel is an engraved group of a Nereid riding across the sea on the back of a marine panther. Here the clumsy drawing of some of the details suggests the possibility of a provincial, rather than Mediterranean, workshop.

A. O. Curle, *The Treasure of Traprain*, 1923.

108. *Lanx*   Plate 121
From the River Tyne, near Corbridge (Corstopitum), Northumberland. Fourth century A.D. Height: 15 inches; width: 19 inches. *Collection of His Grace the Duke of Northumberland*

This rectangular dish, found in the eighteenth century with other silver vessels that have subsequently disappeared, would seem to be the sole survivor of a hoard and was almost certainly the product of a Mediterranean workshop. The raised border bears a running vine-scroll, partly embossed and partly engraved; and within it the whole of the field is occupied by figure-scenes, a large one above and a narrow zone below. The upper scene, which has been convincingly identified as a group of deities worshipped on the island of Delos, shows (passing from right to left) Apollo, with a cloak, buskins, a lyre, bow, and branch, standing in front of a temple with a conical roof and steps (?) leading up to it; his mother, Leto, seated on a cushioned stool; a local goddess, Asteria-Ortygia, standing with a sceptre; Athene, also standing, with an *aegis*, a spear, and a crested helmet, making with her right hand a gesture of greeting to Apollo's twin sister, Artemis, who, clad in a short tunic, cloak, and buskins and holding a bow and arrow, advances towards Athene. Between Apollo and Leto is a globe-topped pillar, between Athene and Artemis are an altar and a tree. In the lower zone (passing from left to right) are the Delian spring (Inopus), issuing from an overturned urn; the hound of Artemis; the palm-tree to which Leto clung when giving birth to her twins; an altar; Apollo's Griffin; and a stylised tree.

The content of the *lanx* is thus completely classical; and classical tradition is reflected in its style. But the lateness of its execution is betrayed by the technique, by the clumsy drawing of the faces and limbs, and by the awkward combinations

of profile heads and frontal torso. Late-antique, too, is the lavish use of delicate incising for such details as ornamental borders on the garments, fillets dangling from the branches of the tree and from the roof of the shrine, background birds in the tree, plants and flowers in the lower zone; and the naïve rendering of the temple steps (?), and the fact that the pillar next to it ends abruptly in mid-air (*cf.* no. 106), likewise demonstrate the second half of the fourth century to be its period.

Here we have, then, a pagan piece that depicts, not symbolic or allegorical mythology, but the recipients of cult at a temple; and the appearance of such a scene at such a date can only be explained as a topical, *ad hoc* allusion to a specific event, namely to the sacrifice offered to Apollo at Delos by Julian the Apostate in 363 when he was *en route* for the Persian war.[3] We may therefore date the *lanx* to *c.* 363 and regard it as a commemorative 'propaganda'-work, emanating from the circle of pagan reaction and probably made at an art-centre not remote from Delos, possibly Ephesus. We may guess that it arrived in Britain among the possessions of some high-ranking Roman official.

Journal of Roman Studies, iv, 1914, pp. 1–12, frontispiece and figs. 1–3; xxxi, 1941, pp. 100–27, figs. 17–9, pls. 8–9 (the *lanx* has a silver-content of *c.* 92.6%).

109. SKILLET   Plate 129
From Backworth, Northumberland. Second century A.D. Height: 3⅜ inches; diameter of bowl: 4¾ inches; length of handle: 4½ inches. *British Museum*

The discovery made at Backworth in 1812 produced one figured vessel, this skillet, equipped with a longish handle and standing on a low foot. Here, as on most silver vessels of this class, the relief-decoration is confined to the flat, horizontally projecting handle, and in this case to its rounded terminal and roughly triangular base where it clasps the rim of the bowl with two spreading arms. In the centre of both terminal and base is an upward-shooting, elongated flower flanked in the former case by two rosettes and tendrils, in the latter case by two running floral scrolls with acanthus-blossoms and rosettes in the spirals and a swan's head hugging the rim on either side. This ornament displays the stylised naturalism in the rendering of plant-forms that characterises second-century A.D. decorative craftsmanship – a date which harmonises with the coins that formed part of the total treasure. The whole design shows traces of gilding and on the stem of the handle is an inscription, in gilt inlaid letters, reading *Matr(ibus) Fab(ius) Dubit(anus?* or *-atus?)*. Fabius was possibly the maker of the skillet, more probably the man who commissioned it as an offering to the Mother-Goddesses, to whom one of the rings that belonged to the hoard was also vowed.[4] Both the style and the technique of

---

1. A. O. Curle, *The Treasure of Traprain*, 1923, pp. 13–9, no. 1, figs. 2–3, pl 5.
2. *Ibid.*, pp. 36–9, no. 30, fig. 17, pl. 17.

3. Cf. the treasure of silver vessels with predominantly pagan subjects found at Kaiseraugst, in Switzerland, in 1961 and connected with Julian the Apostate's visit to that fort in 361 (*Illustrated London News*, 14 and 21 July 1962, pp. 70–1, 98–9), but possibly, in view of the associated coins, deposited some eight years earlier.
4. F. H. Marshall, *Catalogue of the Finger Rings (Greek, Etruscan, and Roman) in the British Museum*, 1907, p. 106, no. 636, pl. 17; *Bonner Jahrbücher*, lxxxiii, 1887, p. 159, no. 359, pl. 3, fig. 4.

the relief-work on this handle is so fully classical that its source is likely to have been, not a British, but a Gaulish, workshop.

Archaeologia Aeliana, ii, 1832, p. 167, pl. 4, fig. 1; *Archaeological Journal*, viii, 1851, pp. 36–7 with two pls.; *Bonner Jahrbücher*, lxxxiii, 1887, p. 159, no. 360, pl. 3, fig. 3; H. B. Walters, *Catalogue of the Silver Plate (Greek, Etruscan, and Roman) in the British Museum*, 1921, pp. 46–8, no. 183, fig. 47, a–b; *Guide to the Antiquities of Roman Britain in the British Museum*, 1922, p. 62, fig. 77; 1951, p. 38, no. 4, pl. 18; 1958, p. 38, no. 4, pl. 18.

110. CASKET WITH LID   Plates 111–2
From the Walbrook Mithraeum, London. Late-third or fourth century A.D. Height: 2½ inches; diameter: 3⅛ inches.
Guildhall Museum, London

This circular lidded casket came to light unstratified, not in a hoard, like nos. 105–9, but by itself, in the north wall of the Mithraeum, where it seems to have been hidden deliberately.[1] Inside it, when it was discovered, was a silver strainer or filter, which had apparently been used with it, but does not seem to have been originally made for it. Of the casket all the wall and the upper surface of the lid are covered with figure-ornament cast in relief and chased and revealing here and there traces of gilding. The designs consist of small-scale figures and groups of men and animals with a few landscape accessories; and a full and detailed description of them will be found elsewhere.[2] Here a brief account of the main elements in the pictures must suffice. The human figures would appear to be those of hunters, clad in short jerkins and breeches, while one of the hunters on the casket wall sports a conical helmet. The animals portrayed are Griffins, elephants, goats, panthers, a boar, a snake, a tapir (?), hippopotami, and lions. On the walls the figures and episodes are arranged in superimposed tiers or storeys. All the figures of men and beasts, both on the lid and on the wall, are essentially three-dimensional, naturalistic, well-proportioned, lively and vigorous in movement. The individual components of the scenes are, in fact, stylistically, as well as technically, in the full stream of Hellenistic art-traditions, and they could, if taken in isolation, rank as the products of an early-to-mid-imperial workshop. But as compositions these designs, on both lid and wall, are wholly devoid of organic coherence, and the effect is that of an 'all-over' carpet- or tapestry-pattern with loosely linked, self-contained units strewn across the field, with a view to covering every scrap of surface with ornamentation. In this respect the casket's affinities are less with the art of the first and second centuries than with late-antique art, as exemplified particularly on mosaic pavements; although much more organic-

ally composed 'all-over' designs had, of course, already appeared in the purely decorative, 'free-style', wild-beast scenes, with or without hunters, of the second-century A.D. red-gloss Gaulish potters' repertory. The fifth-century A.D. mosaics in the great palace of the Byzantine Emperors at Constantinople offer a close parallel to the casket, with their naturalistic figure-groups executed in the Hellenistic manner, but strewn in tiers as self-contained, isolated units across the field.[3] Furthermore, it is a late-antique (fourth-century) mosaic that provides a key to the meaning of what are undoubtedly the strangest figure-groups in the decoration of the Walbrook casket, namely the three on one sector of the lid. There we have two Griffins, each mounted upon the top of a large, rectangular box or chest and each engaged in trying to prise open with its beak the lid of the box in order to get at its contents. The third group shows a man being helped out from the end of a similar box by a companion, while another companion stands on the lid and offers assistance. Reference to the mosaic pavement in the great corridor of the country villa at Piazza Armerina in central Sicily[4] leaves no room for doubt but that the rectangular boxes or chests are crates or cages, set by the hunters for catching wild creatures and also used as travelling-boxes for transporting them alive across the Mediterranean to the places of public entertainment for which they were destined. One such cage appears on this mosaic on wheels and drawn by a pair of oxen;[5] another is slung on a pole and carried along by a pair of huntsmen;[6] others again are ranged on board a cargo-boat.[7] As for the motif of a Griffin perched on top of such a box, a motif shown twice, as we have seen, on the lid of the Walbrook casket, it appears at the right-hand end of the corridor mosaic, where a powerful Griffin facing towards the left sprawls upon the upper surface of a slatted crate, out of one end of which there peeps a human face.[8] It would seem that men were sometimes immured in these receptacles as baits; the beasts would sense their presence and try to tear the cages open in order to reach them; and then, while thus preoccupied, they would the more easily be taken captive by other huntsmen. The third scene on the casket lid represents the succeeding stage in such an episode: the human bait has served his turn and is being released from his confinement. That the Griffin was popularly, at least, believed to exist in the East as a creature that could be hunted is clear from Philostratus' *Life of Apollonius of Tyana*.[9]

The Walbrook casket may, for the reasons given above, be

---

1. See the forthcoming *Report* on the Walbrook Mithraeum. Near the casket there came to light fragments of a silver bowl with late-looking punched decoration, presumably crushed by the nineteenth-century building-operations (pp. 137–8), when the casket itself was mercifully spared by them. This find certainly suggests that the casket and the bowl belonged to a *cache* of purposefully concealed valuable objects.   2. *Ibid.*

3. G. Brett, W. J. Macaulay, and R. B. K. Stevenson, *The Great Palace of the Byzantine Emperors*, 1947.
4. From the very considerable body of literature that Piazza Armerina has already inspired the following items may be cited here: G. V. Gentili (a), *La villa romana a Piazza Armerina* (*Itinerari dei Musei e Monumenti d'Italia*, No. 87), 1951; (b) *ibid.*, ed. 4, 1960; (c) 'I mosaici della villa romana di Piazza Armerina' (*Bollettino d'Arte*, xxxvii, ser. 4, 1952, pp. 33–46, figs. 1–20, pl. 1); (d) *La villa erculia di Piazza Armerina: i mosaici figurativi*, 1959; B. Pace, *I mosaici di Piazza Armerina*, 1955.
5. Pace, *op. cit.*, fig. 19.
6. Gentili (c), p. 39, fig. 14.
7. Gentili (b), fig. 21; Gentili (c), p. 41, fig. 16; Gentili (d), pl. 25.
8. Gentili (a), fig. 16; Gentili (b), fig. 17.   9. iii, 48.

tentatively, at any rate, ascribed to the late-third or fourth century of our era. As regards its place of origin, the piece itself furnishes no evidence. All that we can say is that the provenances or affinities of the late-antique mosaics, with which we have related its decoration, are eastern. The find-spot of the object naturally suggests that it should be described as religious 'table'-ware and that it was employed in Mithraic ritual, perhaps as a container for strained honey, since honey featured in the initiation-rites of the grade of *Leones*.[1] The hunting-scenes could allude indirectly to Mithras in his role as the hunter-down of death and evil.[2] Unpublished.

Figured Bronze-Ware

III. SKILLET WITH HEADS OF BACCHUS AND TWO SATYRS ON HANDLE   Plate 126
From Welshpool, Montgomeryshire. First century A.D. Diameter of bowl: 7 inches; length of handle: 5 inches. *National Museum of Wales, Cardiff (on loan from the Welshpool Borough Council)*

This piece and no. 117 form part of a hoard of decorated bronze vessels found in 1959. The ornament is here confined to the handle, which has a rounded, unfluted stem. At the handle's terminal is an impressive, garlanded Bacchus head, with eyes that were once inlaid with silver. On the upper surface of the handle, at its junction with the bowl, is the head of a youthful Satyr modelled in the round, with stylised arms outstretched to grasp the rim. Immediately below this young Satyr is another and more elderly Satyr head, worked in very low relief, facing in profile to the right, with a *syrinx* depending from it by a pair of strings, while the curved end of a *pedum* projects in front of it. The skillet was certainly imported and probably of Italian workmanship. On the analogy of the figured silver skillets, such as nos. 105 and 109, it may be inferred that at least the more elaborate of their counterparts in bronze were pieces of religious 'table'-ware used for sacrificial purposes in humbler contexts.

Antiquity, xxxiv, 1960, p. 143; *Journal of Roman Studies*, l, 1960, pl. 20, fig. 4; *Antiquaries Journal*, xli, 1961, pp. 22–3, fig. 4, no. 2, pls. 5, b; 7.

112. SKILLET WITH DOG'S HEAD ON HANDLE
                                                   Plate 127
From Canterbury (Durovernum), Kent. First or second

century A.D. Diameter of bowl: 7¾ inches; length of handle: 3¾ inches. *Royal Museum, Canterbury*

This skillet, found in a grave, has a handle with a rounded and fluted stem terminating in a naturalistically modelled dog's head. It was probably imported work, from Italy or Gaul. Skillet-handles with the same type of terminal have been found elsewhere in Roman Britain, in Annandale,[3] in a barrow at Thornborough, in Buckinghamshire,[4] and at Santon Downham, in Suffolk (or at Santon, in Norfolk).[5]

VCH Kent, iii, 1932, pl. 13, fig. 5; J. Ward, *The Roman Era in Britain*, 1911, p. 187, fig. 54, f.

113. SKILLET WITH FLORAL SCROLL   Plate 125
From West Lothian. First or second century A.D. Diameter of bowl: 4¼ inches; height of bowl: 2½ inches; length of handle: 3½ inches. *National Museum of Antiquities of Scotland, Edinburgh*

One class of variant of the deep-bowled, flat-handled type of figured bronze skillet comprises a series of small pieces that are decorated over the greater part of their exterior surfaces with designs in brilliant blue and green, or red, blue, and green, *champlevé* enamelling. Of this very perfect instance, complete with handle, the precise find-spot is not recorded.[6] It carries, *inter alia*, a broad zone of stylised running floral scroll-work on its lower half. A very similar bowl, which apparently never had a handle, was discovered at Braughing, in Hertfordshire.[7] The famous bowl or cup from Rudge, in Wiltshire, is of the same class, but much more ambitious in its ornament. It bears the names of five of the forts on Hadrian's Wall and a conventionalised representation of the masonry and towers of the Wall itself.[8] It is highly probable that all these enamelled pieces, whether handled or handle-less, represent the achievements of local British workshops, the products of which were sometimes exported to neighbouring provinces.[9] But enamelling was, of course, no monopoly of British craftsmen.

Proceedings of the Society of Antiquaries of Scotland, lxvi, 1931-2, pp. 303–5, 353, figs. 14–5, no. 1.

1. Porphyry, *De antro nympharum* 15 (see F. Cumont, *Textes et monuments figurés relatifs aux mystères de Mithra*, ii, 1896, p. 40, no. b).
2. For Mithras as a hunter, see (i) sculptured slab from Dieburg: F. Behn, *Das Mithrasheiligtum zu Dieburg*, 1928, pp. 11–6, pl. 1; (ii) sculptured slab from Rückingen: *Germania*, xxx, 1952, pp. 349–62, pl. 24; M. J. Vermaseren, *Corpus Inscriptionum et Monumentorum Religionis Mithriacae*, ii, 1960, pp. 80–2, no. 1137, fig. 297; (iii) relief from Osterburken: Cumont, *op. cit.*, p. 350, no. 246, pl. 6; (iv) relief from Neuenheim: *ibid.*, p. 346, no. 246, pl. 5; (v) two mural paintings from Dura-Europos: ed. M. C. Rostovtzeff, F. E. Brown, and C. B. Welles. *The Excavations at Dura-Europos: Preliminary Report of the Seventh and Eighth Seasons of Work, 1933–4 and 1934–5*, 1939, pls. 14–5; Vermaseren, *op. cit.*, i, 1956, pp. 68–9, no. 52, fig. 24: (vi) jar from Verulamium: see no. 157. For the *graffito* on the base of the Walbrook casket – ISIAVI, probably a personal name in the genitive case, see *Journal of Roman Studies*, li, 1961, p. 195, no. 16.

3. *Proceedings of the Society of Antiquaries of Scotland*, lxvi, 1931-2, pp. 301–2, fig. 13.
4. Museum of Archaeology and of Ethnology, Cambridge: *Records of Buckinghamshire*, xvi, 1953-4, p. 30, pl. 4, b.
5. *Proceedings of the Cambridge Antiquarian Society*, xiii, 1908-9, p. 160, fig. 11. The find-spot of the hoard from which this vessel comes has been variously identified as Santon Downham, in Suffolk, and Santon, in Norfolk.
6. For an almost identical bowl found at Maltboek, in Denmark, see *Proceedings of the Society of Antiquaries of Scotland*, lxvi, 1931-2, pp. 303–4, fig. 15, no. 3.
7. British Museum: *ibid.*, pp. 302–3, fig. 15, no. 2; *Proceedings of the Society of Antiquaries of London*, ser. 2, iv, 1867–70, pp. 514–6 with fig.; *Guide to the Antiquities of Roman Britain in the British Museum*, 1951, p. 55, no. 2, pl. 21; 1958, p. 56, no. 2, pl. 21.
8. Collection of His Grace the Duke of Northumberland: *Archaeologia Aeliana*, ser. 4, xii, 1935, pp. 310–41, pls. 28, fig. 1; 29.
9. For pieces similar to the Rudge cup, found on the Continent, see the Hildburgh fragment from northern Spain (*ibid.* p. 323, fig. 1, pl. 18, fig. 2) and the bowl in the Musée de Picardie, Amiens (*Journal of Roman Studies*, xli, 1951, pp. 22–4, fig. 4, pl. 3, fig. 1).

114. JUG WITH MASKS AND FEMALE (?) BUST ON HANDLE
Plate 130

From Stanfordbury, Bedfordshire. First century A.D. Height: 6½ inches. *Museum of Archaeology and of Ethnology, Cambridge*

Both this jug and no. 115 were found in late-La Tène burials and may have been imported into Britain, from Italian or Gaulish workshops, just before the Roman conquest. This piece shows two superimposed comic masks in relief on its handle-base escutcheon and, at the junction of the handle with the rim, a human female (?) head and bust, modelled in the round and with arms outstretched on either side to grip the edge.

C. Fox, *Archaeology of the Cambridge Region*, 1923, p. 190, pl. 26, fig. 1.

115. JUG WITH LION ON HANDLE
Plate 131

From Santon Downham, Suffolk, or Santon, Norfolk (see no. 112, note 5). First century A.D. Height: 5½ inches. *Museum of Archaeology and of Ethnology, Cambridge*

On this piece the handle takes the form of an extremely stylised, but effective, lion. The hind-paws occupy the base-escutcheon; the elongated back and rope-like tail compose the stem; while at the junction with the rim are the creature's head and extended forepaws.

Proceedings of the Cambridge Antiquarian Society, xiii, 1908–9, p. 160, pl. 17, figs. 2–3.

116. JUG WITH MASK AND HORSE ON HANDLE
Plate 132

From Canterbury (Durovernum), Kent. First or second century A.D. Height: 7½ inches. *Royal Museum, Canterbury*

A provincial workshop probably produced this piece, with its downturned spout and small, domed, pedestal-base. At the handle-base is a female mask in high relief and at the handle-top is a horse's head, with a mane and forelocks, while the elongated forelegs are stretched (perforce forwards, not backwards, as in Nature) along the rim on either side. This beast has been wrongly identified as a dog.

VCH Kent, iii, 1932, pl. 13, fig. 3; J. Ward, *The Roman Era in Britain*, 1911, p. 187, fig. 54, a; *Catalogue of an Exhibition of Romano-British Antiquities in the Castle Museum, Colchester, July, 1950*, p. 15, no. 34, pl. 4.

117. JUG WITH HANDLE IN FORM OF BOY HERCULES KILLING SNAKES
Plate 133

From Welshpool, Montgomeryshire. First century A.D. Height: 9 inches. *National Museum of Wales, Cardiff (on loan from the Welshpool Borough Council)*

This jug bears a handle of a very rare type, with a stem that consists of the figure of the boy Hercules modelled in the round. He is naked, wears a lion-skin hood, the frontpaws of which are knotted beneath the chin (while the hindpaws grip the rim of the jug) and grasps with both hands the slack body of a dead snake, whereof the tail is whipped round his left leg and ankle. On the escutcheon at the base lies coiled a second dead snake. The child's eyes were once inlaid with silver. This is, indeed, an unusual version of the story, depicting the moment subsequent to the actual strangling of the creatures (the scene that is normally represented) by the infant hero, who is here not a baby of a few months only and also affects the Nemean lion-skin by anticipation. Other instances of the child Hercules with lion-skin hood are a colossal green basalt figure in the Capitoline Museum, Rome,[1] and a marble statuette at Braunschweig.[2]

Antiquity, xxxiv, 1960, p. 143, pl. 16, a; *Journal of Roman Studies*, l, 1960, pl. 20, fig. 3; *Antiquaries Journal*, xli, 1961, pp. 20–2, fig. 4, no. 1, pls. 5, a; 6; *Revue Archéologique*, 1962, pp. 97–101, where an unconvincing attempt is made to interpret the boy as Bacchus.

118. JUG-HANDLE WITH MASK OF OCEANUS
Plate 134

From London. Second century A.D. Height of handle: 8¼ inches. *London Museum, Kensington Palace*

Much of the actual jug is restoration. The only ornament is on the handle-base escutcheon, where there is a large and very finely worked mask of Oceanus, with a pair of winged and curly-tailed sea-beasts intertwined in his hair.

London in Roman Times (London Museum Catalogues, No. 3), 1930, p. 116, frontispiece and pl. 52, b, 1.

119. JUG-HANDLE WITH OX-HEAD AND LIONESS AND CUBS
Plate 135

From London. First or second century A.D. Height: 5⅞ inches. *Guildhall Museum, London*

The stem of this handle is plain. At the base is a highly stylised ox-head, with horns, ears, and eyes, but a palmette in place of the nozzle. At the junction with the rim, at the centre, is a lioness, with a cub on either side of her. These small creatures were crouched along the vessel's edge and face away from their mother, with their hindquarters hunched up. Incised lines and pouncing indicate their markings. This is an attractive piece of provincial work, probably Gaulish.

Unpublished.

120. JUG WITH FIGURE-GROUPS ON HANDLE
Plate 128

From Lesmahagow, Lanarkshire. Second century A.D. Height: 10½ inches. *Hunterian Museum, Glasgow University*

The connection of ideas between the various groups of figure-decoration on the handle of this jug is by no means clear. The groups are arranged in three tiers. Below, on the escutcheon, a small girl stands beside an altar or pedestal, with a bird, probably an owl, perched to the left upon her left hand, while her right hand is raised in a gesture of surprise; beside her, in the field, is an indeterminate object.

1. Ed. H. Stuart Jones, *Sculptures of the Museo Capitolino*, 1912, pp. 275–6, no. 3, pl. 64.
2. P. Arndt, etc., *Photographische Einzelaufnahmen antiker Sculptu en*, nos. 4174–5, 4178 (here Hercules holds a club and a *cornucopiae*).

Above the girl, a crested Corinthian helmet, or possibly a human mask wearing such a helmet, rests on a pile of rocks (?), with a spear, to which fillets are attached, engraved on the background behind it. Above that, again, a small winged Cupid with a flying cloak dances beneath a circular shield, which has a Medusa head as its embossed device and two folds of drapery dangling on either side of it. The workmanship is careful and the jug could have been produced in a good Gaulish studio.

Archaeologia, xvi, 1812, pp. 350–2, pl. 51; J. Macdonald, *Tituli Hunteriani*, 1897, pp. 95–9, pl. 17; *Proceedings of the Society of Antiquaries of Scotland*, lxvii, 1931–2, pp. 298–9, 383, fig. 9.

Figured Pewter-Ware

121. DISH WITH CHRISTIAN SYMBOLS   Plates 137–8
From the Isle of Ely. Fourth century A.D. Diameter: 8½ inches. *Museum of Archaeology and of Ethnology, Cambridge*

Incised on the flat, polygonal flange of this deep dish or bowl with pedestal-foot are Christian motifs – the Chi-Rho monogram, peacocks (symbols of immortality), an owl (?)

(symbol of divine wisdom), Nereids (symbols of baptismal regeneration). The dish could, but need not necessarily, have served a liturgical function. It is possibly native work.

Proceedings of the Cambridge Antiquarian Society, xxxi, 1931, pp. 66–75, pl. 1; *Catalogue of an Exhibition of Romano-British Antiquities in the Castle Museum, Colchester, July, 1950*, pp. 19–20, no. 61. pl. 15.

121a.* DISH WITH FISH   Plate 136
From Icklingham, Suffolk. Fourth century A.D. Length: 7 inches (originally 8½ to 9 inches). *Property of the Earl of Iveagh (on loan to the Museum of Archaeology and of Ethnology, Cambridge)*

This flat, oval dish, one end of which is lost, shows an incised drawing of a fish facing towards the right. The fish was, of course, both a pagan and a Christian religious symbol. But the piece need not necessarily have served a cult- or liturgical purpose. Indeed, its shape suggests that it was used for serving fish at table. It is probably native work and represents the only decorated item in a hoard of pewter objects.

Proceedings of the Cambridge Antiquarian Society, lii, 1959, pp. 6–10, fig. 1; pls. 3, b, 2; 4, a.
*Not in the Exhibition Hand-list.

MISCELLANEOUS WORKS IN METAL
AND OTHER MATERIALS

122. HARNESS-MOUNT WITH SCROLL-DESIGN
                                        Plate 157
From Santon Downham, Suffolk, or Santon, Norfolk (see no. 112, note 5). Mid-first century A.D. Bronze, enamelled. Height: 3¼ inches: width: 2¾ inches. *Museum of Archaeology and of Ethnology, Cambridge*

This mount consists of two main S-shaped elements shown back to back and joined at the centre by a roundel, on each side of which is a *pelta*-shaped hole piercing through the metal. The typically late-La Tène trumpet-scroll design, drawn two-dimensionally, stands out in the burnished bronze against a deep-red *champlevé* enamel background. The mount, like nos. 114 and 115, was found in a late-La Tène burial and probably dates from about the time of the Roman conquest or a little earlier.

C. Fox, *Pattern and Purpose*, 1958, pl. 72, e.

123. MOUNT WITH SCROLL-DESIGNS   Plate 142
From Elmswell, Yorkshire. Second half of the first century A.D. Bronze, enamelled. Width at greatest extent: 9½ inches. *Kingston upon Hull Museum*

This bronze panel, mounted on an iron base, was almost certainly a mount for a casket. The major and lower portion is worked in *repoussé* and carries a formal lyre-pattern scroll-

design of late-La Tène type. The bottom edge is straight, while the sides, sloping inwards, are shaped to follow the curves of the scrolls. Dotted rosettes at the centres of the spirals mark the rhythm of the balanced composition. At the top, across the apex of the triangle, is a narrow horizontal cast strip carrying a running scroll of mainly classical inspiration in *champlevé* red enamelling. The associated evidence suggests for the mount a date between A.D. 60 and 70; and it is a striking instance of the persistence, well into the Roman period in northern Britain, of the genuinely Celtic style of craftsmanship.

A *repoussé* panel with a much more conventionalised lyre-scroll design, found in Great Tower Street, London, represents the style's continuation in the south.[1]

Antiquaries Journal, xx, 1940, pp. 338–57, fig. 1, pl. 52; *Journal of Roman Studies*, xliv, 1954, p. 49; p. 51, fig. 2; pl. 2, fig. 1; C. Fox, *Pattern and Purpose*, 1958, pp. 105–6, fig. 69; *The Studio*, July, 1961, fig. on p. 6.

124. MOUNT WITH RELIEF-FIGURE OF MINERVA
                                        Plate 146
From Lavington, Wiltshire. Third or fourth century A.D. Bronze. Height: 5 inches. *Devizes Museum*

1. British Museum: *Antiquaries Journal*, xx, 1940, p. 346, pl. 53, a; C. Fox, *Pattern and Purpose*, 1958, p. 88, fig. 5.

This unequivocally native work is an oblong plaque, straight at the top and rounded at the bottom, which may have once been mounted on a piece of religious furniture. It confronts us with an excessively naïve, but intriguing, figure of Minerva, crude in technique and unorthodox in detail, yet reminiscent in its pose of the famous classical sculptural type known as that of the Victory of Brescia.[1] The goddess stands to the front, with her left foot raised and resting on the head of a plump owl crouched beside her; and she extends her bare right arm as though to write upon her small, oval shield that is supported vertically on her left knee. Above the shield projects the large, heavy head of Minerva's spear. Her thickly draped and richly pictorial garments consist of a long, sleeveless tunic and an ample cloak, one edge of which hangs down between her legs in a Greek zig-zag fold (*cf.* nos. 27, 30, 72–3). The Medusa head on her *aegis* is oddly sited, not on her breast, but on her flank, and glowers at us from beneath her right arm; and her heavy, square-shaped face, with its enormous, staring eyes, thick, flat nose, and clumsy lips, is crowned, not by a helmet, but by the round-eared mask and skin of what is probably intended for a bear. The little piece is, indeed, an entertaining and by no means unpleasing combination of traditional Graeco–Roman and local British elements.

Journal of Roman Studies, xlv, 1955, pp. 101–2, pl. 30, fig. 1.

125. PHALERA WITH MEDUSA MASK   Plate 147
From Sandy, Bedfordshire. Second century A.D. Bronze. Diameter: 2¾ inches. *Museum of Archaeology and of Ethnology, Cambridge*

This is the best preserved and handsomest of three small metal discs, or 'medallions', of the type known as *phalerae*, circular in shape and each bearing a Medusa mask in relief, which have been unearthed in the southern area of Roman Britain. Objects of this class, carrying Medusa masks and other figures, were worn as military decorations on leather or metal corselets. A complete set of nine silver *phalerae*, eight of them bearing busts or masks, among them a Medusa mask, were found at Lauersfort, in Germany;[2] while a *phalera* with a Medusa mask occupies the central place of honour on the cuirass of the centurion, Marcus Caelius, slain in the battle of the Teutoberger Forest and portrayed in the well-known memorial relief at Bonn.[3] These three British *phalerae* may very well, then, have belonged to soldiers and, since their find-spots are all civilian, have been lost by their owners after retirement from active service; although the possibility of their use as mounts on articles of furniture, chariots,[4] etc. cannot be completely excluded.

The specimen found at Sandy, almost certainly imported from a Gaulish studio, is, in fact, pierced by three rivet-holes, as though for attachment to a metal corselet or to some other object of wood or metal. The very fine, classicised head worked in high relief upon the disc has wings in the hair and has generally been described as Mercury. But the plump, round face wears a definitely feminine appearance; and the wings rule out the interpretations of the head as that of Bacchus or of a youthful Satyr, which have also been proposed for it.[5] Moreover, the hair is very sinuous and snake-like, even if no snakes can actually be discerned in it; and the lightly incised wreath of leaves and berries that surrounds the mask would suit Medusa in her role as goddess of the earth and of fertility.[6]

Proceedings of the Society of Antiquaries of London, ser. 2, xx, 1903–5, pp. 340–1 with fig.; *VCH Bedfordshire*, ii, 1908, p. 11, pl. 2 (top fig.); C. Fox, *Archaeology of the Cambridge Region*, 1923, p. 214; *Bedfordshire Magazine*, v, no. 30, 1956, pp. 233–4 with fig.

126. PHALERA WITH MEDUSA MASK   Plate 148
From Verulamium, Hertfordshire. Second or third century A.D. Two discs of silver with bronze backing. Diameter: 2½ inches. *Verulamium Museum, St. Albans*

This *phalera*, of which the outer silver disc is worked in *repoussé*, is probably of local manufacture. Both the head-wings and the snakes of the Medusa are clearly visible, but the execution is very crude and the piece is damaged. On the bronze backing are the relics of a hinged pin and catch. We may, indeed, be dealing with a disc-brooch, if it had not been pinned to a leather corselet.

R. E. M. and T. V. Wheeler, *Verulamium: a Belgic and Two Roman Cities*, 1936, pp. 212–3, no. 55, fig. 46.

127. CROWN AND HEADDRESS   Plate 141
From Cavenham Heath, Suffolk. Second or third, or possibly late-fourth, century A.D. Bronze. Height: 5¼ inches. *Ipswich Museum*

The most important of the Roman objects, obviously of native origin, in this Suffolk hoard, are a headdress, consisting of five undecorated roundels linked by chains, and two crowns; and there can be little doubt but that these three were items of priestly headgear worn for ritual purposes at some local shrine. Both of the crowns have a high, three-lobed front and a circular headband, front and headband being of a single piece in the case of the larger of the crowns (shown in the Exhibition), whereas in the case of the smaller crown the two portions had once been soldered to one another. Both crowns have metal slips for adjusting them to the heads of different wearers; and both were once richly decked with applied ornaments, jewels and very thin plaques, possibly of precious stones and metals respectively, that had been torn off leaving scars, some of which show traces of figure-work, where they had been soldered to the bronze. The front of the larger crown had, above, a central

---

1. E. Strong, *La scultura romana*, i, 1923, pl. 28.
2. *Germania Romana*, ed. 2, v, 1930, p. 23, pl. 36, fig. 1.
3. *Ibid.*, iii, 1926, pl. 1, fig. 2.
4. E.g. *L'Antiquité Classique*, viii, 1939, pl. 28, fig. 2.

5. *Ibid.*, xv, 1946, p. 127.
6. The second Medusa *phalera* from southern Britain comes from Farley Heath, in Surrey, and is likely to be of local make (Ashmolean Museum, Oxford: unpublished). For the third piece, see no. 126.

jewel flanked by oval plaques and, below, three pedimented *aediculae* or niches, each of which would surely have held the figure of a divinity. The smaller crown shows eight much more irregularly shaped scars, three above and five below; and some of these, at least, must represent figured plaques. On the larger crown, on each side of, and below, the central jewel, are three metal loops, into which feathers of bronze, such as the one actually found with the crowns at Cavenham,[1] could have been inserted.

The crowns do not appear to have been new at the time at which the hoard was deposited at some unknown date. They might have been made in the second or third century and have been buried round about the middle of the fourth century to save them from destruction at the hands of Christian iconoclasts. On the other hand, the approximately known date of the concealment of the very similar objects found in Norfolk (no. 128) raises the possibility that the Cavenham ritual equipment was produced during the pagan revival in Britain in the second half of the fourth century.[2]

Antiquaries Journal, v, 1925, pp. 258–65, pls. 27–8; *Catalogue of an Exhibition of Romano–British Antiquities in the Castle Museum, Colchester, July, 1950*, p. 9, nos. 8–10, pl. 2.

128. CROWN AND DIADEM   Plates 139–40
From Hockwold-cum-Wilton, Norfolk. Second or third, or possibly late-fourth, century A.D. Bronze. Height of crown: 6¼ inches; height of diadem: 3 inches. *British Museum*

The crown and five diadems found on this site in a context of Roman material belong to the same type of religious headgear as no. 127. The diadems have adjustable head-slips and, in front, three upstanding lobes, each of which bears a very thin silver plaque. The designs on these plaques – on three, a crudely drawn male figure, with enormous head, holding a crooked stick and a ball and a very degenerate rendering of the classical vase-and-two-birds motif – betray the local craftsman's hand. The crown consists of a headband surmounted by two arched strips that cross one another above and carry at their point of intersection a round disc and a vertical, projecting spike. At each of the four points at which the strips meet the headband is a roundel with a male human mask in relief at its centre (one mask is now lost). Here again the Celtic hand is (more attractively) evident in the stylised curls of hair and beard that wholly frame the face, in the lentoid eyes, in the wedge-shaped nose, and in the straight, trap-like mouth. These masks may well portray a local god. The Hockwold *cache* must, like no. 127, represent the 'treasury' of some neighbour-

ing temple, again, perhaps, buried to save it from destruction. The holes in which these objects were buried had been dug through a chalk floor, which coin evidence shows to have been occupied to the very end of the fourth century.[3] Their concealment must, therefore, have taken place in the late-fourth century or even later. Crown and diadems could themselves be of much earlier date; but we must obviously reckon with the possibility that their manufacture was connected with the pagan revival in late-fourth-century Roman Britain (*cf.* no. 127).

Journal of Roman Studies, xlvii, 1957, p. 211, pl. 9; *Guide to the Antiquities of Roman Britain in the British Museum*, 1958, p. 62, no. 10, pl. 25.

129. BUCKLE WITH STYLISED HORSES AND DOLPHINS
Plate 153
From Catterick (Cataractonium), Yorkshire. Fourth century A.D. Bronze. Width: 3¾ inches. *In trade, October 1962*.

This is the most impressive specimen, from the point of view of figure-decoration, of the British series of zoomorphic buckles, all probably imported and all, to judge by the evidence afforded by their parallels of continental provenance, of late-Roman date. It is roughly rectangular in shape and shows two confronted and very stylised animals, possibly intended to be horses with incised lines indicating manes, holding the bar on which the buckle's tongue turns between them in their jaws. Two vertically posed dolphins, also stylised, but very recognisable, occupy the buckle's shorter sides. Each dolphin is attached to the back of the head of one of the horses; but between the neck of each horse and its adjacent dolphin is a roughly triangular aperture pierced through the bronze to give the effect of open-work. The four creatures have dot-and-circle eyes and the dolphins' bodies an 'all-over' sprinkling of small round markings. The buckle's nearest parallels are continental – from Warlberla, near Nuremberg,[4] from Bingen, on the Rhine,[5] and from Gellep, in the Ruhr;[6] and so close is the similarity of all four pieces that we may assume them to be the products of a single workshop active in the mid-to-late-fourth century. Although their motifs are, in themselves, Romano–Celtic, their treatment is decidedly Germanic in its flavour; and it seems not unlikely that the market for which they were manufactured was that of the German auxiliaries in the Roman frontier armies.

Other bronze buckles of British provenance show less elaborate versions of the motif of the biting, confronted beasts, without the supporting dolphins. On a piece from Smithfield the buckle proper is almost smothered in a very heavy, square, 'chip-carved' frame of 'geometric' patterns.[7] Three simpler, unframed specimens come from Richborough;[8]

---

1. Ipswich Museum: *Antiquaries Journal*, v, 1925, p. 261, fig. 4; *Catalogue of an Exhibition of Romano-British Antiquities in the Castle Museum, Colchester, July, 1950*, p. 9, no. 11.
2. For a bronze crown somewhat similar in shape to those from Cavenham and possibly also ritual in character, found in the legionary fortress at Vetera (Xanten), in the Rhineland, dating from the first half of the first century A.D., and carrying the well-executed and wholly classical figures of deities and other personages in relief upon its sides and front, see *Germania*, xiii, 1929, pp. 131–2, 2 pls. between pp. 128 and 129; H. Hinz, *Xanten zur Römerzeit*, 1960, fig. on p. 49 Rheinsiches Landesmuseum, Bonn). Plate 251.

3. *Journal of Roman Studies*, xlviii, 1958, p. 142.
4. *Yorkshire Archaeological Journal*, xxxix, 1957, pp. 243–6, fig. 6, no. 12, a.
5. *Ibid.*, fig. 6, no. 12, b.   6. *Ibid.*, fig. 6, no. 12, c.
7. T. D. Kenrick, *Anglo-Saxon Art to A.D. 900*, 1938, p. 45, fig. 7; G. Baldwin Brown, *The Arts in Early England*, iv, 1915, pl. 151.
8. J. P. Bushe-Fox, *Fourth Report on the Excavations of the Roman Fort at Richborough, Kent*, 1949, pp. 122–3, nos. 67–9, pl. 32.

and another such comes from Dorchester.[1] The whole series is of interest as representing the latest phase of provincial metal-work before the breakdown of Roman domination.

Yorkshire Archaeological Journal, xxxix, 1957, pp. 243-6, no. 12, fig. 6, no. 12, pl. 9.

130. FAN-TAILED BROOCH   Plate 154

From Great Chesters (Aesica), on Hadrian's Wall, Northumberland. Late-first century A.D. Bronze, gilded. Height: 4¼ inches. *Museum of Antiquities of the University of Durham and of the Society of Antiquaries of Newcastle upon Tyne (King's College, Newcastle upon Tyne)*

Of the types of *fibulae* that are virtually peculiar to Britain the fan-tailed type claims pride of place in virtue of its most magnificent exponent, this famous and repeatedly published piece. It is adorned with a splendid, balanced relief-design of trumpet-scrolls and it illustrates to perfection the 'high-baroque' phase of late-La Tène workmanship in northern Britain during the Roman period.[2]

Archaeologia, lxxx, 1930, pp. 38-42, pl. 11; E. T. Leeds, *Celtic Ornament in the British Isles down to A.D. 700*, 1933, p. 109, fig. 20, c; C. Fox, *Pattern and Purpose*, 1958, p. 108, pl. 41, c; *Archaeologia Aeliana*, ser. 4, xxxix, 1961, pp. 6, 22, 35.

131. DRAGONESQUE BROOCH   Plate 155

From Carlisle (Luguvalium), Cumberland. Late-first century A.D. Bronze, enamelled. Height: 2⅛ inches. *Carlisle Museum, Tullie House*

An important testimony to the skill and creativeness of Celtic metal-workers in Britain under Roman rule is the dragonesque *fibula*, of which the Graeco–Roman sea-dragon furnished the distant prototype.[3] That creature's upstanding ears, round eyes, and pronged tail can still be recognised, but the fins and forepaws have disappeared. The jaws are curled upwards and finish in a roundel, the body has been flattened out, and the whole monster has been transformed into an S-shaped, two-dimensional Celtic scroll with 'head' and 'tail' exactly corresponding. The joyous, buoyant effect of the design is enhanced by the clasp of the brooch, whipped round the neck above and lashed across the tail below, and by the gay enamelling which so often enlivens examples of this type. This is a recent and particularly fine addition to the series, found in 1956 on a Flavian level. The gilt-bronze is picked out with red and bluish-green enamel.
Unpublished.

132. LID OF SARCOPHAGUS WITH BACCHIC FIGURES
Plate 145

From Holborough, Kent. Second or third century A.D. Lead. Length: 3 ft., 5¾ in.; width at head: 1 ft., 6½ in.; width

at foot: 11 in.; depth of 'trough' of sarcophagus: 1 ft. at head; 10 in. at foot. *Maidstone Museum.*

Britain, as is well known, was particularly rich in lead in Roman times;[4] and of the decorated objects made from those plentiful supplies for the British market, the coffins or sarcophagi are the most imposing. The craft of ornamenting lead coffins with relief-work was practised in several other areas of the Roman world – notably in Roman Gaul and Roman Germany, in the west, and, above all, in the east, in Syria and Palestine, where the art flourished more proliciy and brilliantly than in any other lands.[5] There we find a wealth of motifs both figured and floral in their content and completely classical in style, most of which can be recognised as well-established funerary symbols of death and after-life; and it is to this eastern repertory that we have to turn for parallels to the motifs on some of the British pieces, which, inferior as they are aesthetically to the products of Mediterranean workshops, can claim, as a series, to rival, in interest and variety, their western provincial counterparts.

The method used in manufacturing Roman lead sarcophagi was that of open sand-casting. Matrices of wet sand of the size required for the lead sheets were first prepared and probably held together round the edges by wooden frames. A coffin could be made in two sheets, a smaller one for the lid, a larger one for the bottom and sides. In such cases the second sheet was cast in a matrix shaped like a rectangle from which small squares of identical size had been cut out, one at each of the four corners, in such a way that the inner corner of each square coincided with one of the four corners of the central oblong area reserved for the base; the four sides were then bent up into the perpendicular; and the four angles of the 'trough' so formed were soldered together. Alternatively, the base and the two long sides could be cast in one sheet, the long sides being bent up, while the two short sides were cast separately and soldered on. Or the base and the two short sides could be cast in one sheet, the long sides being cast separately and soldered onto the rest. Or, again, the bottom and the four sides could be cast in five separate sheets and all united by soldering. The sheet for the lid was always slightly larger than the area of the base, so that its four edges could be bent down to overlap the sides.

The ornament was almost certainly produced by a series of positive stamps, either modelled in clay or, much more probably, carved in wood in relief on square, oblong, circular, or elliptical plaques or blocks, or on long strips, as

---

1. Baldwin Brown, *op. cit.*, pl. 152, fig. 10. For a list of bronze buckles from British sites with outward-facing animal heads set back-to-back, see *Antiquaries Journal*, xvii, 1937, pp. 447-8 with fig.

2. A detailed stylistic discussion of this brooch will appear in the forthcoming book on Celtic art in the British Isles by E. M. Jope, of the Queen's University, Belfast.

3. *Antiquaries Journal*, xviii, 1938, pp. 146-53, figs. 1-4; xxxi, 1951, pp. 32-44, figs. 1-9.

4. L. C. West, *Roman Britain: the Objects of Trade*, 1931, pp. 31-4, 39-41; ed. F. Tenney Frank, *An Economic Survey of Ancient Rome*, iii, 1937, pp. 42-5.

5. See especially, *Quarterly of the Department of Antiquities of Palestine*, i, 1932, p. 36, pl. 29; ii, 1933, p. 185; iv, 1935, pp. 87-99, figs. 1-5, pls. 55-60; pp. 138-53, figs. 1-4; *Syria*, x, 1929, pp. 238-51, figs. 1-5, pls. 44-6; xv, 1934, pp. 337-50 with 5 figs., pls. 41-8; xvi, 1935, pp. 51-72 with 9 figs., pls. 12-8; *Journal of Hellenic Studies*, l, 1930, pp. 300-12, pl. 12; lii, 1932, pp. 262-3, pls. 11-2; *Jahrbuch des Deutschen Archäologischen Instituts: Archäologischer Anzeiger*, xlvii, 1932, cols. 387-446, figs. 1-47; li, 1936, cols. 252, 255-81, figs. 1-22; *Berytus*, iii, 1936, pp. 51-75, figs. 1-3, pls. 9-16; v, 1938, pp. 27-46, figs. 1-2, pls. 5-13; vi, 1939-40, pp. 27-61, fig. 2, pls. 5-17; *Mélanges de l'Université Saint-Joseph, Beyrouth*, xxi, 1937-8, pp. 203-12, fig. 1, pls. 52-3.

in the case of borders of running scrolls and garlands. Each motif – figure, mask, shell, vase, column, rosette, etc., or each group of such motifs, in a given design, was modelled or carved on a separate plaque or block; while modelled terracotta, or carved wooden, rods served as stamps for 'cable' and 'bead-and-reel' lines in edgings or 'geometric' patterns. These stamps were pressed face-downwards into the matrix of wet sand so as to imprint in it sharp negative impressions arranged according to the preconceived scheme selected by the craftsman from his copy-book. The stamps, having made their impressions, were then removed; and when the molten lead was poured onto the matrix the negatives left in the sand produced positive figures and patterns standing out in relief on the surface of the sheet. If the plaque or block of a stamp were so pressed into the sand that the background of the figure, etc, was not just flush with, but a little below, the surface of the matrix, a slight ridge would appear in the finished product on one or more sides of the design. It seems unlikely that negative terracotta moulds or wooden blocks carved in 'intaglio' were prepared and left in the matrix when the lead was poured onto it. No terracotta moulds corresponding to well-known coffin-motifs have, so far as the present writer is aware, come to light; and in the case of 'palimpsest' designs, that is, of criss-crossing rods or scroll-borders or of figures superimposed on 'bead-and-reel' and 'cable' lines, etc., moulds, whether of clay or wood, left in the sand-bed, were clearly out of the question. In such 'palimpsests' the upper motif was obtained by pressing the stamp firmly into the bed; that stamp was then removed and the stamp for the lower motif laid circumspectly across the first impression, so as not to blur its outlines, and pressed more lightly into the matrix. It is noteworthy that no positive terracotta stamps for lead sarcophagus-ornamentation are mentioned as found in excavations or as surviving in museums – in Britain or elsewhere. This strongly suggests that such stamps were of perishable wood; and wooden stamps are, in fact, used for casting decorated lead in this country in modern times.

A further argument for holding that the decorative motifs on lead sarcophagi were not all mass-produced in terracotta moulds lies in the fact that when the same motifs are repeated on the same side of a sarcophagus they are seldom completely mechanical replicas of one another. Cases in which such replicas seem to occur could be explained by supposing that a stamp, having made its impression in one part of the matrix, was quickly taken out and pressed in again in another part of it. Indeed, stamps could obviously have been re-used in different parts of the same coffin or for a number of different coffins; and while it is likely that each workshop had its special repertory of motifs and designs, both stamps and copy-books could clearly have circulated from factory to factory, or even from country to country. The irregularities and lack of symmetry displayed by the schemes of some of even the most handsome and elaborate eastern products indicate that the stamps were laid in the matrix by eye. A central motif is, in fact, seldom quite mathematically centred; masks, busts, and figures are often

out of the perpendicular; and balancing motifs, such as shells, are frequently out of line. Blemishes of this kind must have been chiefly caused by careless setting, sometimes, perhaps, by unavoidable shifting of the sand-bed.

The shapes of the British lead sarcophagi are of two varieties, one rectangular, with the ends of equal length, the other tapering, with the longer end at the head and the main axis of the lid set lengthwise, as though to be viewed by a spectator standing at the foot. The second form, one commonly found in Britain,[1] we may take to be a local feature, rarely, if ever, met with in Gaul and Germany and almost non-existent in the eastern areas,[2] where decorated lids are normally rectangular, with centripetal designs viewable from all sides. By far the most interesting lead sarcophagus so far found on a Romano–British site is the present piece, that of a child, unearthed in 1954 on the circumference of a barrow, in which it represents a secondary burial. It is of the tapering variety and was found intact, with the bottom, four sides, and lid complete; although the lid, when brought to light, was in a torn and tattered state, but could be restored by a local plumber's skill almost to its pristine condition. The 'trough' of the coffin is adorned with large scallop-shells (*pectines*), three on each long side and one on each short side. All these shells, which probably allude to the soul's last journey across the ocean to the Blessed Isles and would seem to be peculiar to lead sarcophagi manufactured in this country (as contrasted with the smaller, cockle-shell (*cardines*) species found occasionally on eastern pieces), are carefully and neatly worked, but are not strictly true to Nature, since the lateral, triangular 'ears', which should connect the two ends of the hinge with the sides of the fan-shaped valve, do not appear. The surface of the lid has the Y-shaped formation of 'bead-and-reel' lines frequently found on Gaulish and German, as well as on British, pieces, but on none from eastern provinces; and six scallop-shells are set in pairs to right and left of the stem of the Y. It is noteworthy that of the fourteen scallop-shells that decorate the sides and lid of this coffin, no two are precisely identical.

But what gives the Holborough piece its unique importance in the British series is the group of three full-length human figures arranged in two tiers between the arms of the Y. These figures would appear to be on a higher artistic level than those of the other figured coffins from this country; and furthermore, they belong to a world of funerary imagery not represented elsewhere on sarcophagi from Roman Britain – the world of the Bacchic mysteries.

1. E.g. *Royal Commission on Historical Monuments (England): London iii (Roman)*, 1928, p. 157, pl. 58; *Archaeologia*, xvii, 1814, pl. 25, fig. 2; xxxi, 1846, fig. on p. 308; *Antiquaries Journal*, xxxiii, 1953, pp. 72–4, fig. 1, pl. 17; C. Roach Smith, *Collectanea Antiqua*, iii, n.d., pl. 14; vii, 1880, pls. 19, figs. 1–4; 19 a, figs. 1, 6–7.
2. Of all the coffin-lids illustrated in the articles quoted in note 5, p. 179, only one appears to taper slightly (*Syria*, xv, 1934, pl. 43, no. 9). Another tapering eastern lid, on a late piece with Christian symbols, is in the Musée Lycklama, Cannes. In this case the motifs, the Chi-Rho monogram in an *aedicula* thrice repeated, face towards the head of the deceased, that is, towards the wider end (*Gazette des Beaux Arts*, 1931, ii, pp. 333–5, figs. 25–7).

The three figures were cast as a single unit from an oblong stamp some ten inches high. The impressions made, unintentionally, in the matrix by the lateral and lower edges of the stamp-plaque appear on the lid as slight ridges clearly visible at the sides of, and beneath, the group. Small as they are, these figures are rendered in relatively high relief and in a lively, naturalistic style, with softly rounded contours and plastically modelled heads, limbs, and bodies. Above, nearest to the coffin-head, is a half-draped Maenad standing to the front, naked save for a cloak caught over her left arm and wrapped across her legs. With her right hand she grasps the top of a long *thyrsus*, held vertically. Her features have vanished, but in her hair are traces of what may have been a vine-garland.[1] Beneath the Maenad's feet is a slightly convex horizontal border; and below this are the two other members of the trio. A naked man dances towards the right, with his right leg swung forward in advance of his left leg and foot, on which the weight of his body rests. His left arm and hand are not shown; but with his right hand he seems to be leading by the left hand a naked child, who trots along beside him. That the naked man is a Satyr accompanied by a baby Satyr may be reasonably inferred from his gait and from the presence of the certainly Bacchic figure of the Maenad above him.

The funerary role of Bacchus as saviour and conqueror of death, and of the Maenads, Satyrs, Pans, Sileni, etc. in his train as symbols of the rescued souls of Bacchic initiates in the bliss of paradise (*cf.* nos. 12 and 106), is familiar to every student of Roman eschatological art and thought. Marble sarcophagi, carved in Rome, Italy, Greece, and other Mediterranean areas, with the story of Bacchus and Ariadne, with ecstatic Bacchic processions, or with bands of riotous Cupids, are to be seen in most European and American collections of ancient sculpture. Some such reliefs show child Satyrs among the revellers – that, for instance, on the front of a fine piece found in Rome and now in Baltimore.[2] There can be little doubt but that the Holborough figures are extracts from a Bacchic scene of this kind; and we can surmise that the kinsmen of the child whose bones were found in this sarcophagus, were, if not members of a Bacchic sect, at least conversant with the common stock of doctrines and picture-symbols of Bacchic other-world 'theology'.

For the nearest parallels on lead sarcophagi to the Holborough Bacchic motifs we must turn, not to the western provinces, but to Syria and Palestine, where we find such themes as Satyr masks,[3] masks of Bacchus,[4] a Maenad riding on a panther,[5] full-length figures of the youthful Bacchus,[6]

a Silenus playing on a double-pipe,[7] a Pan,[8] a naked Satyr standing in profile with a *pedum*,[9] a frontal Satyr (or Bacchus?) with a *nebris*, a *thyrsus*, and a *cantharus* (wine-cup),[10] and a Satyr striding to the right with a *pedum* and a bunch of grapes.[11] Thus, in his rendering of Bacchic figures, the designer of the Holborough coffin would seem to betray east-Mediterranean affinities, most probably derived from a copy-book. For the piece's specifically British and definitely non-eastern features – the tapering shape, Y-scheme of decoration on the lid, and large scallop-shells – make it most unlikely that it was manufactured in a Syrian or Palestinian workshop and traded into the province.

What was the purpose of the elaborate and often minutely symbolic ornamentation lavished on these lead sarcophagi, both eastern and western? Sculptured marble coffins were set in chamber-tombs or ranged along road-sides, where they could be seen, admired, and pondered over by the eyes and minds of relatives or passers-by. Lead coffins, on the other hand, were normally hidden away from human sight – encased in outer receptacles of wood or stone or, as in the case of the Holborough piece, enveloped directly in the earth. Once the interment had taken place the decoration would have had no effect on any living persons. It could not have pleased them aesthetically, instructed or comforted them spiritually, or gratified any taste for display. This throws not a little light on Roman after-life ideas. The motifs on these coffins must have been mainly intended for the benefit of the dead, whose souls, while located in paradise, were believed, according to the vague and often confused and inconsistent 'theology' of the age, to inhabit, in some sense, or at least to visit occasionally, the place in which their bones reposed.

Archaeologia Cantiana, lxviii, 1954, pp. 19, 34–46, pls. 13–4.

133. FRAGMENT OF A TANK   Plate 143
From Walesby, Lincolnshire. Fourth century A.D. Lead. Height: 20 inches; width: 21 inches. *Lincoln Museum*

Comparable to the coffins in their monumental proportions and decorated by the same process are the eight tank-like lead vessels found on various sites, all, with one exception, in the southern area of the province. None of them has figured ornament; but two, one from near the Roman villa at Icklingham, in Suffolk,[12] the other from Wiggonholt, in

1. The forms of the breasts, abdomen, and hips are definitely feminine and make the interpretation of the figure as an effeminate featuring of Bacchus very unlikely.
2. K. Lehmann-Hartleben and E. C. Olsen, *Dionysiac Sarcophagi at Baltimore*, 1942, p. 15, fig. 9.
3. *Syria*, xv, 1934, pl. 44, no. 11.   4. *Ibid.*, p. 349, no. 22.
5. *Ibid.*, pls. 46, no. 19; 47, no. 19 (second fig. from top).
6. *Berytus*, iii, 1936, pls. 12, fig. 2; 16, figs. 2, 4; vi, 1939–40, pl. 14, fig. 1; *Jahrbuch des Deutschen Archäologischen Instituts: Archäologischer Anzeiger*, xlvii, 1932, cols. 389–90, figs. 1, 3; cols. 393–4, fig. 5; *Mélanges de l'Université Saint-Joseph, Beyrouth*, xxi, 1937–8, pl. 53.

7. *Syria*, xvi, 1935, p. 58, no. 38.
8. *Berytus*, v, 1938, pl. 5, figs. 1–2; *Journal of Hellenic Studies*, l, 1930, pl. 12 (top fig.).
9. *Berytus*, iii, 1936, pls. 11, fig. 4; 14, figs. 3–4; v, 1938, pl. 9, figs. 1–2; vi, 1939–40, pl. 13, fig. 4; *Jahrbuch des Deutschen Archäologischen Instituts: Archäologischer Anzeiger*, xlvii, 1932, cols. 389–90, figs. 1–3; *Quarterly of the Department of Antiquities of Palestine*, iv, 1935, pl. 55 (upper fig.); *Journal of Hellenic Studies*, l, 1930, pl. 12 (top fig.).
10. C. Clermont-Ganneau, *Album d'antiquités orientales*, 1897, pl. 50, fig. 5; *Berytus*, v. 1938, pls. 10, fig. 2; 11, fig. 2.
11. *Ibid.* vi, 1939–40, pl. 13, fig. 3.
12. British Museum: *Antiquaries Journal*, xxii, 1942, pp. 219–20, pl. 30 *Journal of Roman Studies*, xxxiii, 1943, pl. 8; *Guide to the Antiquities of Roman Britain in the British Museum*, 1951, p. 60, (c), no. 3, p. 63, fig. 30; 1958, p. 62, no. 3, p. 63, fig. 30.

Sussex,[1] carry Christian symbols – the Chi-Rho monogram with alpha and omega in the first case and in the second case the monogram alone. It seems not unlikely that these vessels, even those without Christian symbols, were used for Christian baptism,[2] since all eight pieces are closely akin in style and must be of the same late-Roman date. And a 'font' may be suggested as the function of the lead vessel of which this figured fragment came to light in 1959. The surviving portion is from the wall of just such a tank and it carries in a prominent position a large and well designed Chi-Rho monogram. Above this monogram is the right-hand section of a horizontal, frieze-like panel containing two groups of three human figures each, with a column to the right of the right-hand group and another column between that group and the left-hand group. In view of the presence of the Chi-Rho there would seem to be no question but that these groups have a Christian meaning; for the fact that the stamp for the monogram must have been pressed into the sand-bed in which the vessel's wall was cast denotes the manufacture of the piece for a Christian customer in the first instance.

The columns on the panel would, therefore, represent a Christian building, perhaps a church or baptistery; and indeed the groups might be interpreted as two episodes in the rite of baptism. On the left is a naked woman, whose heavy cloak is slipping to the ground from her right shoulder, with two thickly draped and veiled women standing one on either side of her. Is she a female neophyte, supported by her sponsors, disrobing, and about to enter the baptismal water? On the right are three men fully dressed in cloaks and tunics. Could the central man be a male neophyte with his sponsors, waiting his turn to enter the disrobing-chamber? And was there a scene of an actual baptism in the portion of the frieze that is lost? Such suggestions are only guesses; but they do at least make sense in the context. All the figures have worn surfaces; some have been rather badly damaged; and in no case can the facial features be properly discerned. Their strongly frontal poses and somewhat squat proportions harmonise with the late date that the monogram implies. But the naturalistic, wholly unbarbaric style and the plastically modelled forms indicate that the hands which carved the stamp for the frieze were those of a competent and careful worker.

Journal of Roman Studies, l, 1960, pp. 238–9, pl. 26.

134. TABLE-LEG   Plate 144

From Colliton Park, Dorchester (Durnovaria), Dorset. No criteria for dating. Shale. Height: 19 inches. *Dorset County Museum, Dorchester*

The small carved table-legs of shale from Kimmeridge Bay,

Isle of Purbeck, in Dorset, the most unprepossessing of all the British raw materials used for making decorated objects in the Roman period, provide a signal instance of the British craftsman's adaptation of Graeco–Roman models to a native style and medium.[3] These models were the animal-shaped legs, first, of the small, light, round, three-legged wooden tables a few actual specimens of which have been preserved at various sites,[4] while countless representations of them occur in works of art from all parts of the ancient world, particularly in Hellenistic and Roman funerary banquet-scenes, where they stand beside the couches of the dead;[5] and, secondly, of the larger and much more substantial Roman stone or marble tables, whether round and three-legged or rectangular and upheld by a pair of legs in the form of oblong, carved supports, one at either end.[6] Occasionally reliefs depict the manufacture of wooden legs for tables of the three-legged variety by carpenters using saws and hammers.[7] The legs of the wooden, stone, or marble round tables show, passing from top to bottom, a wedge-shaped tenon to fit into a mortise on the table's under side; the head and neck of an animal (very rarely of a bird) backed against the lower end of the tenon; the creature's breast swelling outwards in a strong, bold curve, leaving a hollow behind it and sometimes sheathed in a calyx of acanthus-leaves; and the sinewy leg of the animal normally terminating in a claw-foot, sometimes in a hoof. On this type of table the animal head is usually that of a panther. But in the case of the oblong supports of rectangular tables from Italian sites, each end of such a support terminates in an outward-facing winged Griffin, prick-eared and sometimes horned, with a long tongue lolling out to meet the outward swell of the breast, sinewy legs, and claw-feet, while a solid slab of carved marble links the backs of the two creatures. Such are the elements of the prototypes followed and adapted, partly, no doubt, from pattern-books, by the British shale-carvers.

Most of the decorated shale objects have come to light, as we should expect, in Dorset, in the neighbourhood of the sources of supply and of the centre of the industry. But the latter's products also travelled far afield, to Somerset (Upper Langridge Farm), to Wiltshire (Cranborne Chase), to Hampshire (Silchester), to London, to Hertfordshire (Verulamium), and even to Leicestershire (Rothley Roman villa). Of the legs from the small three-legged tables by far

---

1. Parham Park, Pulborough, Sussex: *Antiquaries Journal*, xxiii, 1943, pp. 155–7, pl. 28; *Journal of Roman Studies*, xxxiv, 1944, pl. 6.
2. For scenes of early (fourth- or fifth-century) Christian baptism showing the neophyte standing in a small tank or basin, while water flows upon his or her head, see G. Brusin, *Il Reale Museo Archeologico di Aquileia* (*Itinerari dei Museei e Monumenti d'Italia No. 48*), 1936, pp. 12, 45, fig. 26; F. Cabrol, *Dictionnaire d'Archéologie Chrétienne et de Liturgie*, i, ii, 1924, col. 2672, fig. 871.

3. For a full discussion of British shale furniture in general and of most of the individual pieces so far known, see J. Liversidge, *Furniture in Roman Britain*, 1955, pp. 37–53, figs. c–e, 44–65, 69; *Antiquity*, xxiv, 1950, pp. 25–9, pls. 1–4; *Antiquaries Journal*, xxxi, 1951, pp. 193–4, pl. 32, a; *ibid.* xl, 1960, pp. 72–3, fig. 1, pl. 22; *Proceedings of the Somersetshire Archaeological and Natural History Society*, xcvi, 1951, p. 233, pl. 15, fig. 3; *Journal of Roman Studies*, xlix, 1959, p. 130.
4. E.g. Liversidge, *op. cit.*, p. 40 (Casa dell' Atrio Corintio, Herculaneum: unpublished); figs. 59–60 (Panticapaeum: British Museum); figs. 62–3 (Luxor: Musée de Cinquantenaire, Brussels: *cf. Antiquity*, xxiv, 1950, pl. 4).
5. E.g. Liversidge, *op. cit.*, figs. 1, 3–4, 6–13.
6. E.g. *ibid.*, figs. 62–3 c–e; *Antiquity*, xxiv, 1950, pl. 3.
7. E.g. Liversidge, *op. cit.*, fig. 64; *Antiquity*, xxiv, 1950, pl. 2, b.

the best preserved is the present piece. It is complete from the top of the tenon to the bottom of the claw-foot; and here we have the beast's head with pointed ears pricked forward, a hole pierced through behind the lower jaw, the open mouth, the lolling tongue that meets the swelling breast, on which a stylised, fluted feature would seem to represent the acanthus-calyx of the Mediterranean table-legs,[1] and the claw-foot termination. There can be little doubt but that the creature's head corresponds to the heads of Griffins on some of the oblong supports of rectangular tables found in Italy[2] and known in Britain through copy-books, although the wings are omitted. But in the place of the sinewy leg of the Griffin itself the British carver has inserted two very long, slender legs, terminating in a kind of double hoof and running up one on either side of the piece between the claw-foot and the stylised sheath of leaves. These legs must belong to a secondary beast, a deer or an antelope, conceived of, possibly as attacking, much more probably as already partially devoured by, the Griffin, in whose clutches it is struggling. But for this, too, the craftsman had a Graeco-Roman model. For a fragmentary wooden table-leg found at Panticapaeum, in the Crimea, from which the head and claw-foot of the main animal are missing, shows, on the swelling breast, another creature, now unfortunately headless, with extended slender legs and hooves, emerging from an acanthus-calyx.[3] The result of these conflations and variations on the British piece is remarkably effective and very well adapted to the harsh and flaky local medium.

I. A. Richmond, *Roman Britain in Pictures*, 1957, fig. on p. 35 (where it is wrongly described as a chair-leg); *Antiquity*, xxiv, 1950, pl. I, figs. 1–2; J. Liversidge, *Furniture in Roman Britain*, 1955, figs. 44–5.

135. BEAR   Plate 156
From Malton (Derventio), Yorkshire. Third or fourth century A.D. Jet. Length: ⅞ inch. *Malton Museum*

Among the raw materials that were certainly obtained in this country in Roman times and used for carving small figured objects, is Yorkshire jet, the deposits of which lie in the Whitby district. The carvings in this native medium, found on British sites, are of several different types – small independent figures of animals and human beings, knife-handles, small panels with relief-work, 'medallions' also with relief-work, some of which were certainly used as pendants, and the heads of hair-pins. But they nearly all share in common a markedly stylised treatment and a certain crudity of execution which are strongly suggestive of native workmanship. Nearly every type of figured jet object found in Britain can be paralleled in the Roman Rhineland; and the German pieces, when assembled and published,[4] form a very rich and varied collection, much richer and more varied, apparently, than would be any such collection made from

finds in Roman Britain. But since the jet from which the continental objects are carved is identical with that in Yorkshire,[5] while the similarity in style and treatment between those pieces and the British specimens is extremely striking, there would seem to be no reason why the Rhineland and other continental carvings, which are clearly from the same artistic *milieu* as their British counterparts, should not have been worked in Britain and exported ready-made across the Channel. It is most improbable that all Yorkshire jet travelled raw to Germany, some of it returning to these shores in made-up form from German workshops, and that none of the carved objects brought to light in this country were locally produced. For while no half-finished objects or 'wasters' of jet have yet, to the present writer's knowledge, been discovered in the Rhineland,[6] finds of precisely that kind have been made in Yorkshire, for example, in the course of the 1873, etc. railway excavations in York[7] and in the late-Roman signal-station at Goldesborough,[8] proving conclusively the existence of a jet-carving craft in Britain during the Roman period. It may be that the manufacture of carved jet objects for wealthy continental customers represented an important item in the export industry of this province under the later Empire; and that would account for the greater number and, in some cases, more elaborate character of the German, as compared with the British, finds.[9]

Particularly attractive as examples of jet figures in the round are two miniature bears, this one and another from Bootham Bar, York.[10] The Malton bear is effectively characterised, with large, drooping head and humped back. Its forelegs are in one piece and separated by a drill-hole that also passed between the now missing hindlegs, which seem to have been carved in independent pieces. The tiny creature shows no trace of a platform beneath the paws. It was found in a child's grave and was probably the infant's plaything, although it could also have been worn round the neck as a

1. E.g. Liversidge, *op. cit.*, fig. c; *Antiquity*, xxiv, 1950, pl. 3.
2. E.g. Liversidge, *op. cit.*, fig. d.
3. British Museum: Liversidge, *op. cit.*, figs. 59–60.
4. E.g. *Bonner Jahrbücher*, cxlii, 1937, pp. 77–144, figs. 1–12, pls. 19–41.

5. *Ibid.* pp. 83–4.
6. *Ibid.* p. 85: the author of this article, W. Hagen, writes of the 'bisherige völlige Fehlen von Halbfertigware und Abfallstücken in unserem Gebiete'.
7. *A Handbook of the Antiquities in the Grounds and Museum of the Yorkshire Philosophical Society*, ed. 8, 1891, p. 127, item q: 'several blocks of jet in the rough and some pieces partially prepared for pins'.
8. *Archaeological Journal*, lxxxix, 1932, p. 213, item (4): 'several cores or "chucks" from the manufacture of jet rings and bracelets'.
9. The present writer has been informed by Mr. P. J. Adams of the Geological Survey, South Kensington, and by Professor L. R. Moore of the Department of Geology, Sheffield University, that deposits of jet very similar to that from Yorkshire also occur in Württemberg; and it is, of course, theoretically possible that that area may have been the source of the Rhineland carvings. On the other hand, there are, so far as the present writer is aware, no reports of any concentration of jet carved objects, or vestiges of jet-working, in Württemberg during the Roman period. Meanwhile, the trading- and cultural relations between Britain and the Rhineland were particularly close. For the fame of British jet, see Solinus, 22, 11: 'gagates hic [*sc.* in Brittania] plurimus optimusque est lapis'.
10. Sheffield City Museum: *Antiquaries Journal*, xxviii, 1948, pp. 173–5, pls. 25 b; 26, e; *Royal Commission on Historical Monuments (England): York* i (Roman), 1962, p. 142, pl. 70.

bead or amulet, threaded on a string or wire run through the drill-holes between the legs. The York bear, of about the same size as that from Malton, rests on a platform, could clearly have stood by itself, and therefore may have functioned as a toy; but since it has a hole for suspension passing longitudinally through it, between the forelegs and hind-legs,[1] this piece, too, might have been worn as a necklace and have served a twofold role. It is of much the same type of beast as its Malton counterpart, except for the fact that its head does not droop but continues the horizontal line of the back. Two parallels to these Yorkshire bears can be cited from the Rhineland, both equipped with platforms, that from Cologne[2] being nearer to the Malton specimen, while the other, from Trier,[3] is closer to the York example. Yet a third British jet bear, standing on a platform and doubtlessly from the same workshop as its Yorkshire *confrères*, came to light at Colchester.[4]

Antiquaries Journal, xxviii, 1948, pp. 173-5, pls. 25, a; 26, c.

136. RELIEF OF ATYS　　　　　　　　　Plate 152
From Castle Hill, Whitton, near Ipswich, Suffolk. Third or fourth century A.D. Jet. Height: 2⅜ inches. *Ipswich Museum*

The only British instance known to the present writer of a jet plaque with carving in relief is the vertical, straight-sided piece from the Roman villa on this Suffolk site. It tapers towards the top and carries a figure of Atys seen in profile to the right and terminating at about the waist in a roughly straight line. The short, completely straight upper edge seems to be original, but the lower edge is broken and on the missing portion was probably the god's lower half. Atys wears a Phrygian cap on his long, curly hair and a cloak that leaves exposed the right arm, which is bent up at the elbow, while the right hand grasps a pomegranate. The workmanship is undoubtedly native, as the wedge-shaped nose, large, lentoid eyes, shown in full in the profile face, and the heavy jowl betray. A somewhat similar plaque, surviving as a fragment, on which appear portions of a standing male figure, came to light at Trier.[5]

Proceedings of the Suffolk Institute of Archaeology and Natural History, xxi, 1933, p. 254, pl. opp. p. 248, fig. 55.

137. MEDALLION WITH MEDUSA HEAD　　Plate 149
From Strood, near Rochester, Kent. Fourth century A.D. Jet. Maximum diameter: 1¾ inches. *Ashmolean Museum, Oxford*

The class of figured jet objects from Roman Britain of which the greatest number of examples has so far come down to us is that of the round or oval medallion-like pendants with relief-work. Seven specimens are known, some with hollow

lugs at the top of the design for suspension round the neck, while those not so equipped are likely to have once been inserted in metal frames that were provided with these attachments. Many more examples with several of the same motifs, have been found in the Rhineland.[6] Three British pendants bear Medusa heads, a motif, found not infrequently on continental specimens, that was obviously intended to ward off evil from the wearer of the ornament. One piece from York[7] and one from London[8] have frontal Medusas of the normal type. But this third piece, found in a cemetery, is of a most unusual and wholly native character. It shows a quiet, kindly face in profile to the right, with the hair arranged in chunky masses, each of which is engraved with incised lines. But the wings, which are detached from the head, are in full-face and the four snakes, instead of being twisted in the hair and tied in a knot below the chin, are deployed symmetrically on either side of the head to fill the field of the pendant. Here the native craftsman was clearly somewhat ill at ease with his Graeco-Roman model.

C. Roach Smith, *Collectanea Antiqua*, i, 1848, pl. opp. p. 17, fig. 5; *Archaeologia*, lxvi, 1914-5, p. 572, fig. 5; E. T. Leeds, *Celtic Ornament in the British Isles down to A.D. 700*, 1933, p. 97, fig. 29, a; *Archaeologia Cantiana*, lxix, 1955, pp. 217-9, pl. 1.

138. TWO MEDALLIONS WITH FAMILY GROUPS
Plates 150-1
From York. Fourth century A.D. Jet. Maximum diameters: 2¼ inches. *Yorkshire Museum, York (Eburacum)*

Another popular motif on Rhineland pendants is that of the portrait-bust; and of this three specimens are known from Britain, all from York. Of the two pieces shown in the Exhibition, one carries two frontal busts, a woman on the left and a man on the right, wearing the dress and hair-style of the fourth century; while the second pendant bears three frontal busts, a family group also late in character, consisting of a woman on the left, a man on the right, and a child in front of them. A third medallion has a single draped female bust, also facing to the front and again of fourth-century style, with the hair bunched on either side of the face and brought forward in a roll above the brow.[9] It seems unlikely that these busts were true portraits, taken from the life; and, indeed, in the case of the pieces exported to the Continent from Britain such a possibility is obviously ruled out. Much more probably they were stock 'portraits', chosen for their general suitability to given purchasers or recipients – a man and woman for a married pair, a man, woman, and child for members of a family, a young female for a girl, and so forth. G. Home, *Roman York*, 1924, pl. opp. p. 176; I. A. Richmond, *Roman Britain in Pictures*, 1947, fig. on p. 5; *Royal*

---

1. The present writer owes this information to Mr. John Bartlett, formerly of the Sheffield City Museum.
2. *Ibid.* pp. 174-5, pl. 25, d; *Bonner Jahrbücher*, cxlii, 1937, pl. 29, fig. 1 (on right).
3. *Antiquaries Journal*, xxviii, 1948, pp. 174-5, pl. 25, c; *Bonner Jahrbücher*, cxlii, 1937, pl. 29, fig. 1 (on left).
4. Colchester and Essex Museum, Colchester: unpublished.
5. *Bonner Jahrbücher* cxlii, 1937, pl. 41, fig. 2, no. K 7.

6. *Bonner Jahrbücher*, cxlii, 1937, pls. 30-1.
7. Yorkshire Museum, York: G. Home, *Roman York*, 1924, pl. opp. p. 176; *Royal Commission on Historical Monuments (England): York* i (*Roman*), 1962, p. 142, pl. 68.
8. Ashmolean Museum, Oxford (no. 1948.72): unpublished.
9. Yorkshire Museum, York: G. Home, *Roman York*, pl. opp. p. 176.

Commission on Historical Monuments (England): York i *(Roman)*, 1962, p. 142 (where it is suggested that the three-busts piece may be of shale, not jet), pl. 68.

139. CAMEO WITH BEAR DEVOURING GOAT Plate 158
From South Shields (Arbeia), County Durham. Second or third century A.D. Indian sardonyx. Length: 1⅞ inches. *Museum of Antiquities of the University of Durham and of the Society of Antiquaries of Newcastle upon Tyne (King's College, Newcastle upon Tyne)*

This famous bear cameo is very likely to be of non-British workmanship. The stone is oval and the animal itself is worked in the white upper layer against the background of the rich translucent brown of the lower layer. Its humped back and shaggy coat are sensitively rendered and it stands towards the right, with the head slightly raised and the ears

flattened back, holding between the cruel claws of its forepaws its prostrate prey, the head of which projects beyond them. The prey would appear to be a goat. Its ears, eyes, nostrils, mouth, and beard can be readily discerned; and in front of the ears are two bumps, the tops of which have broken surfaces, suggesting that they represent the stumps of horns. Since it is improbable that an Indian sardonyx would have been imported unworked into Britain, the South Shields bear can hardly have been modelled on a beast seen locally. But the drawing and the modelling are very realistic and the artist might have worked from a British bear exported to some Mediterranean arena. Bears were a recognised product of this country in antiquity.

Archaeological Journal, XXXV, 1878, pp. 103–7 with pl.; *Archaeologia Aeliana*, ser. 2, X, 1885, pp. 263–4 with fig.; I. A. Richmond, *Roman Britain*, 1955, p. 162, pl. 6; *Archaeologia Aeliana*, ser. 4, XXXIX, 1961, p. 34, pl. 8, fig. 1.

FIGURED GLASS

140. BOWL WITH NILOTIC MOTIVES   Plate 160
From the Roman and Saxon Cemetery, Girton College, Cambridge. First or second century A.D. Light-green glass. Diameter: 7⅜ inches. *Museum of Archaeology and of Ethnology, Cambridge (on loan from Girton College)*

Of the earliest known pieces of cut and engraved glass from British sites the most complete is this shallow bowl, probably made in Egypt. The design is incised in outline within a circle on the exterior of the base and shows a very naturalistically rendered duck, seen three-quarters from behind, with outspread wings, in a setting of Nilotic plants.

E. J. Hollingworth and M. M. O'Reilly, *The Anglo-Saxon Cemetery at Girton College, Cambridge*, 1925, pp. 32–3, pl. 12.

141. BOWL WITH BACCHIC SCENE   Plate 159
From Colliton Park, Dorchester (Durnovaria), Dorset. Fourth century A.D. Glass with bluish tinge. Diameter: 7½ inches. *Dorset County Museum, Dorchester*

This hemispherical bowl of Rhineland origin bears on its exterior a Bacchic scene that can be looked at equally well from either side of the glass and is worked in a combination of cutting and engraving, with *pointillé* grooved and shaded details. In the central roundel on the base is the bust of a Satyr with a *pedum*, while circling about it, on the vessel's sides, is a frieze of five dancing figures, two Maenads and three Satyrs. The Maenads whirl along with their heads tossed back in ecstasy; they wear long, sleeveless, crinkly Greek tunics, that leave one breast and one leg exposed; and they hold in one hand a *thyrsus*, while with the other hand they grasp a bunch of reeds from which depends a tambourine (?). The Satyrs are naked and hold in one hand a *pedum*, in the other a bunch of reeds, similar to that which the Maenads

grip, but ending below in a heart-shaped object that might be some form of musical instrument. The general effect is one of vivid movement, conveyed by means of quick, sure lines by the hand of a thoroughly competent draftsman.

Proceedings of the Dorset Natural History and Archaeological Society, LX, 1939, pp. 55–6, pl. 3; *Journal of Roman Studies*, XXIX, 1939, p. 219, pl. 32.

142. BOWL WITH HUNTING-SCENE   Plate 161
From Wint Hill, Banwell, Somerset. Fourth century A.D. Greenish glass. Diameter: 7½ inches. *Ashmolean Museum, Oxford*

This segmental bowl is undoubtedly the finest and most spectacular of the fourth-century glasses found in Britain with mainly engraved subjects, products of the famous glasshouses of Cologne. The scene, a lively hare-hunt, is carried out wholly in free-hand engraving, without any signs of facet-cutting, and is worked on the exterior, but meant to be viewed from the inside of the bowl, through the glass, since from the outside the inscription – *vivas cum tuis pie S* (= ΠΙΕ ΖΗΧΗC)[1] – is read in retrograde. In the upper part of the picture a mounted horseman gallops to the right between two trees. He wears a short, long-sleeved tunic, adorned with a series of small circles, and a cloak that flies out behind him in the breeze and in his right hand he brandishes a whip. Below, in a setting of smaller trees and shrubs, two smooth-coated hounds, wearing collars just below their shaggy ruffs, are hot in pursuit of a long-eared hare which they are driving to the right towards a net. The feet of all the animals are casting shadows rendered by short lines of cross-

1. A mixture of Latin and Greek: 'Long life to you and yours: drink and good health to you'.

shading; and there is emphasising cross-shading just inside the outlines of all the figures. Short, sharp jabs give expression to the texture of the pelts of the horse, hare, and dogs. The draftsmanship throughout is sensitive and vigorous – superior to that of the Wint Hill bowl's nearest parallel, a bowl with a hare-hunt in the Rheinisches Landesmuseum, Bonn, which shows a mounted hunter, above, and, below, two collared hounds rounding up a hare into a net towards the right.[1] Two adjoining fragments of a bowl of the Wint Hill type, found at Chesters, depict the head and nude right shoulder of a rider and the greater part of the horse's head and neck, turned towards the left and possibly from a hunting-scene, although normally such scenes are orientated rightwards.[2]

Country Life, 30 May, 1957, p. 1090 with fig.; *Journal of Roman Studies*, xlvii, 1957, p. 232, no. 24, pl. 14; *Journal of Glass Studies*, ii, 1960, pp. 45–81, figs. 1–39. The last is a definitive and richly illustrated study and description of the bowl by D. B. Harden, together with a catalogue of the glasses belonging to its group, a commentary on its technique and style, and a discussion of its affinities, date, and place of manufacture.

1. *Journal of Glass Studies*, ii, 1960, pp. 53–4, no. 2, figs. 10, 15, 30. Plate 254.

2. Chesters Museum: *ibid.*, p. 64, no. 22, fig. 28; *Archaeologia Aeliana*, ser. 4, xxxvii, 1959, pp. 47–8, fig. 7, no. 1. Two tiny morsels of another such bowl, with a design that cannot now be identified, were found in a Roman house at Great Staughton, in Huntingdonshire (*Journal of Glass Studies*, ii, 1960, p. 64, no. 23, fig. 29).

FIGURED POTTERY

143. FIGURINES FROM CHILD'S GRAVE Plate 172
From Colchester (Camulodunum), Essex. Second half of the first century A.D. Height of tallest standing figurine: 6⅜ inches; length of longest reclining figurine: 5 inches. *Colchester and Essex Museum, Colchester.*

Of the terracotta figurines that have come to light in this country in Roman contexts the great majority were imports from abroad. Such was certainly the case with the earliest and probably the best-known series of objects of this kind, the group from a child's grave in one of the Colchester cemeteries. These date from soon after the foundation of the *colonia* in 49–50, before factories for the manufacture of pottery at this level could have been established locally; and two of the items from this collection, lead-glaze unguent-pots in the form of an ibex and a hare respectively (no. 153), are definitely first-century imported pieces. If, then, the figurines in this group that depict oldish men standing or reclining do represent, as has been suggested,[1] 'a caricaturist's version of the hard-faced, flap-eared Italian types', to which the Centurion Facilis, portrayed on the pre-*colonia* Colchester tombstone (no. 81), obviously belonged, and if they indicate that the veteran colonists could 'with a pawky humour laugh at themselves'[2] on some occasions, they must have been commissioned from abroad with these ideas in mind, not carried out to order on the spot.

Of the twenty figurines (exclusive of the hare and ibex unguent-pots) in the whole grave-group the nine shown in the Exhibition were undoubtedly intended to compose a light-hearted banqueting-scene with diners and reciters. Four, three male and one female, are recumbent. The men, who are all draped, have very realistically portrayed, clean-shaven, heavily fleshy faces. One scratches the back of his head, another rests his right hand against his left cheek, the third clutches his wine-cup with both hands firmly. The woman is also fully draped and has prominent eyes and scraped-back hair. Of the five standing male figures one, who wears a short, sleeved tunic and rests his hands against his breast, might be a slave. The other four, who wear togas, bend forward each over the tray, supporting what appears to be a partly unrolled scroll, that he carries in both hands. These would be reciters.

T. May, *Catalogue of the Roman Pottery in the Colchester and Essex Museum*, 1930, pp. 251–2, pl. 75, fig. 3b.

144. FIGURINE OF GENIUS CUCULLATUS Plate 171
From Reculver (Regulbium), Kent. Second or third century A.D. Original Height: *c.* 6 inches. *Royal Museum, Canterbury*

This fragment of a votive terracotta figurine was found, in association with late-second-to-early-third-century pottery, some eight-hundred feet west of the 'Saxon Shore' Roman fort. That it was an import from the Rhine-Moselle district is certain, in view of the fact that its closest parallels have come to light in that area. It is the central portion of a somewhat clumsily modelled, dwarfish figure of a Genius Cucullatus (*cf.* nos. 76–7, 159), wearing a short, long-sleeved tunic, from below which two small, spindly legs emerge. In its dumpy and impossible proportions this terracotta vividly recalls a stone statuette of a Genius Cucullatus from Birdoswald.[3] The right hand, which rests against the body, grips a scroll comparable to that so often seen in the hands of the Genius' more sophisticated Graeco-Roman counterpart, Telesphoros, where it betokens the secrets of healing lore, as it does here. The fingers of the left hand of the Reculver figure are spread across the folds of the tunic, while the *cucullus*, which forms a V-shaped fold upon the chest, is not drawn over the head, but is thrown back upon the shoulders.

Archaeologia Cantiana, lxvi, 1953, pp. 86–91 with fig., pl. 1; *Collection Latomus*, xxviii, 1957, pp. 467–8, no. 14, pl. 63, fig. 4.

1. *Archaeological Journal*, ciii, 1947, p. 60.
2. *Loc. cit.*

3. Carlisle Museum, Tullie House: J. C. Bruce, *Lapidarium Septentrionale*, 1875, p. 209, no. 419 with drawing; *Collection Latomus*, xxviii, 1957, p. 461, no. 4, pl. 63, fig. 3.

145. FIGURINE OF SEATED MOTHER-GODDESS WITH DOG   Plate 173

From Canterbury (Durovernum), Kent. Second or third century A.D. Height (without head): 5½ inches. *Royal Museum, Canterbury*

This pipe-clay figurine, which is as yet unique in Roman Britain, shows a seated Mother-Goddess ensconced, in strict frontality, in a high-backed chair and holding on her lap with both hands a small dog with alert, pricked ears (*cf.* no. 72). This personage can, without difficulty, be identified as the Fertility- and Mother-Goddess Nehalennia, whose cult was popular in Roman Gaul and Germany, particularly along the lower Rhine.[1] The dog a well-known symbol of the underworld and of healing, is one of Nehalennia's constant attributes on the Continent. The style of the Canterbury piece displays a pleasing combination of formalism, in Nehalennia's pose, and naturalism, in the rendering of her dog.

Archaeologia Cantiana, lxv, 1952, pp. 131–3, pl. 1; lxx, 1956, pp. 192–200.

146. SEATED FIGURE OF MOTHER-GODDESS WITH TWO INFANTS   Plate 175

From London. Second or third century A.D. Height (without head): 4½ inches. *London Museum, Kensington Palace*

Imported into Roman Britain from the Allier district of France were the pipe-clay figurines that represent the Dea Nutrix, a Mother-Goddess seated in a basket-chair and giving suck, generally to two babies, as in this example, occasionally to a single infant. In this case the head is lost, but where it has been preserved the hair is gathered on the crown of the head into a species of coronal or top-knot and there is a certain charm in the serious, intent expression of the youthful features. Here again, as in no. 145, the pose is hieratic, but strikes a pleasing note of maternal homeliness and of simplicity. As has been already noted,[2] the resemblance between the Gaulish figurines and the sixth-century B.C. stone statuette of a *kourotrophos* – a seated Mother-Goddess giving suck to a pair of infants – from Megara Hyblaea in Sicily[3] is extremely close; and the ultimate dependence of the Roman provincial clay figurines on a long-established classical prototype needs no further proof.

The finds in Roman Britain of the Dea Nutrix are almost entirely confined to the south-east corner of the country, with special concentrations in London and at Canterbury, apart from outlying single finds made at Chester, Wroxeter, Exeter, and in Essex respectively.

London in Roman Times (*London Museum Catalogues, No. 3*), 1930, p. 48, pl. 21, no. 5; *Archaeologia Cantiana*, lxxi, 1957, pp. 38–46, pls. 1–4.

147. FIGURINE OF VENUS WITH CUPID   Plate 174

From Colchester (Camulodunum), Essex. Second or third century A.D. Height (without head, but including base): 5⅜ inches. *Colchester and Essex Museum, Colchester.*

By far the most popular and widespread class of votive pottery figurines in the province, the offerings of the less well-to-do in the humbler types of public temples or in private shrines, consisted of the pipe-clay 'Venuses', whose origin and distribution have already been fully studied.[4] These 'Venuses' are of two main types, one half-draped, where the goddess holds in one hand the upper edge of her garment, which is gathered in a roll round her hips, and touches a tress of her hair with her right hand – a version of the goddess that was produced in the Cologne region factories from the end of the first century onwards and is represented in Britain by five joining fragments found on the temple site at Springhead (Vagniacae), in Kent.[5] The second, and, so far as Britain is concerned, by far the commoner, type shows the goddess naked, clutching with her left hand a bunch of drapery that hangs down beside her left leg and touching a tress of her hair with her right hand.[6] The 'Venus' of this second type stands on a bell-shaped pedestal and her hair is often tied in a kind of 'bow' on the crown of the head; and figurines of this type reached Britain from the centre of their manufacture in the Allier district of France. Both in their types and in their style these 'Venuses', for all their special connections with the poorer strata of the provincial populations, are purely classical, derived from the traditional Graeco–Roman renderings of Venus and Aphrodite. But it was the after-life, fertility, and health-bringing aspects of the Roman goddess that formed the most important link between her and the Celtic deity who assumed her art-forms. This is clear from the fact that such figurines have frequently been found, both in Britain and abroad, in association with sacred springs and other healing waters and that other pieces have come to light in graves.

As a distribution-map of finds of pipe-clay 'Venuses' reveals,[7] the cult of the goddess spread northwards into the area of Hadrian's Wall and westwards as far as the borders of Wales. But the main concentration lay south and east of the line of the Foss Way, particularly in Londinium, with other important centres at Silchester, Richborough, Verulamium, and Colchester; while of the northern sites York has so far proved to be the most prolific. The 'Venus' figurines are, in fact, essentially a feature of art and religion in the civil zone of Britain and we may suspect that in the military regions

1. A. Hondius-Crone, *The Temple of Nehalennia at Domburg*, 1955.
2. *Archaeologia Cantiana*, lxxi, 1957, p. 41.
3. L. von Matt, *Ancient Sicily*, 1960, pl. 52.

4. *Archaeologia Cantiana*, lxxii, 1958, pp. 60–76 with fig., pls. 1–2; pp. 107–8.
5. *Ibid.* pl. 1, a. Pl. 1, b depicts a complete example from Horperath, Kreis Mayen, in Germany.
6. *Ibid.* pl. 2, a; *London in Roman Times* (*London Museum Catalogues, No. 3*), 1930, pl. 21, figs. 1–4; R. E. M. and T. V. Wheeler, *Verulamium: a Belgic and Two Roman Cities*, 1936, pl. 61, figs. 1, 3–5; *Guide to the Antiquities of Roman Britain in the British Museum*, 1951, p. 62, no. 5, p. 63, fig. 30; 1958, p. 62, no. 5, p. 63, fig. 30. For a full list of specimens, with references, see *Archaeologia Cantiana*, lxxii, 1958, pp. 71–6.
7. *Ibid.* fig. on p. 69. *Cf.* also a piece from Godmanchester, Huntingdonshire: *Archaeological News Letter*, vii, 1, 1961, pp. 11–2 with fig.

their importation was largely due to the civilian elements inhabiting the extra-mural settlements, the *canabae* and *vici* of the fortresses and forts.

A 'Venus'-type of a no less classical, but somewhat different, kind is this piece from Colchester. Here the goddess, unfortunately headless, is again completely nude, rests her right hand against her breast, and touches with her left hand the head of Cupid, who stands beside her left leg and holds a mirror up towards his mother. The figurine provides still further evidence of a taste for Graeco–Roman art-forms in the less wealthy Romano–British *milieux*.

Unpublished.

148. SHERD WITH MAENAD AND VINE   Plate 169
From Leicester (Ratae Coritanorum). First half of the first century A.D. Height: 3⅛ inches; width: 2⅜ inches. *Leicester Museum*

This is a sherd of the red-gloss ware with moulded decoration known as Arretine, from the centre of its manufacture at Arretium (Arezzo), in Tuscany. Its production ran from *c.* 30 B.C. to *c.* A.D. 30, when it was ousted from the markets of the Empire by the so-called 'samian', the red-gloss output of the south-Gaulish pottery-industry. It is, then, extremely probable that some of the Arretine pieces found in Britain reached this country before A.D. 43 and rank as pre-conquest imports. Arretine was the best and most expensive non-metallic table-ware of Augustan and Tiberian times. It must have been costly to import into the island and only wealthy Britons, presumably Belgae, could have afforded it. Here we may have an interesting instance of the penetration of pre-conquest Mediterranean pottery wares by way of trade into a relatively northern area of Celtic Britain. The Jewry Wall site at Leicester yielded evidence of a native settlement (*c.* A.D. 35–50), which probably represents a northward expansion of the Belgae in the years immediately preceding the Roman conquest.[1] On the other hand, this pot might have reached the site of Leicester with the Roman army's northward advance.

The pot from which the sherd came was by the Arretine potter Cornelius.[2] The piece shows a Maenad wearing a tunic, a *nebris*, and boots. She holds a vine-tendril and stands against a background that is strewn all over with large bunches of grapes and vine-leaves.[3]

Antiquaries Journal, xiii, 1933, pp. 58–9 with drawing (where the sherd is wrongly attributed to the potter M. Perennius).

149. SHERD WITH GLADIATOR   Plate 183
From York (Eburacum). *c.* A.D. 160–200. Height: 3 inches; width, at base: 2½ inches. *Museum of Archaeology and of Ethnology, Cambridge*

This sherd is from a 'form 45' bowl and bears a design in what might be termed 'negative relief'. The ornament, instead of standing out from the surface of the pot, was cut into its walls, before the clay had hardened, by means of faceted and incised lines – in fact, an imitation in clay of cut-glass decoration. Examples of such continental Gaulish red-gloss and black-gloss are relatively rare in Britain and they show, for the most part, stylised leaves and flowers.[4] But occasionally pieces of a more ambitious character reached these shores. Here we have the figure of a fighting gladiator drawn with not a little verve and accuracy. Preserved are the trunk and limbs (the head is unfortunately gone) of a *retiarius* (net-man) lunging towards the right, but all shown frontally. The champion, who wears fringed drawers, holds a trident horizontally across his abdomen, while the *gladius* (short sword) of his now lost opponent to the right of him is pointed at his breast. The outlines are carried out in facets, and the details and the shading of the trunk and legs are delicately incised.

Antiquaries Journal, xxxiv, 1954, pp. 233–4, fig. 1, pl. 27, b.

150. SHERDS REPRESENTING PAN MASK AND MEDUSA MASK   Plates 180–1
From Winchester (Venta Belgarum), Hampshire. Late-second or early-third century A.D. Pan diameter: 1¾ inches; Medusa diameter: 1⅛ inches. *Property of W. J. Turner, Esq.*

Among the most impressive types of *appliqué* decoration on black-gloss pottery from central Gaul are the frontal masks of Pan and Medusa, of which these two pieces are examples. Of the other Pan masks from British sites two were found at Silchester,[5] two at Alchester,[6] and one at York, where it is accompanied by a large pine-cone.[7] The Medusa mask has as yet no parallels of British provenance. The *appliqué* motifs on vessels of this type were cast in separate moulds and luted onto the pot's exterior (*cf.* Introduction, p. 11).

Unpublished.

151. SHERD REPRESENTING SILENUS MASK   Plate 187
From Verulamium, Hertfordshire. Late-second or early-third century A.D. Diameter: 1⅜ inches. *Property of the Verulamium Excavation Committee*

This black-gloss frontal mask of a Silenus is of the same type as no. 150.

Unpublished.

152. POT WITH TWO VINE-LEAVES, MAENAD MASK, AND SILENUS MASK   Plate 182

1. K. M. Kenyon, *Excavations at the Jewry Wall Site, Leicester*, 1948, pp. 4, 9–10.
2. *Ibid.*, p. 59.
3. For a very similar Arretine motif, see G. H. Chase, *The Loeb Collection of Arretine Pottery*, 1908, pl. 21, no. 131.
4. E.g. H. B. Walters, *Catalogue of Roman Pottery in the Department of Antiquities, British Museum*, 1908, pp. 386–8, fig. 233; *Guide to the Antiquities of Roman Britain in the British Museum*, 1958, p. 31, pl. 3 (right-hand upper fig.); *Journal of Roman Studies*, xlvii, 1957, p. 226, pl. 15, fig. 3.
5. Collection of His Grace the Duke of Wellington (on loan to the Reading Museum): *Antiquaries Journal*, xxxvii, 1957, p. 38, nos. 20–1, pl. 14.
6. Ashmolean Museum, Oxford: *ibid.* p. 40, nos. 28, a–b, pl. 14.
7. Yorkshire Museum, York: *ibid.* pp. 40–1, no. 29, pl. 14.

From Verulamium, Hertfordshire. Late-second or early-third century A.D. Height 4⅞ inches. *Property of the Verulamium Excavation Committee*

This is an almost intact two-handled black-gloss beaker, in shape a variant of 'form 74' and with *appliqué* decoration of the same type as that of nos. 150–1. Here there are two naturalistically modelled vine-leaves, the frontal mask of a Maenad, and the mask of a Silenus seen in profile to the right. *Antiquaries Journal*, xli, 1961, p. 75, pl. 21, a.

153. TWO UNGUENT-POTS IN FORMS OF HARE AND IBEX   Plates 162–3
From Colchester (Camulodunum), Essex. Mid-first century A.D. Height of hare: 4¼ inches; height of ibex: 3 inches. *Colchester and Essex Museum, Colchester*

A rarity from British sites are examples of the decorated lead-glaze wares, of which the centre of production was St. Rémy-en-Rollat, in the Allier district of France. These two moulded pots carry a yellowish glaze. The hare is crouching on the ground, with its head turned back and raised vertically to form the spout. The ibex is also lying down, with its forelegs tucked beneath it, and the spout of the vessel rises from behind its tall horns. The modelling of both beasts is sensitive and naturalistic. They belong to the same grave-group as no. 143.
R. J. Charleston, *Roman Pottery*, 1955, pl. 33, a–b.

154. JAR WITH MOTTO AND FLORAL DESIGN   Plate 192
From Verulamium, Hertfordshire. Late-second or early-third century A.D. Height: 8 inches. *Property of the Verulamium Excavation Committee*

Characteristic products of the Rhenish potteries in the late-second and early-third centuries are the vessels, mainly in the form of bulbous jars or beakers and elongated flagons, some with indented walls, on which the designs are traced in thick, opaque, white paint, with occasional touches here and there of thick, golden-yellow paint, on a more or less glossy red or black or dark-brown coat. The most attractive designs consist of bold and flowing floral scrolls of classical derivation, neatly and truly drawn, as by sure and expert hands, and often containing clusters of round, berry-like blobs; but there are also vertical floral sprays, unattached leaves and clusters, and some non-representational, abstract patterns, such as plain discs, rings and lines of blobs, and series of stylised vertical features. The designs may, further, be accompanied by mottoes, the letters of which either run continuously or are separated from one another by clusters, discs, etc.[1] One such black-gloss beaker of British provenance, that with the motto SVAVIS which was found in the 'basement-room' of the Lullingstone villa (*cf.* no. 10), has been generally accepted as a continental import.[2] But with regard

to many other colour-coated British finds of this type, particularly those that have come to light at, or in the region of, a well-known centre of pottery manufacture, such as the Nene Valley, in the Peterborough (Castor) area, and Colchester, there is a strong possibility that we are dealing, not with imported, but with home-made vessels, despite the fact that they resemble pieces of Rhenish provenance extremely closely in shapes, in decorative motifs, in the style in which these motifs are carried out, and in the mottoes. If they were made in Britain their makers would have been either British potters working from imported models or immigrants from the Continent who had established factories in promising localities in the island and may have had in their employ some native apprentices. Only after some years of experience in the spectrographic analysis of clays shall we be able to distinguish home- and foreign products in this field with real assurance (*cf.* Introduction, p. 11).
Among those pots of which the principal ornamentation takes the form of floral patterns is this jar or beaker with a dark-brown coat, stylised sprays, and the motto DA MERVM ('Wine, please').
Unpublished.

155. JAR WITH HARE AND HOUNDS   Plates 178–9
From Verulamium, Hertfordshire. Late-second or early-third century A.D. Height: 9 inches. *Property of the Verulamium Excavation Committee*

The best and rightly the most admired of all the native wares of Roman Britain is that with a matt or slightly burnished black or brown coat and relief-work carried out in the *en barbotine* technique (*cf.* Introduction, p. 11). This is 'Castor' ware *par excellence*, so called from the village of Castor on the north bank of the Nene, near Peterborough, in the area of which, and in the adjacent districts, have come to light, from the early-nineteenth century onwards, the kilns that produced it. To what extent experienced potters from the Continent settled there and assisted native enterprise in the running of this industry, we do not know. However, there can be little doubt but that the Nene Valley kilns were among the most productive in the province; and the wares that they turned out enjoyed a wide distribution to many parts of Britain, including military sites on the northern frontier.
'Castor' pots are often classed as 'coarse' ware, although their style and fabric place them on a level far above that of other products of the native potteries and could justly claim for them the title of British 'fine' ware. But this does not imply that the skill of the designers was by any means always equal to their courage in attempting the more ambitious subjects. Indeed, from the purely aesthetic standpoint, it is the pots with the less elaborately representational themes that form the most attractive 'Castor' series. Among these the most popular subject was the animal-hunt, of which this jar or beaker offers a good example. Here, in a setting of stylised floral scrolls and sprays, svelte, long-eared hounds, with slender legs and eager tongues, pursue a plump, round-eyed hare. On other pieces the dogs are collared and stags are

1. E.g. *Germania Romana*, ed. 2, v, 1930, pls. 29, fig. 5; 30, figs. 1–2; R. J. Charleston, *Roman Pottery*, 1955, pls. 70–3.
2. Lullingstone Museum: *Archaeologia Cantiana*, lxiii, 1950, p. 19, no. 23; fig. 8; G. W. Meates, *Lullingstone Roman Villa*, 1955, pl. 38. Plate 255.

included in their prey. The chase, as here, whirls from right to left in a broad frieze round the body of the pot; and we need not doubt but that this theme made a special appeal to the hunt-addicted Celtic populations, both civilian and military, of the north-western Roman provinces. On the best pieces, for instance on this piece and on a pair of jars from Corbridge,[1] the animals are rendered with a verve and a restrained naturalism that are wholly satisfying to the eye and with an admirable clarity and sureness of draftsmanship. That the subject-matter and the style of the 'Castor' hunt-pots reached Britain from the Continent is obvious. It is enough to quote such Gaulish pieces as the red-gloss *olla* (squat jar) found at Felixstowe[2] and a red-gloss jar and a black-gloss jar from Niederbieber.[3] But it seems that in Britain the colour-coated hunt-pot enjoyed a quite outstanding vogue. Unpublished.

156. Jar with Arena- and Circus-Scenes   Plate 193
From the region of Castor (Durobrivae), Northamptonshire. Late-second or early-third century A.D. Height: 9⅞ inches. *Peterborough Museum*

On this fragmentary pot are combined an arena-scene and a circus-scene very crudely modelled in *en barbotine* technique. There is a pair of duelling gladiators, one with a straight, the other with a curved, sword; and then, between two rudely shaped pilasters, a lively and unusual episode – a female acrobat leaping from the back of a quadruped of indeterminate species, facing to the right, onto the back of a leftward-facing, spotted panther. The colour-coating is of lightish-brown; but the details of the figures in relief are painted in darker-brown, while some very stylised floral scrolls are sketched, in the flat, in another shade of brown paint on the background.

VCH Huntingdonshire, i, 1926, pp. 242–3, no. 12, pl. 5; *Antiquaries Journal*, XXXIX, 1959, p. 92, pl. 23.

157. Jar with Mithras, Hercules, and Mercury   Plate 190
From Verulamium, Hertfordshire. Late-second or early-third century. Height: 8¼ inches. *Verulamium Museum, St. Albans*

On this fragmentary jar are preserved substantial portions of three deities boldly modelled in *en barbotine* technique and all identifiable by their dress and attributes. Mithras appears in his role as hunter (*cf.* no. 110), holding a bow and wearing his Phrygian cap and a tunic, the skirt of which is all bespangled with rosettes and crosses: his legs and feet are lost. Of Hercules we have the abdomen, legs, and feet, his bow, gripped in his left hand, and part of the lion-skin draped across his left arm; and of Mercury there survive the legs and feet, with wings at the ankles.

Archaeologia, XC, 1944, pp. 121–2, fig. 20, nos. 1–1a.

158. Jar with Gladiators, Hunters, and Animal-Hunt   Plates 176–7
From Colchester (Camulodunum), Essex. Late-second or early-third century A.D. Height: 8½ inches. *Colchester and and Essex Museum, Colchester*

The Nene Valley was not the only centre for the manufacture of colour-coated pots with *en barbotine* relief-work. It would appear to be virtually certain that the fine series of vessels with this type of decoration that the *colonia* of Camulodunum and its immediate neighbourhood have yielded was the product of the city's own kilns. Whether Colchester and the Nene Valley simultaneously received from the Continent the stimulus for making wares of this type, or whether the latter area received it from the former (and Roman Colchester's connections with the Rhineland were long-established and particularly strong), is not at present clear.

This piece, the so-called 'Colchester vase', shows two *venatores* (arena-hunters), one naked, save for an abbreviated loin-cloth, and grasping a short stick, the other equipped with a belt and arm-guards and brandishing a whip above the head of an infuriated bear. To the right of this group a different arena-scene confronts us – a pair of gladiators in combat. The 'Samnite' on the left has a crested visor-helmet, a cylindrical shield, arm-guard, belt, loin-cloth, greaves, and a short sword. His opponent on the right is a *retiarius* wearing arm-guards, a belt, a loin-cloth, and boots; he points with the first finger of his right hand towards the 'Samnite' as a sign that he is beaten, and, indeed his net has vanished and his trident lies useless on the ground beneath the 'Samnite's' feet. Above the *venatores* are inscribed their names – 'Secundus' and 'Mario'; the 'Samnite' is labelled 'Memno sac (= 'secutor') viii (perhaps the number of his victories)', the *retiarius*, 'Valentinu(s)'; and then we read 'legionis xxx'. The Thirtieth Legion was, of course, stationed in the Rhineland, not in Britain. But this need not imply that the jar was a Rhenish import. Some legions may have had their own troupes of gladiators and *venatores* to provide them with entertainment (as well as to act as the commander's bodyguard);[4] and the names on this jar could be those of 'stars' attached to the Thirtieth Legion, but famed throughout the northern provinces.

On the back of this jar there is a two-tiered animal-hunt, producing an 'all-over', tapestry-like effect which is extremely decorative. In each zone a hound, a hare, and stags speed towards the right, while stylised floral sprays occupy the background.[5]

R. J. Charleston, *Roman Pottery*, 1955, pl. 65; *Transactions of the Essex Archaeological Society*, n.s., XXV, 1955, pl. 8, fig. 1.

---

1. Corbridge Museum: *Archaeologia Aeliana*, ser. 3, v, 1909, pp. 417, 419, fig. 45; ser. 4, XXXV, 1957, pp. 191, no. 89; 229, fig. 10.
2. British Museum: R. J. Charleston, *Roman Pottery*, 1955, frontispiece.
3. E. Gose, *Gefässtypen der römischen Keramik im Rheinland*, 1950, p. 15, no. 164, pl. 10; p. 17, no. 197, pl. 13.

4. *Cf.* Tacitus, *Annals* i, 22; Suetonius, *Tiberius* 72.
5. For another jar from Colchester wholly encircled by two superimposed zones of hounds chasing hares and hinds towards the left, see *Transactions of the Essex Archaeological Society*, n.s., XXV, 1955, pl. 8, figs. 2–3.

159. Fragmentary Jar with Hunt of Hunch-backed Genii Cucullati   Plate 186

From Colchester (Camulodunum), Essex. Late-second or early-third century A.D. Original height of pot: *c.* 9 to 12 inches. *Colchester and Essex Museum, Colchester*

An enigmatic and, so far as the present writer knows, unique representation in *en barbotine* of a *venatio* (arena-hunt) is on this piece, which has a dark, chocolate-coloured coat and touches of other colours used here and there upon the figures. Of the *venatores* three are visible. One, on the left, survives entire and is naked and hunch-backed and wields a long knife; the second, on the right, is preserved from head to thighs, wears pants that are strengthened with metal studs, a waist-belt, braces, and armlets, has a guard on his left arm, and with his right hand flourishes a whip in the face of a snarling bear; while of the third hunter, on the left, above the first, only one leg, swathed in a puttee, and the foreparts of his dog, remain. Other quarry are a hare, a quadruped, of which portions of the legs are left, and, most surprisingly, four long-cloaked and hunch-backed hooded dwarfs, presumably Genii Cucullati (*cf.* nos. 76–7, 144). Of these one, at whom a hound is barking furiously, still stands erect, another is in process of falling to the ground, while two lie already prostrate. The import of this comic situation so far eludes us.

Collection Latomus, xxviii, 1957, pp. 468–9, no. 15, pl. 62, fig. 4 (from a drawing by M. R. Hull).

160. Fragment of Jar with Jupiter Dolichenus   Plate 188

From the region of Castor (Durobrivae), Northamptonshire. Late-second or early-third century A.D. Height: 2¼ inches; width: 3⅛ inches. *Peterborough Museum*

Another class of Nene Valley pottery showing scenes with human and animal figures has designs that are, like the floral scrolls, other floral motifs, and mottoes (*cf.* no. 154), carried out in opaque white paint, but with occasional touches of colour. This type of decoration was, of course, again of Rhineland origin. But we may with confidence assign to local factories the fragments displaying the technique which have been found in the Castor area. For while some of the figures are reasonably well drawn, others exhibit extreme naïvety (*cf.* Introduction, p. 11).

In the Rhineland were produced tall-necked motto-jugs with scrolls 'inhabited' by birds and quadrupeds.[1] A jug of the same type from Trier carries a row of half-figures of Seasons emerging from calyces of leaves;[2] while from Trier also comes an exceptionally fine motto-jar adorned with four roundels, each of which contains the bust of a god or personification.[3] The two Trier vessels are gay with touches of brilliant polychromy; and, similarly, on some of the British pieces the white paint is enlivened by yellow-brown

details. But as in the case of *en barbotine* wares, so in that of the painted series, the British potters seem to have outdone their continental masters in their enterprising choice of more varied and more complicated figure-scenes. Among the subjects represented are this head and bust of Jupiter Dolichenus, wearing his conical Syrian hat (*cf.* nos. 34 and 161) and a cuirass and brandishing a double-axe (*cf.* no. 161).

Antiquaries Journal, xxxix, 1959, pp. 92–3, no. 1, pl. 24, fig. a.

161. Mould for *Appliqué* Figure of 'Wheel-God'   Plates 164–5

From Corbridge (Corstopitum), Northumberland. Third century A.D. Height: 5¾ inches. *Corbridge Museum*

This mould is to be associated with a series of native grey and buff vessels, mainly large jars, carrying relief-decoration in *appliqué* on their walls (*cf.* Introduction, p. 11). In this case, and in several other cases, only the 'negative' moulds used for the casting have survived to us; and this, the most famous of the group, the so-called 'Harry Lauder' mould, depicts an outlandish bearded Celtic god. He is shown frontally, with a conical helmet, crooked club, oblong shield, and wheel, the last attribute suggesting that he may be the 'Wheel-God' Tanaris (or Tanarus).[4] Almost certainly by the same hand is the figure, also found at Corbridge, in 1958, of a bearded Smith-God – this time the 'positive' figure, applied to a large, grey, globular jar, just below the rim, came to light – with a conical cap, an *exomis* (slipped tunic), boots, hammer, tongs, and an anvil in the field beside him.[5] He may be a Celtic form of Vulcan. Thirdly, in precisely the same style and again from Corbridge, is a set of four sherds, from similar grey jars, the most informative of which carries what has been interpreted as part of the bearded figure of Jupiter Dolichenus, wearing a tunic and his conical Syrian hat (*cf.* nos. 34 and 160), while in his right hand he brandishes a double-axe (*cf.* no. 160).[6] Another of the fragments has incised upon it the potter's signature, Alletio. We have, thus, abundant evidence for the local manufacture at Corbridge of figured vessels of this type, for which both the fabric and the wide lattice-scoring that some of the sherds display suggest a third-century date.

Archaeologia Aeliana, ser. 3, vi, 1910, pp. 224–6, fig. 6.

162. Jar with Smith's Tools, etc.   Plate 191

From Colchester (Camulodunum), Essex. Late-second or third century A.D. Height: 8⅝ inches. *Colchester and Essex Museum, Colchester*

Inanimate objects in *appliqué* on the walls of pots are represented by the decoration on two more or less complete

---

1. F. Oelmann, *Die Keramik des Kastells Niederbieber*, 1914, p. 36, fig. 12. Cf. *Trierer Zeitschrift*, i, 1926, p. 8, fig. 8, a, pl. 3, fig. 2.

2. E. Gose, *Gefässtypen der römischen Keramik im Rheinland*, 1950, p. 18, no. 214, pl. 15; *Trierer Zeitschrift*, i, 1926, p. 8, fig. 8, c, pl. 3, fig. 3. Cf. *ibid.* pp. 9–10, figs. 9–10 for sherds of a painted pot with Planetary Deities.

3. Oelmann, *loc. cit.*; *Trierer Zeitschrift*, i, 1926, pp. 1–17, pls. 1–2.

4. P. Lambrechts, *Contributions à l'étude des divinités celtiques*, 1942, pp. 64–80; *Journal of Roman Studies*, xxxix, 1949, p. 21, pl. 1. That the form Tanarus was current in Britain we know from the dedication I(ovi) O(ptimo) M(aximo) Tanaro from Chester: *Corpus Inscriptionum Latinarum*, vii, no. 168.

5. Corbridge Museum: *Journal of Roman Studies*, xlix, 1959, p. 106; *Archaeologia Aeliana*, ser. 4, xl, 1962, pp. 35–6, no. 1, pl. 4, fig. 1. Plate 256.

6. Corbridge Museum: *ibid.* ser. 4, xxi, 1943, p. 193, pl. 10G, fig. 1. More probably this god is another rendering of the Celtic Vulcan, with a *pilleus* and a hammer (*ibid.*, ser. 4, xl, 1962, p. 36, no. 2, p. 4, fig. 2).

large jars, of which this is one, and on fragments of others of the same style and fabric. All carry smith's tools and other implements, sometimes very carefully and neatly shaped, deployed round the vessel's shoulders. This jar has a whitish coat and bears tongs, an anvil, a hammer, and a wedge. The second whole pot, from Canterbury, is of grey, sandy clay: its emblems are a hammer, wedge, tongs, anvil, and rope, together with the relics of a human face (cf. no. 164).[1] A fragment from Colchester, with a dull-white coat, has tongs, hammer, and an anvil;[2] on a sherd from Chester-le-Street, in County Durham, an axe, tongs, and what might be the frame for a plumb-line are applied;[3] and scraps of grey vessels found in the fort at Malton and at Elmswell, in Yorkshire, show hammers, tongs, wheels, etc. and in some cases human arms, presumably from full-length figures of the type portrayed on the mould and sherds from Corbridge (cf. no. 161).[4] All that one can say as to the date of these jars is that they are best associated with the second half of the period of Roman occupation of this island. Possibly they served a ritual purpose, in the cult of Vulcan or of some native patron of smiths and other workers in related trades.

T. May, *Catalogue of the Roman Pottery in the Colchester and Essex Museum*, 1930, pp. 146–7, fig. 3; *Proceedings of the Society of Antiquaries of Newcastle upon Tyne*, ser. 2, x, 1921–2, pl. opp. p. 20 (lower fig.).

163. MOULD FOR MASK FOR JUG-NECK   Plates 166–8

From Horspath, near Oxford. Third century A.D. Height: 2⅜ inches. *Ashmolean Museum, Oxford*

The jugs made in Britain with a human, generally female, mask, cast in a mould and applied to one side of the neck (or fashioned by pressing the clay of the jug into a mould held against its neck), form a late series of third- and fourth-century date. These masks, taken as a whole, display considerable divergencies from one another in style, technique, and fabric. Some are wholly classical in type, with naturalistic and plastically modelled hair and facial features. Others are more crudely and coarsely worked, with stylised hair and sometimes with painted details. This mould for casting a female face and neck for a jug-mask of the classical variety is a remarkable and, it seems, unique object in that the outside of the mould has been pulled by the native potter into the shape of a grotesque male face.

Oxoniensia, xvii–xviii, 1952–3, pp. 231–4, pl. 21, a–e.

164. TWO FACE-POTS   Plates 185, 189

From Colchester (Camulodunum), Essex. Late-second or third century A.D. Heights: 10⅛ and 10½ inches. *Colchester and Essex Museum, Colchester*

These pots belong to a class of squat, globular jars of buff clay, usually equipped with three small handles and forming a large and homogeneous series, which were manufactured in the kilns of Colchester. On the upper part of one side of the exterior of each such jar strips and lumps of clay have been applied free-hand (not from moulds) to form the lewdly expressive features of a human face – a wedge-shaped nose; small, lentoid eyes beneath broadly arching brows, the hairs of which are indicated by incisions; a tiny, provocative mouth, now round and button-like, now straight and mocking; and a pair of large, impressionistic ears. Below the mouth on some pots a semi-circle of incised dots suggests a beard; and in several cases what appears to be a phallus has been added at a slightly lower level than the face. On one such jar two goat-horns spring upwards from the junction of the brows, indicating that the features are those of a grotesque Pan; and it seems likely that these vessels had a quasi-religious function in some form of fertility-worship. The secondary use at Colchester of some of them as burial-urns would thus be readily explained.

T. May, *Catalogue of the Roman Pottery in the Colchester and Essex Museum*, 1930, pp. 143, 276, 289, pls. 51a–2; 90, no. 13; R. J. Charleston, *Roman Pottery*, 1955, pl. 92; *Guide to the Antiquities of Roman Britain in the British Museum*, 1951, p. 36, no. 23, fig. 17; 1958, p. 36, no. 23, fig. 17; M. R. Hull, *Roman Colchester: a Brief Account*, 1961, lower fig. on p. 37; *Roman Colchester*, 1958, p. 285, nos. 288–9, fig. 120.

165. HEAD-POT DEPICTING WOMAN   Plate 194

From York (Eburacum), Fishergate. Early-third century A.D. Height 11⅝ inches. *Yorkshire Museum, York*

Akin to the face-pots (no. 164) and possibly derived from moulded glass prototypes[5] is an extremely crude, but expressive variety of native figured jar with a white or buff coat and mould-cast in the form of a human head and neck, the facial features being very roughly modelled in relief. This piece shows a woman with hair that is parted in the centre and conceals the ears, after the manner of Julia Domna's coiffure. The eyebrows are hatched and the huge eyes are diamond-shaped; and the mouth is small and smirking. Here the details are incised; but on other head-pots, such as those from Lincoln,[6] Colchester,[7] the Castor area,[8] and York,[9] there are painted black or brown details.

---

1. Royal Museum, Canterbury: unpublished.
2. Colchester and Essex Museum, Colchester. M. R. Hull, *Roman Colchester*, 1958, p. 128, fig. 57, no. 2; p. 144, no. 2.
3. *Proceedings of the Society of Antiquaries of Newcastle upon Tyne*, ser. 2, x, 1921–2, pp. 19–21 with plate (upper fig.); *Antiquaries Journal*, ix, 1929, pp. 156–8, fig. 1 and p. 255.
4. Malton Museum: ed. P. Corder, *Roman Malton and District Report*, No. 7, 1950, p. 32, no. 12, pl. 6, b.
5. E.g. a moulded glass head of a negro, said in one place to have come from Pompeii, in another, to have been found at South Shields (Arbeia), County Durham: Museum of Antiquities of the University of Durham and of the Society of Antiquaries of Newcastle upon Tyne (King's College, Newcastle upon Tyne): *Archaeologia Aeliana*, ser. 3, xi, 1914, p. xxi; ser. 4, xxxvii, 1959, pp. 55–6, pl. 5, fig. 4.
6. British Museum: H. B. Walters, *Catalogue of Roman Pottery in the Department of Antiquities, British Museum*, 1908, p. 427, no. M 2761, fig. 283; *Guide to the Antiquities of Roman Britain in the British Museum*, 1922, pp. 118–9, fig. 134; 1951, p. 36, no. 24, pl. 5; 1958, p. 36, no. 24, pl. 5: the inscription reads: D(e)O MIIRCVRIO.
7. Colchester and Essex Museum, Colchester: Benham's Colchester, 1948, fig. on p. 96; M. R. Hull, *Roman Colchester*, 1958, p. 285, no. 292, fig. 120.
8. Peterborough Museum: *VCH Huntingdonshire*, i, 1926, pl. 3, fig. 3.
9. Yorkshire Museum, York: *Royal Commission on Historical Monuments (England): York* i (Roman), 1962, pl. 29, no. H.2133.

Royal Commission on Historical Monuments (England): York i (Roman), 1962, pl. 29, no. H.2132.

166. CAKE-MOULD WITH SCENE OF IMPERIAL SACRIFICE   Plate 184

From Silchester (Calleva Atrebatum), Hampshire. Early-third century A.D. Diameter: 4¼ inches. *Collection of His Grace the Duke of Wellington (on loan to the Reading Museum)*

Circular terracotta moulds used for decorating cakes and other pastries with figured ornament are not uncommon finds in Roman contexts on the Continent, particularly in the onetime Danubian provinces, where the subjects depicted on those objects include portraits of imperial persons, scenes in which an Emperor is involved, religious scenes, and miscellaneous representations.[1] But in Roman Britain only one such mould has so far come to light, this piece, found during the 1890–1909 excavations at Silchester. The clay of which the mould is made is probably of local origin; but we cannot tell whether a British potter himself created the design that we see on it or made his 'negative' from another craftsman's 'positive' model, perhaps an imported one.

The right-hand portion of the scene (to describe it from a cast taken from the mould), which is displayed within a roundel, has been broken off. But the picture certainly contained no more than the four surviving figures, two of whom, both male, face towards the left, while the other two, one male and one female, are turned towards the right. In the centre, between the two groups of figures, is a sacrificial tripod; and from the facts that two, possibly three, of the male figures are wearing laurel-wreaths and that three *vexilla* occupy the background, above the heads of the quartet, we may deduce that the sacrifice is being conducted by imperial persons and has a military connotation of some kind. The man on the extreme right, who stands in front of his companion, is obviously the most important person in the scene; and from his long, flowing, pointed beard and from the hair-style of the woman on the left, which is unequivocally that of the Empress Julia Domna, we may

1. *Laureae Aquincenses,* i, pp. 312–41, pls. 48–75 (*Dissertationes Pannonicae,* ser. 2, x, 1938).

further deduce that Septimius Severus is the Emperor in question here. The two other male figures would then be Caracalla on the right and Geta on the left; and since both are bearded and both, probably, laureate, the scene cannot be earlier than 209, the year in which the younger brother, Geta, was elevated to the rank of Augustus to which Caracalla had attained in 198. The dress of the males is semi-military – a tunic and a *sagum* (cloak); and the design, if made in Britain, could portray a thanksgiving sacrifice on the occasion of a victory in Severus' British war. If the model had been imported from abroad, the original intention could have been to commemorate some other, possibly oriental, victory in a scene that was adapted at Silchester to a British context.

The ultimate source of the potter's picture could have been a medallion- or coin-type, otherwise unknown to us, or some official painting or relief. At any rate, both the general style and the content are wholly Roman, while the somewhat clumsy drawing of the figures almost certainly betrays a provincial artist's hand.

Antiquaries Journal, xxxviii, 1958, pp. 237–40, pl. 25.

167. LAMP WITH VINE-SCROLL   Plate 170

From Verulamium, Hertfordshire. Fourth century A.D. (?). Length: 4¾ inches. *Verulamium Museum, St. Albans*

This very well preserved pear-shaped lamp was found in the nineteenth century unstratified. It has a deeply sunk, fluted centre and a handsome, stylised running vine-scroll on the rim. Its straight-sided nozzle is of the type normally seen on terracotta lamps of the second century A.D. from east-Mediterranean sites.[2] But a piece of the late-antique or quasi-Christian class affords a close parallel both to the nozzle-form and to the deeply sunk centre of the British example.[3]

Unpublished.

2. H. B. Walters, *Catalogue of the Greek and Roman Lamps in the British Museum,* 1914, pls. 34–5.
3. *Ibid.,* p. 201, no. 1341, fig. 302. A very similar lamp, with a vine-scroll on the rim, a straight-sided nozzle, and a deeply sunk, fluted centre has been found at Same, in Cephalonia, in Greece (*Bulletin de Correspondence Hellénique,* lxxxiv, 1960, pp. 731, 733, fig. 6, b).

FRESCO PAINTING

168. FLORAL SPRAY   Plate 200

From the Basilica, London. Second century A.D. (?). Height: 5½ inches. *London Museum, Kensington Palace*

This naturalistic spray of grey-green dark and light leaves, with dark-brown stems and yellow buds, is shown against a red background. It is impressionistically rendered, doubtlessly by a foreign artist, in a style reminiscent of painting at Pompeii and Stabiae.

London in Roman Times (London Museum Catalogues, No. 3), 1930, pp. 38–9, pl. 11.

169. PEOPLED FLORAL SCROLL FROM FRIEZE
Plates 195, 197

From Verulamium, Hertfordshire. Second century A.D. Height: 5 feet; length: 12 feet. *Property of the Right Hon. the Earl of Verulam (on loan to the British Museum)*

This is the most ambitious surviving piece of fresco floral painting that has so far come to light in Roman Britain. It was found in Insula xxi, 2 of the Roman city and appears to have run along the top of the north-west wall of the courtyard of the house, where a substantially roofed corridor must have sheltered it. At the top of the frieze a dark-red border, curving slightly forward, marks the junction of the wall and ceiling; and the frieze itself is filled with a running scroll of leaves and flowers forming spirals, four of which remain, painted on a yellow ground. This scroll is 'peopled' by frontal masks of felines, probably panthers, alternating with full figures of pheasants shown in profile, the centre of each spiral housing one of these creatures. Birds and beasts are reddish-brown, with realistic shading and modelling. The stems and tendrils of the scroll are dark-green; the leaves are light-green; while between each pair of spirals, turned alternately up and down, is a funnel-shaped motif, pale-green from its pointed end to its mouth, where it terminates in three large red-brown, sharply pointed petals. This feature is best interpreted as an almost closed acanthus-flower emerging from a leaf-calyx and seen in profile. Similar, but more conventionalised, flowers fill the spaces between the spirals of the running ivy-scroll on the Dorchester (Dorset) Oceanus mosaic[1] and on a mosaic border from Cirencester[2] and of the floral scrolls bordering hexagons on a Silchester mosaic;[3] while still more stylised flowers appear between the spirals of the running floral scroll that borders the Venus lunette in the *triclinium* pavement (no. 191), and of the scrolls flanking bowls in the corners of the large square of the Ganymede pavement (no. 190), of the Bignor villa,[4] between the spirals of the floral scroll that separates two 'geometric' panels on a pavement from Verulamium itself,[5] and between the spirals of two floral scrolls on a mosaic from Woodchester.[6] It would seem that copy-books that included scrolls with this special feature, which is not normally encountered in scrolls in any medium from continental and Mediterranean lands,[7] were in circulation in Roman Britain during a period of several centuries. Again, while the foreparts of animals emerging from flowers, or figures of complete beasts standing in or running through the foliage, constantly occur in the centres of the spirals in running scrolls throughout the Roman world, the present writer knows of no other instance of only the masks of animals in such positions.[8] The painter of this frieze doubtlessly came from abroad.

Antiquaries Journal, xxxvii, 1957, p. 14, pls. 4, a; 5.

170. FRAGMENT OF CEILING   Plates 196, 198
From Verulamium, Hertfordshire. Second century A.D. Height: 6 feet, 9 inches; width: 6 feet, 6 inches, *Verulamium Museum, St. Albans*

1. *Proceedings of the Dorset Natural History and Archaeological Society,* xlix, 1928, pl. opp. p. 98.
2. Prof. Buckman and C. H. Newmarch, *Illustrations of the Remains of Roman Art at Cirencester,* 1850, pl. 6, fig. 2.
3. *VCH Hampshire,* i, 1900, pl. 5.
4. S. Lysons, *Reliquiae Britannico-Romanae,* iii, 1817, pls. 5, 8–9, 19.
5. R. E. M. and T. V. Wheeler, *Verulamium: a Belgic and Two Roman Cities,* 1936, pls. 40; 46, a.
6. S. Lysons, *An Account of the Roman Antiquities Discovered at Woodchester in the County of Gloucester,* 1797, pls. 19–20, fig. 3. *Cf.* The presence of the same feature between the spirals of a fragmentary floral scroll found in 1959 at Chichester: Chichester Museum.
7. See *Papers of the British School at Rome,* xviii, 1950, pp. 1–43 with I fig., pls. 1–26.   8. *Ibid.*

This fragment belonged to the ceiling of the southern arm of the corridor, surrounding the courtyard of the house, in which no. 169 came to light. It has been put together from many pieces that had fallen, face-downwards, directly onto the corridor's tessellated floor and were covered by the fragments of plaster, adorned with *candelabra* and floral swags on a bright-red ground, which had fallen from the corridor's south wall.[9] Since this corridor was only seven feet, nine inches wide, only about one foot is lost here of the total width of the painted ceiling. The design, which is carried out on a purple ground, consists of a series of interlacing octagons, outlined in ornamental yellow lines and arranged symmetrically in rows. Twenty octagons survive, sixteen more or less completely and four in part only. The centre of each octagon contains a rectangular panel; and in each of the sixteen remaining panels is either the figure of a naturalistic dove or, in two cases, the frontal mask of a panther-like feline, very similar to the feline masks inhabiting the running scroll (no. 169). The feline heads are yellow; the doves are mainly yellow, with red-brown feather-markings. The lines that enclose the rectangular panels are foliated, while foliated diagonal intersecting lines, decked with barley-heads, connect the corners of the panels.[10] In each of the elongated hexagons formed by the interlacings of the octagons is a string of three green-and-white flowers joined by leafy yellow stems. The octagons and panels were clearly meant to imitate coffering; and the fact that the doves are set at different angles to one another must imply that the painting was intended to be viewed from below. The general effect is very gay, tasteful, and delicate, the product of a well-trained foreign painter, in a style that would have graced a house or tomb in Rome; and as the relic of a painted ceiling this fragment, together with no. 171, is so far unique of its kind in Roman Britain.[11]

Antiquaries Journal, xxxix, 1959, pp. 17–8, pl. 1.

171. FRAGMENT OF CEILING   Plate 202
From Verulamium, Hertfordshire. Second century A.D. Height: 2 feet. *Property of the Verulamium Excavation Committee*

This ceiling-fragment, which is much less well preserved than no. 170, comes from the same house and from another part of the same corridor. The design is the same, but the background of this portion is red instead of purple.

Antiquaries Journal, xl, 1960, p. 17.

172. PORTICO OF COLUMNS ON DADO   Plate 201
From Verulamium, Hertfordshire. Second century A.D. Height: 6 feet, 9½ inches. *Property of the Verulamium Excavation Committee*

9. *Antiquaries Journal,* xxxvii, 1957, p. 13, pl. 3, a.
10. For similar barley-heads, combined with leaves and berries and linking squares and roundels, see the much-restored painted frieze or dado from Silchester (*Archaeologia,* lv, 1896, pp. 249–51, fig. 5).
11. For the relics of a much later and much more elaborate painted ceiling from the Constantinian hall that preceded the earliest church on the site of the Cathedral at Trier, see *Trierer Zeitschrift,* xviii, 1949 (Beiheft), pp. 45–51, figs. 1–2, pls. 5–6, Beilage 1–5.

This fragment was found in Insula xxviii, 3 of the Roman city and had fallen in pieces face-downwards from the south-west wall of a room in the house. The design is painted in varying shades of reddish brown and shows a colonnade. The columns are set with spaces of roughly four feet between them; each is about three feet, six inches high, stands on a low base, is crowned by a lotus-leaf capital, and has a net-work pattern on its shaft. The spaces between the columns are filled with somewhat crudely rendered 'marbling', while below the column-base is a dado of 'marbled' panels with darker-brown plain borders.

Antiquaries Journal, xxxix, 1959, p. 13.

173. FIGURE OF CUPID   Plate 199
From Leicester (Ratae Coritanorum). Second century A.D. Height: 11⅝ inches. *Leicester Museum*

This fragment displays a centrally placed, inward-curving dark-green arch with imitation coffering on its soffit. Within the arch there stands towards the front a Cupid, with scarlet hair, blue butterfly-wings, and a blue garment, holding a *pedum* in his right hand and a basket (?) in his extended left hand. The stylised, unnaturalistic colouring and the somewhat clumsy drawing may betoken the hand of a native painter.

Journal of Roman Studies, xlix, 1959, p. 113, pl. 17, fig. 2.

174. LIFE-SIZE FEMALE FOOT   Plate 203
From the Ickleton Villa, Cambridgeshire. Fourth century A.D. (?). Height: 9 inches; width: 13 inches. *Museum of Archaeology and of Ethnology, Cambridge*

The piece carries the right foot of a running or dancing female figure, with the hem of her skirt swirling round her ankle. She may have been a Nymph or Maenad. At any rate, she represents the relic of an important, large-scale painting, probably a mythological scene. That such scenes did adorn the walls of Romano–British villas we know from at least three discoveries.[1]
There are no external criteria for dating the fragment. But since the elaborate equipment of country villas is known to date, in general, from the fourth century (see Introduction, pp. 12–3), we may with some confidence assign this painting to that period.

Proceedings of the Cambridge Antiquarian Society, xliv, 1950, pp. 14, 17, pl. 4, a; *Antiquity and Survival*, ii, 4, 1958, p. 382, fig. 9.

1. (i) Otford, Kent: *Journal of Roman Studies*, xvi, 1926, pp. 238, 244, no. 26, fig. 68; *VCH Kent*, iii, 1932, p. 122, pl. 5 (upper fig.); *Catalogue of the Greek, Etruscan, and Roman Paintings and Mosaics in the British Museum*, 1933, pp. 56–7, no. 84, fig. 64 (where the fragment with the human figure is reproduced upsidedown); (ii) Lullingstone, Kent: *Journal of Roman Studies*, xlviii, 1958, p. 149; (iii) Comb End, Gloucestershire: S. Lysons. *Reliquiae Britannico-Romanae*, ii, 1817, pl. 1.

175. FRAGMENT OF CHRISTIAN PAINTING   Plate 204
From the Lullingstone Villa, Kent. Fourth century A.D. Original height: *c.* 2 feet, 8 inches. *Lullingstone Museum*

This fragmentary figure is one of a row of six figures, each of which occupied an intercolumniation of a portico of seven columns painted on the west wall of a room on the eastern side of the villa. The painted wall-plaster from that room had fallen into the 'basement-room' below (*cf.* no. 10), when the house met its end in a fire in the late-fourth or early-fifth century and the walls and floor of the upper room collapsed. The wall-paintings in this room were quite certainly Christian and it, together with the smaller rooms adjoining it, are very likely to have formed a house-church or domestic chapel. The complete scheme of the design on the west wall and the order in which the six figures were arranged was recovered through the acumen and skill of Mr. C. D. P. Nicholson, who undertook the arduous task of piecing the fragments of plaster together.
Of this figure the major portion has survived. It is a young man with flaming red hair and dark, lustrous eyes. He stands to the front and wears rich robes with edgings of pearls. Behind his shoulders is a curtain run on a thin rod or cord. This indicates that the youth is to be thought of as already dead when the painting was carried out, since in third- and fourth-century funerary art, both pagan and Christian, a curtain is constantly draped behind the representation of the departed. It is probably a symbol of the vault of heaven, where the dead person has gone to dwell.
Of the five other figures in the portico three, at least, had their arms extended laterally, with the palms of the hands turned outwards, in the attitude of an *Orans* or early-Christian at prayer. They are praying, probably, for the young man's soul.

G. W. Meates, *Lullingstone Roman Villa*, 1955, pp. 126–34; figs. 10–1, pls. 42–4; ed. R. L. S. Bruce-Mitford, *Recent Archaeological Excavations in Britain*, 1956, pp. 99–103, figs. 37–8, pl. 19, a.

176. FRAGMENT OF CHRISTIAN PAINTING   Plate 205
From the Lullingstone Villa, Kent. Fourth century A.D. Original diameter: *c.* 2 feet, 8 inches. *Lullingstone Museum*

From fragments of painted plaster from the 'basement-room', that yielded the fragments of no. 175, Mr. C. D. P. Nicholson pieced together the greater part of a large-scale Chi–Rho monogram painted in brilliant red against a white ground and surrounded by a polychrome wreath of leaves and flowers. Judging by the spot in the 'basement-room' in which these fragments came to light, we may assume that the monogram was painted at the western end of the chapel's (?) south wall.
It has fortunately proved possible to place in position, more or less, the essential features of this design and to obtain a reasonably accurate general impression of it. We have the vital centre-piece, carrying the intersection of the vertical stem of the Rho and the diagonal arms of the Chi; and in the middle of the point of crossing is the mark of the end of one

of the arms of the compass with the other arm of which the painter traced the line of the circle that the surrounding garland was to follow. There are also faint, but certain, traces of the Rho's rounded head. The existence of the garland is assured, not only from the compass-mark, but also from fragments carrying both sections of it and either portions of the plain white background of the monogram or scraps of the monogram itself. There is also sure evidence that a *taenia* (ribbon) secures the wreath below; and that on the fluttering ends of the *taenia*, on either side, is perched an inward-facing bird, between whose beak and the lower edge of the wreath there falls through the air a cluster of six dark-red seeds or berries. It would seem probable that at least one quasi-Ionic column flanked the wreath on the spectator's right, since we have two adjoining fragments that depict a section of the wreath (left) and part of a column-cap (right) and another fragment carrying a further section of the wreath (left) and what looks like a fluted column-shaft (right). It is also possible that one or more columns stood below the wreath and monogram, since what may be part of a column-cap is seen immediately below a portion of the left-hand *taenia*-end on one and the same fragment. There are thus sufficient data for reconstructing all the really significant elements in the scene on a basis of certainty and for adding, on a basis of fair probability, some secondary details.

A striking parallel to this monogram design is provided by the carving in the central panel of a well-known mid-fourth-century marble columned sarcophagus (found in the Domitilla Catacomb and now in the Lateran Christian Museum), on which the four lateral panels show scenes from Our Lord's Passion.[1] The two innermost colonnettes support a shell-shaped semi-dome, from the crown of which emerges the head of an eagle holding in its beak a laurel-wreath that encircles a large-scale, very prominent Chi-Rho monogram. The ends of the *taenia* that binds the wreath below fly out on either side, carved in low relief against the background. The bottom of the wreath rests on the top of the vertical stem of a cross-like feature, on each of the horizontal arms of which is perched an inward-facing bird, pecking at the wreath. Beneath the arms of the Cross two sleeping Roman soldiers are seated. The monogram, wreathed in victor's laurel, does, in fact, represent Our Lord rising from the Holy Sepulchre, the place of which is taken by the Cross. Life is triumphant over death, Easter Sunday over Good Friday. The Cross has become the banner of the Victor; and it has been suggested[2] that the soldiers' attitudes were intended to recall those of conquered barbarians crouched beneath a pagan Roman trophy. The birds are Christian souls feeding on the life-giving garland, just as at Lullingstone the birds eat seeds or berries falling from the wreath; and the busts of Sun and Moon in the angles above the springs of the semi-dome on the sarcophagus denote the wonderment of Nature at the victory, of which the eagle is again a pagan symbol. It may well be that this Lullingstone monogram symbolised the Resurrection and that, if there were columns below the wreath, they suggested the architecture of the Tomb.

Still more fragmentary portions of two more painted Chi-Rho monograms have come to light in the villa – one from the east wall of the chapel (?), the other from the room adjoining it on the north. Each is in a wreath.

G. W. Meates, *Lullingstone Roman Villa*, 1955, pp. 135–42, 145, figs. 12–3, pls. 45–7; ed. R. L. S. Bruce-Mitford, *Recent Archaeological Excavations in Britain*, 1956, pp. 103–4, fig. 39.

2. *Loc. cit.*

1. No. 177: C. van der Meer and C. Mohrmann, *Atlas of the Early Christian World*, 1958, pp. 142–3, 145, figs. 466–7.

MOSAICS

177. SCALLOP-SHELL   Plate 206
From Verulamium, Hertfordshire. Second century A.D. Height: 10 feet, 9 inches; width: 15 feet, 9 inches. *Verulamium Museum, St. Albans*

This pavement came to light in the apse of a room of a house built *c.* A.D. 130–50. It displays a great fan-shaped scallop-shell, the flutes of which are white with blue shading turning to mauve near the white hinge. The 'ears' of the shell are white, yellow, and orange and the shell is splendidly set off against an orange background, which is contained by a narrow wave-pattern border. The piece at once recalls the Hemsworth, Dorset, apse design.[1] But here there is no Venus poised upon the shell to distract the eye from its superbly decorative quality. Outside the design are two plain borders, first a broader one of orange and then a narrower yellow one.

R. E. M. and T. V. Wheeler, *Verulamium: a Belgic and Two Roman Cities*, 1936, pp. 144–5, pl. 39.

178. OCEANUS   Plate 207
From Verulamium, Hertfordshire. Second century A.D. Height: 8 feet; width: 7 feet, 11½ inches. *Verulamium Museum, St. Albans*

The house in which this piece was laid dates from *c.* 160–90. The pavement consists of a square with a wide key-pattern border enclosing an inner square panel. In the border are reserved four small oblong panels, one on each side, each containing an outward-facing chalice. The central square holds an imposing bust of Oceanus, with impressive, plastically modelled facial features and muscular neck and

1. *Catalogue of the Greek, Etruscan, and Roman Paintings and Mosaics in the British Museum*, 1933, pp. 99–100, no. 33, pl. 30. Plate 257.

shoulders. From the shaggy hair spring, not the usual lobster-claws, but what appear to be the claws or legs of some other sea-beast,[1] and the god wears a thick and neatly trimmed beard, instead of the loose, flowing beard that is usually characteristic of him. The colours used are red, white, grey, buff, and black.

R. E. M. and T. V. Wheeler, *Verulamium: a Belgic and Two Roman Cities*, 1936, p. 146, pls. 41; 45, a.

179. LION DEVOURING STAG   Plate 208
From Verulamium, Hertfordshire. Second century A.D. Dimension of square: 11 feet, 9 inches. *In situ (covered over)*

Excellently preserved is this polychrome pavement, with central figured panel. A heavily maned, tawny lion is striding towards the left, while below its head are seen the head and antlers of a stag, the remainder of which is to be imagined as either already devoured by, or concealed behind, the beast of prey. Three slightly curving red lines, running down beneath the lion's jaws, indicate the victim's blood. The lion is sturdily built and plastically modelled and shaded, with bright high-lights on head, flanks, haunches, and legs. Outside this central *emblema*, in each corner of the rich 'geometric' frame, is a neatly drawn, two-handled chalice, worked in yellow, white, and red. The figure-scene is a notably dramatic and pictorial piece, the work of an extremely competent and well-trained mosaicist.

Antiquaries Journal, xl, 1960, pp. 17–8, pls. 1; 3, b: *Journal of Roman Studies*, l, 1960, p. 227, pl. 25, fig. 1; *The Studio*, July, 1961, fig. on p. 7.

180. FOUNTAIN   Plate 209
From Verulamium, Hertfordshire. Second century A.D. Dimension of square: 8 feet. *Verulamium Museum, St. Albans*

This pavement is virtually complete. Its scheme of design is a grid of five squares and four rectangular panels; and the central and largest square is occupied by a slender, two-handled, yellow chalice, outlined in black. Two jets of pale-blue water spurt from the vessel's mouth and two yellow dolphins, outlined in black and sporting scarlet snouts, fins, and tail-prongs, dive down on either side with their tails entwined in the handles of the chalice.[2] The draftsmanship is

1. It has been suggested (*Journal of the British Archaeological Association*, ser. 3, xviii, 1955, p. 15; *Archaeologia Aeliana*, ser. 4, xxxix, 1961, p. 70) that these projections are horns and that the bust represents a Celtic horned god. But the protuberances do not look like antlers; and in view of the wholly Graeco-Roman content of the other three second-century figured mosaics at Verulamium, the present writer is still inclined to favour the Oceanus interpretation. For projections very similar to those on the Verulamium bust, on the top of an Oceanus mask on a mosaic from Dorchester, see *Proceedings of the Dorset Natural History and Archaeoligical Society*, xlix, 1928, pl. opp. p. 98. *Cf.* the projections springing from the heads of two Tritons on a marine mosaic in the Domus dei Dioscuri at Ostia: G. Becatti, *Scavi di Ostia* iv; mosaici e pavimenti marmorei, 1961, i, p. 120; ii, pl. 214.
2. A fourth-century pavement from the villa at Downton, Wiltshire, mainly 'geometric', shows in its central roundel a fluted chalice of which the two handles take the form of dolphins: Salisbury Museum: *Annual Report of the Museum*, 1956–7, pp. 9, 14, pl. 1.

sketchy and suggests the hand of a somewhat indifferent craftsman, but the general effect of the picture is gay and attractive. In two of the lateral, rectangular panels there is a stylised ivy-scroll.

Antiquaries Journal, xxxix, 1959, p. 13, pl. 4, a; *Journal of Roman Studies*, xlix, 1959, p. 123, pl. 13, fig. 2.

181. THREE SEASONS   Plates 210–2
From Cirencester (Corinium), Gloucestershire. Second century A.D. (?). Diameter of roundels: 4 feet, 9 inches. *Corinium Museum, Cirencester*

These are extracts from an elaborate, gaily coloured pavement consisting of a square with an eight-octagon grid, found in Dyer Street. Of the octagons, each of which seems to have enclosed a figured roundel, two had vanished, one had almost disappeared, and one was badly, another slightly, damaged at the time of the pavement's discovery. The corner-roundels hold each the outward-facing bust of a girl with seasonal attributes – Spring half-draped, crowned with leaves and flowers and accompanied by a bunch of flowers and a bird; Summer naked, wreathed with corn and flowers and equipped with a sickle and a bunch of corn-ears; Autumn draped, garlanded with grapes and vine-leaves, and armed with a pruning-knife, her other attribute being lost, as is also the whole of Winter. Summer and Autumn are excellently drawn and modelled, whereas Spring, with her hard, harsh lines, is by a less skilled hand.

Prof. Buckman and C. H. Newmarch, *Illustrations of the Remains of Roman Art in Cirencester*, 1850, pls. 2 opp. p. 38; 3, opp. p. 42; 4, opp. p. 44; 5, opp. p. 43.

182. MARINE SCENE   Plate 213
From Cirencester (Corinium), Gloucestershire. Second century A.D. (?). Dimensions not recorded. *Lost*

This pavement, found in Dyer Street in 1783, is now only known from S. Lysons's fine coloured drawing of it. The drawing shows part of a marine scene and the original would appear to have been one of the best-drawn and most classical in style of all the British figured mosaics. The figures that survived when the discovery was made were: part of a Nereid riding on a sea-beast; a flying Cupid clutching the wheel of a chariot that had once, presumably, carried Neptune; part of a second Cupid mounted on a dolphin; one hand of a third Cupid; a sea-lion, a sea-horse, and part of another sea-beast; a dolphin, a conger, a crab, other fish, and shells. The colours used were white, black, grey, brown, red, and yellow. Such a piece could have been laid in any quarter of the Mediterranean area, even in Rome itself.

S. Lysons, *Reliquiae Britannico-Romanae*, ii, 1817, pl. 7; Prof. Buckman and C. H. Newmarch, *Illustrations of the Remains of Roman Art in Cirencester*, 1850, pp. 29–31.

183. CYPARISSUS AND STAG   Plate 219
From Leicester (Ratae Coritanorum). Fourth century A.D. (?). Height of octagon: 3 feet, 4 inches; width of octagon: 3 feet, 4 inches. *Leicester Museum*

This octagonal panel was found near All Saints' Church about 1675. The figure-group that it contains shows Cyparissus, naked but for a scarf-like cloak, standing in front of, and holding by the collar, the beloved stag that he accidentally slew. The animal turns its head affectionately towards the youth; and a winged Cupid on the left, about to shoot an arrow from his bow, symbolises the mutual devotion of the boy and beast. Of Cyparissus' eventual transformation into a cypress-tree no hint is given in the picture: the story may have been continued in other panels that have vanished. The scene is portrayed with feeling; but the uncouthness of much of the drawing is suggestive of a late date. Fragments of white, grey, cream-coloured, black, and brown marble have been used by the mosaicist, together with cubes of bluish-grey, reddish-brown, and yellow limestone, of brown and citron sandstone, and of red terracotta.

VCH Leicestershire, i, 1907, pp. 192–4, pl. 3 (lower fig.); W. Fowler, *Engravings of the Principal Mosaic Pavements, etc.*, 1804, pl. 11 (Cambridge University Library copy).

184. WOLF AND TWINS   Plate 220
From Aldborough (Isurium Brigantum), Yorkshire. Fourth century A.D. (?). Height: 4 feet, 6 inches; width: 4 feet, 4½ inches. *Leeds City Museum*

This square panel depicts a Roman legendary subject – the She-Wolf nurturing the Twins beneath the *Ficus Ruminalis*. The grey trunk of the tree, which is very stylised, is on the left and it bends at the top horizontally towards the right across the upper portion of the field, where it puts out branches and oval, pointed, red and yellow leaves that bear no resemblance to fig-leaves. The Wolf stands towards the left against a yellow background, with her head facing the spectator and her righ forepaw raised and kicked out behind as though to indicate the Twins, who, instead of sucking her, are executing a kind of jig below her belly, where the craftsman has not attempted to render teats. The infants have grey heads and waist-belts, while the rest of them is carried out in red. The animal is grey, with white eyes and thick, wide, red lips that seem to grin with satisfaction; and her ears are pointed and upstanding, more like those of a cat or of a lynx than of a wolf. The picture, which is framed by a border of somewhat crudely drawn diamonds, is almost comic in its extreme naïvety. Yet the choice of the topic, the time-honoured symbol of Eternal Rome, presupposes at least some religious, mythological, and literary interest and knowledge on the part of the patron who commissioned the design.

H. Ecroyd Smith, *Reliquiae Isuriacae*, 1852, supplementary coloured pl.

185. ORPHEUS AND BEASTS   Plate 221
From the Barton Farm Villa, just outside Cirencester (Corinium), Gloucestershire. Fourth century A.D. Dimension of square: 14 feet, 8 inches. *Corinium Museum, Cirencester*

The figured portion of this polychrome pavement consists of a square in which are inscribed three concentric circular borders framing a central roundel. The latter is, to a large extent, complete and shows Orpheus seated, with a Phrygian cap, short tunic, flying cloak, and boots, and playing on a large lyre. On either side of his head faintly coloured tendrils occupy the background. To the right of him is a long-tailed, now headless, animal, probably a fox, and a portion of the picture on the left of him is lost. The inner border holds a file of seven birds, some wholly, others in part, preserved, strutting clockwise towards the left and separated from one another by stylised trees. The flock includes a peacock, a heron (?), and a goose (?): an eighth bird has disappeared. The middle, and narrowest, border contains a stiff garland of conventionalised, shaded laurel-leaves, arranged in rows of three; while the outer, and widest, border has a procession of quadrupeds slinking along in the same direction as the birds. These are separated by stylised, bushy trees and between, and below the bellies of, the beasts are also still more stylised, faintly coloured tendrils springing from the earth. Of the six animals that originally formed the company three are virtually intact – a lion, a tiger, and a scaly-coated leopard (?). There are also the foreparts of what may have been a bear; but of the other creatures only the merest fragments are preserved. Behind the animals' paws are short, wavy, horizontal lines suggesting shadows.

A number of the features of this pavement occur on nos. 186 and 187, while nos. 186 and 187 have other common features. There can be little doubt but that all three pavements were the products of the same firm of mosaicists and that the firm was established in Corinium. A lost Orpheus pavement from Cirencester itself, found in Dyer Street and known from a drawing,[1] again displayed some of the distinguishing elements of the Barton Farm, Woodchester, and Chedworth mosaics.

Prof. Buckman and C. H. Newmarch, *Illustrations of the Remains of Roman Art in Cirencester*, 1850, pl. 7 opp. p. 32; *Journal of the British Archaeological Association*, xxv, 1869, pls. 2–6; *Transactions of the Bristol and Gloucestershire Archaeological Society*, xxxiii, 1910, pp. 69-77, pl. between pp. 68 and 69.

186. ORPHEUS AND BEASTS   Plate 222
From the Woodchester Villa, Gloucestershire. Fourth century A.D. Over-all dimensions of mosaic room: 49 feet square. *In situ (covered over)*

This is the largest and most sumptuous of the polychrome pavements in the rich country house found below the village churchyard at Woodchester, near Stroud. It covered the floor of the *oecus*, or chief reception-room, in the centre of the main residential block. It is a square framed by a broad border with designs purely abstract in character, apart from four fluted chalices in roundels, enclosing an inner square, in each corner of which stood one of the four columns that

[1] K. J. Beecham, *History of Cirencester and the Roman City Corinium*, 1888, pl. opp. p. 266.

supported the roof of the chamber. Inscribed within the inner square is a circle composed of three concentric figured friezes, the inner one of which apparently enclosed an octagon. But of that only one angle has survived and the figured decoration that it doubtlessly once contained has been completely lost. Orpheus himself, of whom the left leg, with the lyre resting on his knee, and part of the skirt of his tunic have remained, is in the inner frieze and interrupts, on the outer side, its border which is composed of a wreath of rows of three shaded laurel-leaves of precisely the same type as that on no. 185. On the right of Orpheus are the tail and hindlegs of a fox, while stylised trees, of the same type as those in the bird-frieze on no. 185, and birds, the latter moving in procession towards Orpheus from either side, filled the remainder of the frieze. Among the birds can be distinguished a peacock, a pheasant scratching its chin, a dove, and perhaps a duck. The central frieze holds quadrupeds slinking along clockwise. Of these nine survive wholly or in part and in the gap that has been torn in the mosaic two more could have been accommodated had there been no tree between them. Large, bushy trees, exactly resembling those in the beast-frieze on no. 185, separate most of the existing beasts, although between the tiger and the stag and between the stag and the leopard there are only the faintly coloured tendrils which are likewise seen below the bellies of the animals and are again identical in type with those on no. 185. It would seem that the mosaicist had some difficulty with the spacing of his quadruped procession. The other beasts that we can identify are a bear, a winged Griffin, a lion, the head of another feline, and the hindquarters of a horse. These creatures cast the same small, wavy shadows as do their kinsmen from Barton Farm. The outer frieze shows just below the leg of Orpheus a bearded Oceanus mask, with the claws and legs of a sea-creature sprouting from the hair, from which springs, to right and left, a stylised, running floral scroll (cf. no. 187). Lastly, in each of the spandrel-shaped spaces between the circle and the corners of the inner square was a pair of reclining female figures, mainly nude. In one of these angles, that which holds the only remaining column-base, the pair survives almost entire – two Water-Nymphs wearing diaphanous cloaks and each leaning on a urn from which water flows. Of the second pair all but the head and left arm of a naked girl, together with the booted foot of her companion, can be seen. Of the third pair we have the legs only, while the fourth had been destroyed.

S. Lysons, *An Account of the Roman Antiquities Discovered at Woodchester in the County of Gloucester*, 1797, pls. 6–10; *Reliquiae Romano-Britannicae*, ii, 1817, pls. 22, 26–7; *Transactions of the Bristol and Gloucestershire Archaeological Society*, v, 1880–1, pp. 142–7, pls. 16–24; xlviii, 1926, pp. 75–96, pls. 1, 3–10.

187. THREE SEASONS AND FLORAL SCROLL

Plates 214–7

From the Chedworth Villa, Gloucestershire. Fourth century A.D. Dimensions of Seasons triangles: length: 4 feet, 10 inches; height 2 feet, 5 inches; dimensions of scroll-panels: length: 8 feet, 4½ inches; width: 1 foot, 6¾ inches

These mosaics are laid in the *triclinium* (dining-room) of the house. The room is divided into two portions. In the triangles at the corners of the northern pavement were the full-length polychrome figures of four small, dancing boys in the guise of Seasons. Autumn had disappeared, but the other three are perfectly preserved. Winter wears a hood, a flying cloak, a short, half-sleeved tunic, and perhaps leggings; in his right hand he holds a dead hare, in his left, a bare branch; and on either side of him is a heavy leaf-spray. Spring is naked, save for a narrow 'scarf' fluttering about his waist; he holds a bird and a flower-basket and is flanked on either side by a stylised ivy-leaf, while faintly coloured tendrils, similar to those already noted on nos. 185 and 186, occupy the background. Summer, who, unlike the other two, has wings, is completely nude and holds in his right hand a wreath, in his left a flower (?)-basket and a corn-ear (?): the same heavy leaf-sprays flank him as in the case of Winter.

The pavement in the southern section of the room is 'geometric', apart from two horizontal panels, on two of its opposite sides, each of which holds a handsome, stylised, running floral scroll that springs to right and left from a centrally placed bowl. The colours used in these panels are varying shades of brown and greyish-green; and the treatment of the scrolls is exactly the same as that in the outer scroll-border of the central roundel on no. 186.

M. and C. H. B. Quennell, *Everyday Life in Roman Britain*, 1952, figs. 102–3; L. Cottrell, *Seeing Roman Britain*, 1956, fig. 30; G. M. Durant. *Journey into Roman Britain*, 1957, pl. opp. p. 217.

188. SEASON

Plate 218

From the Bignor Villa, Sussex. Fourth century A.D. Height of octagon: 2 feet, 2¼ inches; width of octagon: 2 feet, 2¼ inches. *In situ*

Of this pavement many figures had already been destroyed when the house was excavated. The mosaic as a whole was divided into two large squares; and each of the corner octagons of one of these squares must have held a Season, although only the bust of Winter is preserved. It is a striking figure, muffled in a grey and brown hooded cloak, with expressive facial features and a dead, bare branch as attribute.

S. Lysons, *Reliquiae Britannico-Romanae*, iii, 1817, pls. 13, 15, 22.

189. MEDUSA MASK

Plate 223

From the Bignor Villa, Sussex. Fourth century A.D. Diameter of roundel: 3 feet, 2 inches. *In situ*

This is in the central octagon of a 'geometric' piece. Within a roundel is a vigorously drawn Medusa mask with stylised hair and writhing snakes emerging from it. The colours used are black, white, blue-grey, yellow, pink, scarlet, and crimson.

S. Lysons, *Reliquiae Britannico-Romanae*, iii, 1817, pls. 27–8.

190. RAPE OF GANYMEDE   Plate 224
From the Bignor Villa, Sussex. Fourth century A.D. Diameter of roundel: 7 feet, 2 inches. *In situ*

This polychrome mosaic shows, within a central roundel, Ganymede, a plump, fair-skinned youth, naked save for boots and a red, fluttering cloak. He is being carried up to heaven by a very large and naturalistically rendered yellow eagle. The roundel is inscribed in a square, in each corner of which is a bowl holding leaf-sprays.

S. Lysons, *Reliquiae Britannico–Romanae*, iii, 1817, pls. 5, 7.

191. VENUS AND CUPIDS AS GLADIATORS
                                          Plates 225–6
From the Bignor Villa, Sussex. Fourth century A.D. Height of lunette: 2 feet, 4 inches; length of frieze: 14 feet, 8 inches. *In situ*

This polychrome piece covered the floor of the apsed *triclinium* of the house. The lunette in the apse, which is very well preserved, has a broad border filled by a highly ornamental running floral scroll, which springs to right and left from the mouth of a fluted bowl at the centre of the chord. Within this border, in a roundel, is the delicately drawn bust of Venus, nimbed, diademed, and draped, with her dark hair falling loosely in strands upon her shoulders. On each side of her a leafy swag, on which a bird is perching, unites the roundel with the border, while in the field are two fruit-and-leaf-sprays and two *cornuacopiae*. This lunette is connected with the main rectangular area of the chamber by a narrow frieze along the chord, in which nine winged Cupids, dressed and armed as gladiators, are practising under the direction of three winged Cupid trainers, who wear tunics of late-antique style. Here the draftsmanship is somewhat clumsy, but the movements and gestures of the troupe are expressive and lively.

S. Lysons, *Reliquiae Britannico–Romanae*, iii, 1817, pls. 16, 19, 23.

192. RAPE OF EUROPA   Plate 229
From the Lullingstone Villa, Kent. Fourth century A.D. Width of figured panel: 8 feet. *In situ*

The mosaics of the villa's apsed *triclinium*, built *c.* A.D. 330, fall into two distinct, but closely related, parts, on the east, a rectangular area, on the west, an apse, raised above the other by a step nine inches high. The figure-decoration of the pavement in each compartment faces towards the west; and outside the semi-circular mosaic picture in the apse, between it and the curving western wall of the *triclinium*, is a broad, horse-shoe-shaped area of large plain *tesserae*. On this would have stood the *sigma* (curved table) and the couches of the diners, who could thus have viewed the pavements to full advantage, from the proper angle, as they dined.[1]
The upper and larger portion of the background of the pavement in the apse is white and represents the sky; the lower and smaller segment is of dark-blue *tesserae* to indicate the sea. A spirited bull bounds across the sea towards the right, his hind-hooves touching the water, his forelegs extended through the air horizontally. On the creature's back, facing the spectator, while her knees are turned towards the tail, sits Europa, half-draped in a diaphanous cloak, which hangs behind her and is then drawn forward to swathe the legs. Arched above her head she holds a veil or 'scarf' that flutters in the breeze. She wears a bracelet, two armlets, and a necklace. The somewhat fatuously gratified expression on the bull's countenance suggests his pleasure in his prize. On the left a winged Cupid playfully twists the animal's tail, while a second winged Cupid on the right strides ahead, looking back towards the pair as he makes a gesture of encouragement. All the figures are drawn in red outline and are completely two-dimensional and flat, without modelling or shading of any kind, except in the hair and faces, where some yellow and purple *tesserae* are used. But the whole effect of the design is gay and full of movement and the draftsmanship is careful and assured. It seems likely that the mosaicist who laid this pavement, and the most important figured portions of that in the other section of the room, was of continental origin and training. Above the Europa scene, and facing in the same direction, is an inscription written along the chord of the apse in two lines. It is an elegaic couplet that scans correctly and is of quite respectable Latinity:

> *invida si ta[uri] vidisset Iuno natatus*
> *iustius Aeolias isset adusque domos*

('If jealous Juno had seen the swimming of the bull she would with greater justice on her side have repaired to the halls of Aeolus').
Here there is, of course, an allusion to the first book of the *Aeneid*, where Juno is described as persuading the god of the winds to raise a storm to overwhelm Aeneas on his voyage to Italy; the implication being that a plot of this kind to submerge her faithless consort would have been more excusable. The couplet would have been meaningless to anyone who did not know his Virgil (*cf.* no. 200).[2]
Archaeologia Cantiana, lxiii, 1950, pp. 44–5, pls. 1, b; 5, b; G. W. Meates, *Lullingstone Roman Villa*, 1955, pp. 34–46, pls. 5, 8–9; ed. R. L. S. Bruce-Mitford, *Recent Archaeological Excavations in Britain*, 1956, pp. 92–4, pls. 17, b; 18, b.

193. BELLEROPHON AND CHIMAERA   Plate 228
From the Lullingstone Villa, Kent. Fourth century A.D. Width of figured panel: 7 feet. *In situ*

---

1. *Cf.* the similar arrangement of the mosaic pictures in the apsed *triclinium* in the 'House of the Buffet Supper' at Antioch on the Orontes in Syria (D. Levi, *Antioch Mosaic Pavements*, 1947, ii, pl. 23, a).

2. The only other British mosaic certainly depicting the Europa story is that found in the villa at Keynsham, near Bristol, and now displayed in the Visitors' Reception Hall in Messrs. Fry's Chocolate Factory at Somerdale. There Europa is already seated on the bull's back and is encircling its neck with a garland. But the animal has not yet left *terra firma* and one of Europa's companions is offering it a basket of flowers (*Archaeologia*, lxxv, 1926, p. 128, pl. 17, fig. 1).

In the centre of the lower, rectangular floor of the villa's *triclinium* is a cushion-shaped area or square with sagging sides, forming a panel with a white ground in which another lively figure-group, is depicted. This, like no. 192, is drawn in flat, two-dimensional, but black, instead of red, outline and shows a white, winged Pegasus rushing towards the right with Bellerophon upon his back. The hero wears a red cloak and red boots and is thrusting with his spear, composed of alternating red and white cubes, at the Chimaera, a monster with a lion's head, a serpent's tail, and the here somewhat unconvincingly delineated head and shoulders of a goat emerging from the centre of the back. The fire-breathing creature runs rapidly below the belly of the horse and in the same direction. In each corner of the 'cushion' is a sea-beast, a sea-lion or perhaps a dolphin; and within the field, to left and right of Bellerophon and Pegasus, are two dumbbell-shaped, striped objects, which have been oddly identified as 'pillars'.[1] They are actually mussel-shells, with their two valves open and connected by an abnormally thick and massive hinge.[2] This association of Bellerophon with water admits of two explanations. On the one hand, the scene at Lullingstone may illustrate the Roman 'simultaneous' method of narration, which comprises within a single picture two successive episodes of the same story: Bellerophon crosses the sea from Greece and slays the Chimaera in Lycia. On the other hand, the aquatic motifs could allude to Bellerophon's role as a maritime hero.[3] (For the different standards of workmanship on this mosaic, see Introduction, p. 14).

This rendering of the story of Bellerophon, so far unique in Roman Britain, takes its place in a series of twelve known ancient representations of the myth in mosaic-work. The earliest of them is on a late-fifth-century B.C. pebble pavement from Olynthus, in northern Greece, the latest on the fifth-century A.D. mosaic in the peristyle of the early-Byzantine imperial palace in Constantinople.[4] At Lullingstone, in each of the corners of the square that contains the central 'cushion' is the bust of a Season in a roundel. Winter wears a hooded cloak; Spring has a bird; while Summer, crowned with somewhat lean corn-ears, seems to have usurped the place next to Winter usually occupied by Autumn, who, once next to Spring and presumably wreathed with grapes and vine-leaves, vanished in a fire, probably the final fire that destroyed the villa. Since the Seasons accompany Bellerophon on two other Roman-age mosaics, from Nîmes and from Ravenna, this association is unlikely to be due to chance or merely 'decorative'. If the slaying of the monster denotes the soul's victory over death (*cf.* Introduction, p. 14), the Seasons would be an allegory of its everlasting bliss in paradise.

1. *Archaeologia Cantiana*, lxiii, 1951, p. 46.
2. *Cf.* the similar renderings of mussel-shells on mosaics from Jurançon, Basses Pyrénées (*Inventaire des mosaiques de la Gaule et de l'Afrique*, i, 1; *Narbonnaise et Aquitaine*, 1911, no. 409) and Dougga, Tunisia (*ibid.*, ii, 1: *Tunisie*, 1913, no. 560).
3. *Gallia*, xi, 1953, p. 267.
4. *Ibid.*, xvi, 1958, p. 266.

Archaeologia Cantiana, lxiii, 1950, pp. 45–7, pls. 1, b; 5, a; G. W. Meates, *Lullingstone Roman Villa*, 1955, pp. 26–32, pls. 3–7; ed. R. L. S. Bruce-Mitford, *Recent Archaeological Excavations in Britain*, 1956, pp. 92–4, pls. 17, b; 18, a.

194. FISH   Plate 230
From the Lufton Villa, Somerset. Fourth century A.D. Length of each side of octagon: 8 feet. *In situ (covered over)*

The ambulatory of the octagonal plunge-bath in this country house near Yeovil contained a figured pavement that for Britain is again unique – panels containing a row of fish along each of seven of the sides. The mosaic on one of these sides has been destroyed; and the eighth side has a design of 'geometric' patterns, faultily set by a careless, no doubt local, craftsman, since its lateral motifs do not correspond in size. Of the six existing fish-panels, one of which was represented in the Exhibition, two contain four fish, three five fish, and one six fish, including two eels or congers, each entwined about the body of another fish, making a total of twenty-nine surviving. The fish are drawn in a somewhat summary, but lively, style, many of them blowing from their noses clusters of bubbles as they swim along to right or left. They are worked on a white ground in six different colours – white, yellow, pink, red, blue, and black. Among them a sharp-nosed creature like a sword-fish can be detected; but the rest are schematic and conventional, less naturalistic than ornamental, and their individual equation with particular species is not possible. These are certainly not local river-fish of southern Britain, based on the craftsman's personal observation of Nature. They are copy-book creations; and for those, all over the Roman world, the marine fauna of the Italian coasts furnished the ultimate models. It was in the first centuries B.C. and A.D. that such models were established; and by the third and fourth centuries A.D., and in distant lands, the copies of these grew more and more stylised, with hard, conventionally ringed eyes, flattened tails, and stiff dorsal fins, all features that are found on the fish at Lufton.

Proceedings of the Somersetshire Archaeological and Natural History Society, xcvii, 1952, pp. 91–112, pls. 6–9.

195. ORPHEUS AND BEASTS   Plate 232
From the Brading Villa, Isle of Wight. Fourth century A.D. Dimension of square: 8 feet, 2 inches. *In situ*

This pavement in the centre of the long, narrow Room VI of the house consists of a square framing a circle. In the circle is the best-preserved, and in many ways the most attractive, of all the British renderings of Orpheus himself, who is seated on a light-grey rock to the front, wearing a scarlet Phrygian cap and a scarlet cloak and playing on a gold and grey lyre with scarlet strings. To the right and left of him are four spell-bound creatures – a red-capped ape, worked in light-grey with red outlines, and a dark-grey peacock on the left, a small, dark-grey bird and a long-tailed yellow fox on the right. The link between Orpheus and the birds and beasts is more intimate in this scheme[1] than in that of nos. 185 and 186, where they circle in separate zones round their enchanter. This Orpheus group is, on the whole, superior to all the other scenes and figures on the Brading pavements and might have been by a foreign master. In the four corners between the circle and the square are the remains of human heads, crudely drawn in black outline, that could be Seasons.

J. E. Price and F. G. Hilton Price, *A Description of the Remains of Roman Buildings at Moreton, near Brading, Isle of Wight*, 1881, pl. opp. p. 10.

196. ASTRONOMER   Plate 233
From the Brading Villa, Isle of Wight. Fourth century A.D. Dimension of square: 3 feet, 6 inches. *In situ*

This square polychrome mosaic is in the centre of the panel of the pavement linking the two main rectangles of which the floor of Room XII of the house is composed. It contains a half-draped, bearded personage seated on a cushioned chair, whom we may with confidence identify as an astronomer. To the left of him is a sun-dial on a pillar, and below these, resting on a three-legged stool, is a globe, at which the man is pointing with a rod. A vase, from which projects a spray of foliage, stands on the ground in the lower right-hand corner of the picture.[2] If the generally religious meaning of these pavements be admitted, this astronomer might be regarded as an embodiment of the intellectual wisdom that was, according to Roman after-life ideas, one of the roads to immortality.

J. E. Price and F. G. Hilton Price, *A Description of the Remains of Roman Buildings at Moreton, near Brading, Isle of Wight*, 1881, pl. between pp. 16 and 17.

197. SCENE WITH COCK-HEADED MAN   Plate 231
From the Brading Villa, Isle of Wight. Fourth century A.D. Height of panel: 2 feet, 5 inches; width of panel: 4 feet. *In situ*

This is one of the five surviving panels of an original set of nine which made up the grid on the pavement of Room III of the house. It carries an enigmatic scene – a small gabled building with a red, tiled roof and a door approached by a ladder or steps, which ascend the side of the grey hill or mound which the building crowns. On the left stands a personage with a red cock's head and a human body, clad in a long-sleeved, short, grey tunic, with scarlet stripes, and a yellow cape, perhaps the cock-headed Gnostic Abraxes. On the left, at different levels, are two grey, winged Griffins, facing to right and left respectively. The present writer knows of no other work of ancient art that can throw any light on the meaning of this picture. Meanwhile, it may be suggested that the scene depicts some mystic initiation, in

which the neophyte wears a bird-mask, with the ladder or steps as a symbol of the soul's ascent to heaven, represented by a temple, and the Griffins as guardians of the dead.

J. E. Price and F. G. Hilton Price, *A Description of the Remains of Roman Buildings at Morton, near Brading, Isle of Wight*, 1881, pl. opp. p. 8.

198. CHARIOT-RACE   Plate 227
From the Horkstow Villa, Lincolnshire. Fourth century A.D. Length: 19 feet, 5 inches. *British Museum*

The scene in this oblong panel is the best-preserved section of the pavement from this house. It is, in fact, complete, apart from a gash across the centre and a fairly small lacuna in the right-hand lower corner. It depicts a circus-race, with the *spina* (central wall), which terminates at either end in a pair of conically capped *metae* (turning-posts), running across the centre of the field. Above the *spina* is a *biga* (two-horse chariot) advancing to the left. It seems to have lost a wheel, and to the right of it we see a horseman who has dismounted in order to assist the discomfited *auriga* (charioteer) pitching headlong from his chariot. To the right again is a second horseman, riding leftwards and waving a lasso. Below the *spina* three *bigae* are galloping towards the right. The horses are worked in buff, red, and bluish-grey: the men have brown, buff, and red clothing, late-antique in type, while their faces are outlined in brown. The drawing of the men is clumsy, but the horses are, relatively, very well done, with varied, naturalistic poses and vivid movements. In the context of the Orpheus scene, which forms the subject of one of the fragmentary sections of this pavement, the horsemen and charioteers are unlikely to have carried any specifically local or topical allusion – to horse-breeding in the Horkstow area or to aristocratic sports in the circus of the *colonia* at Lindum.[3] If the Orpheus is associated, as it well may have been, with other-world ideas, the circus-scene – a common copy-book motif – could have served here as an allegory of the race of life and of the soul's final victory.

W. Fowler, *Engravings of the Principal Mosaic Pavements, etc.*, 1804, pl. 2 (Cambridge University Library copy); S. Lysons, *Reliquiae Britannico-Romanae*, i, 1813, pls. 5–6; *British Museum Quarterly*, ii, 1927–8, pp. 44–6, pl. 24; *Catalogue of the Greek, Etruscan, and Roman Paintings and Mosaics in the British Museum*, 1933, pp. 108–9, 112, no. 36p, fig. 124; *Guide to the Antiquities of Roman Britain in the British Museum*, 1951, p. 58, (b), no. 1, pl. 22; 1958, p. 58, (b), no. 1, pl. 22.

199. NEPTUNE, ETC.   Plate 234
From the Frampton Villa, Dorset. Fourth century A.D. Dimensions not recorded. *In situ (covered over)(?)*.

The villa at Frampton (Maiden Newton), eight miles north-west of Dorchester, yielded to the excavators three remarkable late mosaics, now lost, or at any rate long since reburied and inaccessible. Their disappearance is all the more regrettable inasmuch as they are among the richest and most interesting

1. The closest parallel to this scheme of composition is that of an Orpheus mosaic found at Ptolemais in Cyrenaica (*Journal of Roman Studies*, lii, 1962, pp. 13–8, fig. 1, pls. 1–7).
2. For the seated figure of an astronomer, possibly Anaximander, holding a sun-dial, see the mosaic from the Johannisstrasse, Trier (K. Parlasca, *Die römischen Mosaiken in Deutschland*, 1959, pls. A, fig. 1; 28, fig. 2). Plate 258.

3. I. A. Richmond, *Archaeological Journal*, ciii, 1947, p. 68; *Roman Britain*, 1955, p. 123.

pavements that have come to light in Britain. One (that shown in the Exhibition) is of no small significance for the study of Romano-British Christianity.

This is the famous Neptune and Chi-Rho mosaic, a pavement that consists of two figured squares, one larger than the other, linked by a narrow 'geometric' strip. From the side of the larger square projects an apse, with a chalice in a panel at its apex and across its chord a border, of which the sacred monogram in a roundel forms the central feature, while a floral scroll runs on either side of it. The square is framed all round by a border, in each of the four lengths of which is a dolphin procession; while on the side adjacent to the apse, but within the square, is an inscription[1] running to right and left of a centrally placed head of Neptune facing towards the apse and with a pair of dolphins issuing from his mouth. The head breaks through the dolphin procession at this point, as does also, in the centre of the side adjacent to the smaller square, a figure of Cupid, flanked by birds and, above them, by the remnants of another text.[2] In the centre of the larger square is a roundel containing the figure of a hunter, whose horse is rearing above a feline.[3] Outside the roundel, in the corners of the square, are small square panels, each with a figure-group (one of which is lost) illustrating the story of Venus and Adonis. Between these squares are four lunette-shaped sectors, the decoration of three of which has disappeared, while in the fourth we can detect remains of water-birds. Beyond the linking 'geometric' strip, in the smaller main square of the pavement, Bacchus is seated on a leopard in a large roundel, which is flanked on two sides of the square by rectangular panels, one showing a hunter in pursuit of a stag and a bear (?), the other a second hunter attacking a lion.

The large and centrally placed Chi-Rho in the apsed compartment of this pavement would seem to indicate that the owner of the Frampton villa, who had this mosaic laid, was a Christian or had close Christian contacts. If that were so, the pagan motifs of the two main squares, including the Neptune and the verses in his honour, do not appear to have troubled him. He would, no doubt, have interpreted them, as his pagan contemporary neighbours would have done, as symbols of the after-life, of death, rebirth, and paradise.

S. Lysons, *Reliquiae Romano–Britannicae*, i, 1813, pl. 5; T. D. Kendrick, *Anglo-Saxon Art to A.D. 900*, 1938, pl, 21.

200. SCENES FROM VIRGIL   Plate 235
From the Low Ham Villa, Somerset. Fourth century A.D. Over-all dimensions of mosaic: 13 feet square. *Castle Museum, Taunton*

1. F. Bücheler, *Anthologia Latina: Carmina Latina Epigraphica*, 1895–7, no. 1524: *Neptuni vertex regmen sortiti mobile ventis/scultum cui caerulea es[t frons] delfinis cincta duob[us]*. The Latin, which appears to be written in heptameters, can be construed as: 'The head of Neptune, to whose lot fell the kingdom (of the sea) scoured by the winds, is figured here, his deep-blue brow girt by a pair of dolphins'.
2. *... nus perfici ullum/... gnare Cupido.*
3. This cannot be Bellerophon slaying the Chimaera, for the back of the feline, which is shown in Lysons's drawing as well preserved, has no goat's head growing out of it.

The discovery at Low Ham, two-and-a-half miles east of Langport, of this remarkable polychrome mosaic, depicting the romance of Dido and Aeneas, was due to a somewhat unromantic circumstance, to a farmer digging a grave for a diseased sheep in 1938. Part of the site of the interment can, indeed, be detected in one corner of the pavement, where *tesserae* have been displaced; and the operation did, in fact, come within a few inches of wrecking the decorated area completely. But the burial at any rate succeeded in throwing up the Roman tiles which suggested the presence of a villa and led to the first trial-excavation in 1945. In 1946 the mosaic was gradually cleared and found to cover the *frigidarium* (cold bath) of the baths of an exceptionally large country house.

The mosaic consists of a central square panel surrounded on all four sides by two long and two rectangular panels, making in all five pictures, which are divided from one another by guilloche borders. The central picture has an octagonal frame of plait-pattern, while the two long scenes are each completely enclosed in a guilloche border and by an inner narrow black line. The work is carried out against a white background in vivid colours – scarlet, crimson, white, yellow, gold, blue, grey, brown, and black being the chief ones employed; and all the *tesserae* are of local materials. The style of the drawing, the associated coins and pottery, and the floor-layers under the mosaic suggest for the latter a mid-fourth-century date. It is unlikely to be earlier than *c.* A.D. 350. Naïve as their figures are aesthetically, these pictures are yet, as an archaeological document, of very great importance, first as bearing witness to the standards of literary culture attained by fourth-century villa dwellers in this country and secondly in view of their relation to the fascinating question of book-illustration in the Roman world (*cf.* Introduction, p. 15).

The four scenes that enclose the centre-piece face outwards towards the walls of the *frigidarium*. Those to the right of and above the central picture (when this is viewed the right way up) illustrate *Aeneid* Book i, those to the left of and below it, *Aeneid* Book iv. The story begins on the right-hand side (Scene I), where three ships, representing the Trojan fleet, have arrived at the African coast near Carthage. These are drawn very crudely, with bird-heads at prow and stern, a single sail, and a series of St. Andrew's crosses adorning the bulwarks, below which oars resembling knitting-needles stick out diagonally. In the first ship, on the left, can be seen the heads of two men with the upper parts of two shields – unless the dome-shaped object between the men is not a shield, but the case in which Anchises salvaged the *sacra* from the sack of Troy. The second ship contains a helmeted head, probably that of the Palladion, also saved from Troy,[4] the head of a woman, probably a priestess, and

4. The bringing from Troy of the Palladion is not explicitly recorded in Virgil's text, but the reverse-type of a *denarius* of Julius Caesar, which depicts Aeneas escaping from the city with his aged father, Anchises, on one arm and the Palladion in his other hand, shows that this tradition was current in the poet's time (H. A. Grueber, *Coins of the Roman Republic in the British Museum*, 1910, ii, p. 469, nos. 31–5; iii, pl. 110, no. 20).

that of a youth wearing a Phrygian cap, who may be Ascanius, Aeneas' son. The third ship holds only one man, who is handing a large wreath or collar to another man, so placed in this picture, when viewed from the bottom, that he seems to be lying on his back; and behind his shoulders are the traces of the sheep's burial.

This man, who wears a striped cloak and holds a spear over his left shoulder, is almost certainly Achates, the faithful companion of Aeneas, sent by the latter, after his arrival at Dido's court, back to the Trojan ships to fetch Ascanius and presents for the Queen. These included a collar set with pearls and a double diadem, bejewelled and of gold:

> colloque monile
> baccatum et duplicem gemmis auroque coronam
> (Aen. i, 654–5),

one of which the mosaicist has depicted. And Achates' curious position within the framework of Scene I is best explained by supposing that we have here a conflation of two scenes in the original book-illustration or copy-book which the craftsman was adapting – first, a scene in which Achates would have been shown facing the ship to receive the gift from the man standing in it, and, secondly, one in which he would have been represented as hastening back to Carthage with it. It is with Scene II that the figure of Achates is aligned, although he is outside its framework.

In this four-figure picture we have no direct illustration of particular words of Virgil, but a kind of paraphrase of the last hundred lines (657–756) of Book i of the Aeneid, of the passage immediately preceding the famous banquet at which Dido entertained her Trojan guests. Venus has sent Cupid, disguised as Ascanius, first to Aeneas and then to Dido, to stir in their hearts a mutual vivus amor (Aen. i, 721); and Cupid's task has been very successfully accomplished, for Aeneas and Dido have clearly become intensely interested in one another and are exchanging sidelong glances. Aeneas stands on the left, with his leg crossed, and supports himself on his spear. He is bearded and wears a Phrygian cap – a form of headgear which, unlike Ascanius, he never sports in earlier works of art, a cuirass with a broad belt and with striped and pleated 'skirt' and sleeves, and leather boots. On the right is Dido – not Anna, the Queen's sister and confidante, as the excavators have described her, but the second of the protagonists, balancing Aeneas and too conspicuous to be a minor character. She wears a bluish-white transparent 'skirt' and a red 'scarf' thrown round her naked shoulders. On the crown of her head is a large round curl, a feature which distinguishes the figure that is unquestionably Dido in the next two scenes. Her right hand is raised, with the forefinger pressed against the chin, in the familiar Roman gesture expressive of such emotions as wonder, admiration, bewilderment, or confusion.[1] As contrasted with her guest's swarthy skin, the Queen's flesh is white, and so is that of Venus, who stands between the lovers, but slightly with-

drawn from them, with her right arm and hand thrown affectionately round the shoulders of Cupid-Ascanius, the boyish figure on her right. The goddess is completely naked, wearing only a semicircular diadem or crown, the mark of Venus Genetrix (mother of Aeneas and foundress of the Julian House), necklace, armlets, and a fourfold breast-and-back chain, with a large oval jewel on the centre of the breast, catching together the chain's four segments, to which a similar jewel on the centre of the back doubtlessly corresponded.[2] It looks as if the painting or statue, from which the figure of the Low Ham Venus was derived, was lighted from the left, since it is the opposite side of the legs and thighs that is shaded. The mosaicist unfortunately forgot the black tessera that should have marked the pupil of the right eye, with the result that the goddess appears to be winking violently. Cupid-Ascanius, who has the white flesh of childhood, wears a red Phrygian cap, a red dalmatic over a white, long-sleeved tunic with coloured wrist-bands, and red shoes and leggings. In his right hand he holds a spear.

The second long panel (Scene III) presents the famous hunting-episode of Aeneid iv. On the left is Dido on a grey mount, wearing a large round curl, a small cap or helmet with pointed peak, a striped cloak that billows out behind her, while the other end is twisted scarf-like round her otherwise naked form, and short boots. Aeneas, in the centre, rides a jet-black horse and is naked, save for a Phrygian cap, a striped, flying cloak, and boots. He turns his head back towards the Queen as though to indicate to her that they have been outstripped by the boy Ascanius, seen on the right on a greyish–white pony and in the same dress as in the previous scene. The boy's cloak flies out behind him, as he gallops along in full career, just as Virgil describes him:

> at puer Ascanius mediis in vallibus acri
> gaudet equo, iamque hos cursu, iamque praeterit illos
> (Aen. iv, 156–7).

Here no landscape effects have been attempted.

The next panel, the second short one (Scene IV), depicts the climax of the story – the embrace of Dido and Aeneas in the cave in which they have sheltered from the storm. No actual cave is shown, but a couple of very stylised, windswept trees indicate the rustic setting and the tempest. The lovers stand locked in one another's arms – Dido on the left, wearing her large round curl and peaked cap or helmet, bootless, and completely naked save for a 'scarf' twined about her, Aeneas on the right, having donned, in addition to the Phrygian cap and boots of Scene III, the sleeved, belted, and 'skirted' cuirass of Scene II, but with no cloak visible. Finally, within the central octagon, Venus, the divine 'stage-manager', appears again (Scene V), a statuesque figure silhouetted against her cloak, which she is in the act of throwing off as she grasps a corner of it in either hand. She affects the same headdress, that of Venus Genetrix, as in Scene II, but lacks the necklace, the armlets, and the fourfold breast-

---

1. A Pompeian wall-painting shows Aeneas making just the same gesture when he first catches sight of Dido on arriving at her court (*Memorie della Reale Accademia di Archeologia, Lettere e Belle Arts* (Società Reale di Napoli), iii, 1918, pl. opp. p. 114).

2. An actual fourfold chain, of gold and of late-Roman date, with central ornaments for breast and back, was found in Egypt and is now in the British Museum (W. Dennison, *Studies in East Christian and Roman Art*, 1918, pp. 149–50, no. 15, pls. 39–40).

and-back chain. The goddess is flanked on either side by a winged, naked, and torch-bearing Cupid. The Cupid on her right stands with his eyes closed, legs crossed, and torch reversed, in the attitude of mourning. His companion on the left of Venus darts swiftly along towards his mistress, with open eyes, alert gaze, and torch erect, while a fold of drapery perhaps the 'scarf' of Venus, passes horizontally across his abdomen. The torches are not wedding-torches, since the torch held downwards spells death. Indeed, the Cupid on our left alludes to Dido, who died, that on the right to Aeneas, who surmounted the temptations of the love-affair and lived to fulfil his mission. In other words, the dominating theme of what otherwise appears to be a purely literary pavement is a moral and religious one, that of death as a source of life, of which Venus is one of many symbols.

The Low Ham mosaic takes its place in a cycle of ancient illustrations of Virgil's text executed in the Roman age in various media – in wall-paintings, on mosaic pavements, in sculptured reliefs, on medals or medallions, and in manuscripts. The most important and spectacular series of such pictures are those contained in the two illustrated MSS of Virgil now in the Vatican Library (see Introduction, p. 15). The miniatures of the earlier MS (c. A.D. 400) are very eclectic in character, being reminiscent of works of art of all periods from the first to the fourth century A.D. The illustrations of the later MS (generally dated c. 500, by some, to the early-fourth century) are far less classical in style: some are, indeed, almost medieval in appearance. Of the pictures of the earlier (?) codex the most relevant to our mosaic is no. 11, which depicts Aeneas at Dido's court and Achates hurrying off, spear in hand, to fetch the gifts from the Trojan ships (Plate 260). Picture no. 15 in the later (?) codex shows the cave-scene, but in a very different vein from that at Low Ham. Dido and Aeneas sit primly side by side in a cupboard-like cave, into which they seem to have been packed sardine-wise, while outside it hunters and horses shelter themselves as best they can from the drenching rain (Plage 261). The Virgilian wall-paintings are mostly from Pompeii and date from the first centuries B.C. and A.D. But those from the villa at Otford, in Kent, are probably of the fourth century.[1] The

other Virgilian mosaics belong to various epochs in the imperial period; while the reliefs and medallions are mainly of the first and second centuries A.D. The distinguishing mark of the Low Ham mosaic, as contrasted with all these other works of art has been already noted (see Introduction, p. 15). Our pavement supplies definite indications that the design was imported into Britain from abroad and that the piece was worked in this country by a local craftsman closely following an imported copy-book, or, possibly, by a visiting craftsman who brought his copy-book with him. The subject-matter suggests North Africa, the horses are of a type frequently met with on Tunisian and Algerian mosaics, and both Dido's large round curl and Venus' breast-and-back chain are best paralleled on a pavement depicting the Three Graces from Sabratha, in Tripolitania.[2] Further, it may be noted that in order to see the outward-facing Scenes I–IV to full advantage, one must obviously stand, not on the mosaic, but outside it. Yet the walls of the *frigidarium*, on the floor of which the pavement lay, came within a few inches of the picture: only by flattening oneself against those walls most uncomfortably could one have enjoyed those scenes the right way up. The design was, in fact, originally intended for a quite different context, for a central space surrounded by a passage-way or ambulatory, enabling one to walk round the Virgilian mosaic and examine these outward-facing scenes in comfort. Indeed, in the case of two at least of the Mediterranean pavements, known to the present writer, with continuous outward-facing scenes enclosing a central panel, one at Villelaure, in southern France,[3] the other at Oudna, in Tunisia,[4] there is to be found just such an ambulatory, in the first example, floored only with 'geometric' patterns, in the second example, separated from the pictures by a colonnade.

Journal of Roman Studies, xxxvi, 1946, p. 142, pl. 11; C. A. Ralegh Radford and H. S. L. Dewar, *The Roman Mosaics from Low Ham and East Coker* (Somerset County Museum Publications, No. 2), 1954.

1. *Catalogue of the Greek, Etruscan, and Roman Paintings and Mosaics in the British Museum*, 1933, pp. 56–7, no. 84, fig. 64 (where the fragment with the human figure is reproduced upsidedown).

2. Unpublished. Plate 259.
3. *Inventaire des mosaïques de la Gaule et de l'Afrique*, i, 1: *Narbonnaise et Aquitaine*, 1911, no. 105; *Bulletin Archéologique du Comité des Travaux Historiques et Scientifiques*, 1903, pl. 1.
4. C. Daremberg, E. Saglio, and E. Pottier, *Dictionnaire des antiquités grecques et romaines*, iii, 2, 1904, s.v. *musivum opus*, p. 2113, fig. 5249.

ADDENDUM to No. 12, p. 130, col. 1, note 1
Cf. also (i) a crudely worked marble group from Ankara, showing Bacchus standing between Pan, on his left, and Silenus mounted on a panther and backed against a tree-trunk, on his right: Museum of Antiquities, Istanbul: G. Mendel, *Catalogues des sculptures grecques, romaines, et byzantines*, iii, 1914, pp. 602–4, no. 1392; (ii) a small amber group, 10 inches high, from near Esch (N. Brabant), in Holland,

showing Bacchus with *thyrsus* and a drinking-horn, supported by a Satyr and with a panther crouching at his right side, while a vine-tree forms a background to the figures: Centraal Noordbrabants Museum, Den Bosch: *Bulletin van de Vereeniging tot Bevordering der Kennis van de antieke Beschaving te 'S-Gravenhage*, xxxvii, 1962, pp. 61–7, figs. 1–2. The present writer owes these two references to Dr. M. J. Vermaseren.

GLOSSARY OF LATIN AND GREEK TERMS

aedicula niche

aegis upper garment, normally with Medusa mask, worn by Jupiter, Minerva, and some Emperors

aerarius copper-smith

ansa handle

auriga charioteer

balteus sword-belt

biga two-horse chariot

caduceus serpent-staff

canabae civil settlement outside a fortress

candelabrum lamp-stand

cantharus wine-cup

cardo cockle-shell

cingulum militiae military belt

cista mystica sacred casket

civis Carnutenus native of the Chartres region of France

cornucopiae horn of plenty

denarius standard Roman silver coin

Domus Divina Divine (i.e. Imperial) House

duplicarius petty officer

emblema central ornament or panel, circular or rectangular

exomis slipped tunic

fibula brooch

Ficus Ruminalis legendary fig-tree in Rome

focus fire-place on an altar

frigidarium cold bath

gladius short sword

ἱππικὰ γυμνάσια (*hippica gymnasia*), cavalry-sports

iuventus 'Youth Organisation'

kourotrophos nursing-mother

lanx flat dish or tray

lapidarius stone-mason

Leo Mithraic grade of 'Lion'

manes spirits of the dead

meta turning-post of a circus

modius corn-measure

mystes initiate

nebris fawn-skin

oecus reception-room

olla jar

Orans early-Christian at prayer

palaestra place of exercise

Pater Mithraic grade of 'Father'

patera dish

pecten scallop-shell

pedum shepherd's curved throwing-stick

pelta crescent-shaped shield used by Amazons

petasos round hat

phalera circular decoration for cuirass, harness, etc.

pilleus pointed cap

retiarius gladiator fighting with a net

sacra sacred objects

sagum military cloak

scultor [sic] sculptor

secutor 'pursuer', a light-armed gladiator

sestertius standard Roman bronze coin

sigma curved table

spina central wall of a circus

stele tombstone

stephane diadem or other headdress

suovetaurilia sacrifice of pig, sheep, and ox

syrinx Pan-pipe

taenia ribbon

Tauroctonos Bull-Slayer, title of Mithras

tessera cube of marble, stone, or terra-cotta used in mosaic-work

thiasos revel-rout

thyrsus Bacchic staff

tibicen piper

triclinium dining-room

turma squadron

tympanum tambourine

venatio arena-hunt

venator arena-hunter

vexillarius maker of military standards

vexillum military standard

vicus civil settlement outside a fort

vitis centurion's vine-staff

SHORT GENERAL BIBLIOGRAPHY

A. The History and Archaeology of Roman Britain

R. G. Collingwood, *The Archaeology of Roman Britain*, 1930.

R. G. Collingwood and J. N. L. Myres, *Roman Britain and the English Settlements*, ed. 2, 1937.

I. A. Richmond, *Roman Britain in Pictures*, 1947.

M. P. Charlesworth, *The Lost Province or the Worth of Britain*, 1949.

I. A. Richmond, *Roman Britain* (*The Pelican History of England I*), 1955.

A. L. F. Rivet, *Town and Country in Roman Britain*, 1958.

ed. I. A. Richmond, *Roman and Native in North Britain*, 1958.

Guide to the Antiquities of Roman Britain in the British Museum, 1922, 1951, 1958.

Ordnance Survey Map of Roman Britain, ed. 3, 1956.

B. The Kindred Continental Provinces and Their Art

O. Brogan, *Roman Gaul*, 1953.

E. Espérandieu, *Recueil général des bas-reliefs, statues et bustes de la Gaule romaine*, 1907–38, with an additional volume on *La Germanie romaine*, 1931.

Germania Romana: ein Bilder-Atlas, ed. 2, 1924–30.★

H. Schoppa, *Die Kunst der Römerzeit in Gallien, Germanien und Britannien*, 1957.★

M. Probé and J. Roubier, *The Art of Roman Gaul*, 1961.★

W. Deonna, *L'art romain en Suisse*, 1942.★

F. J. Wiseman, *Roman Spain*, 1956.

Ars Hispaniae, ii, 1947.

A. M. Pidal, *Historia de España: España Romana*, ed. 2, 1955.

C. The Art of the Graeco-Roman World

Cambridge Ancient History, viii, ch. 21, 1930; ix, ch. 20, 1932; x, ch. 17, 1934; xi, ch. 20, 1936; xii, ch. 16, 1939.

E. Strong, *Art in Ancient Rome*, 1929.

P. Ducati, *L'arte in Roma*, 1938.★

E. Strong, *Roman Sculpture from Augustus to Constantine*, 1907.

E. Strong, *La scultura romana*, i, 1923; ii, 1926.

D. E. Strong, *Roman Imperial Sculpture*, 1961.

R. P. Hinks, *Catalogue of Greek, Etruscan, and Roman Paintings and Mosaics in the British Museum*, 1933 (introductory essay).

D. Levi, *Antioch Mosaic Pavements*, 1947 (introductory essay).

A. Maiuri, *Roman Painting*, 1933.★

R. J. Charleston, *Roman Pottery*, 1955.

E. van der Meer and C. Mohrmann, *Atlas of the Early Christian World*, 1958.★

★Mainly a Picture-Book.

ACKNOWLEDGEMENTS

OBJECTS in this catalogue were reproduced by courtesy of the following owners. The numbers refer to the Catalogue.

His Grace the Duke of Bedford: 27
Mrs. C. M. Bennett: 15, 17, 22, 23, 26
Mrs. K. Harding: 86
Mrs. D. M. E. Hollond: 1
The Right Hon. the Earl of Iveagh: 121a
J. Jones, Esq.: 50
Lt.-Colonel G. W. Meates: 175, 176, 192, 193
His Grace the Duke of Northumberland: 108
D. Oglander, Esq.: 195, 196, 197
Capt. H. Tupper: 188, 189, 190, 191
The Right Hon. the Earl of Verulam: 169
His Grace the Duke of Wellington: 52, 60, 166

The Corporation of the City of Bath: 25, 91
University Museum of Archaeology and of Ethnology, Cambridge: 2, 3, 5, 56, 114, 115, 121, 122, 125, 149, 174
The Mistress and Fellows of Girton College, Cambridge: 140
Royal Museum, Canterbury: 51, 112, 116, 144, 145
Carlisle Museum, Tullie House: 33, 42a, 44, 58, 74, 89, 131
The Grosvenor Museum, Chester: 84
The Trustees of Chesters Museum: 30, 35, 59, 67, 68, 75, 93
Cirencester Urban District Council: 19, 31, 34, 72, 73, 76, 95, 181, 185
Colchester and Essex Museum: 21, 46, 81, 83, 143, 147, 153, 158, 159, 162, 164
The Trustees of Corbridge Museum: 42, 47, 62, 92, 94, 161,
The Wiltshire Archaeological and Natural History Society, Devizes: 124
Dorset Natural History and Archaeological Society, Dorchester: 40, 134, 141
Dumfries Burgh Museum: 45
The National Museum of Antiquities of Scotland, Edinburgh: 9, 80, 97, 98, 99, 100, 107, 113
The Hunterian Museum, Glasgow University: 120
City of Gloucester Museums: 7, 63, 66, 82, 96
The Trustees of Housesteads Museum: 77

Ipswich Museum: 127, 136
Kent County Council: 10
Kingston upon Hull Museums: 123
Leeds City Museums: 184
City of Leicester Museums and Art Gallery: 148, 173, 183
Lincoln City and County Museum: 133
The Trustees of the British Museum: 1a, 16, 43, 48, 54, 55, 87, 101, 105, 106, 109, 128
The Worshipful Company of Goldsmiths : 64
The Guildhall Museum, London: 12, 20, 24, 36, 37, 38, 61, 110, 119
The London Museum: 29, 32, 69, 118, 146, 168
Maidstone Museum: 132
The Trustees of Malton Museum: 135
The National Trust: 78, 187
Joint Museum of the University of Durham and Society of Antiquaries of Newcastle upon Tyne: 41, 53, 65, 70, 71, 104, 130, 139
County Borough of Northampton Museum and Art Gallery: 4
City of Norwich, Castle Museum: 102, 103
The University Museum, Nottingham: 79
The Ashmolean Museum, Oxford: 13, 39, 137, 142, 163, 182, 198, 199
Peterborough Museum Society: 156, 160
Verulamium Museum, St. Albans: 28, 126, 157, 167, 170, 177, 178, 180
The Librarian, Public Library, South Shields: 85
Somerset County Museum, Taunton: 200
The Verulamium Excavation Committee: 151, 152, 154, 155, 171, 172, 179
Welshpool Borough Council: 57, 111, 117
Winchester City Museums: 8, 150
The Rector, Woodchester, Gloucestershire: 186
Yeovil Museum: 194
The Yorkshire Museum, York: 6, 11, 18, 49, 88, 138, 165

Negatives or prints for reproduction were generously lent by the following:
Lt.-Colonel G. W. Meates (175, 176); The National Museum of Antiquities of Scotland, Edinburgh (97); The Institute of Archaeology, London University (179, 180); the Ashmolean Museum, Oxford (182, 199; Haverfield Library 186)

INDEX OF NAMES

The references are to the numbers of the Catalogue.

INDEX OF PLACES

The references are to the numbers of the Catalogue.

Strainer (Cat. no. 110)